Borrowed Dreams

May McGoldrick

A SIGNET BOOK

SIGNET
Published by New American Library, a division of
Penguin Group (USA) Inc., 375 Hudson Street,
New York, New York 10014, U.S.A.
Penguin Books Ltd, 80 Strand,
London WC2R 0RL, England
Penguin Books Australia Ltd, 250 Camberwell Road,
Camberwell, Victoria 3124, Australia
Penguin Books Canada Ltd, 10 Alcorn Avenue,
Toronto, Ontario, Canada M4V 3B2
Penguin Books (N.Z.) Ltd, Cnr Rosedale and Airborne Roads,
Albany, Auckland 1310, New Zealand

Penguin Books Ltd, Registered Offices:
Harmondsworth, Middlesex, England

First published by Signet, an imprint of New American Library,
a division of Penguin Group (USA) Inc.

ISBN: 0-7394-3434-9

For Judy Spagnola.
Thank you for all you do.

Chapter 1

London
January 1772

"We are going in the wrong direction!" Instead of turning west at the ancient Temple Bar, the carriage had turned east on Fleet Street, and the driver was now whipping his team through the busy traffic going into the City. The lawyer raised the head of his cane to the roof of the carriage to get the attention of the driver, but the touch of Millicent's gloved hand on his sleeve made him stop.

"He is going where he was directed, Sir Oliver. There is an urgent matter I need to see to at the wharves."

"At the wharves? But . . . but we are already somewhat pressed for time for your appointment, m'lady."

"This shall not take very long."

He sank back against the seat, somewhat relieved. "Since we have a little time then, perhaps I could ask you a few questions about the secretive nature of this meeting we have been summoned to attend this morning."

"Please, Sir Oliver," Millicent pleaded quietly. "Can your questions wait until after my business at the wharves? I am afraid my mind is rather distracted right now."

All his questions withered on the man's tongue as Lady Wentworth turned her face toward the window and the passing street scene. A short time later the carriage passed by St. Paul's Cathedral and began wending its way down through a rough and odorous area in the direction of the Thames. By the time they crossed Fish Street, with its derelict sheds and warehouses, the lawyer could restrain himself no longer.

"Would you at least tell me the nature of this business at the wharves, m'lady?"

"We are going to an auction."

Oliver Birch looked out the window at the milling crowds of workmen and pickpockets and whores. "M'lady, I hope you intend to stay in the carriage and that you will allow me to instruct one of the grooms to obtain what you are looking for."

"I am sorry, sir, but it is essential that I see to this myself."

The lawyer grasped the side of the rocking carriage as the driver turned into the courtyard of a tumbledown wreck of a building on Brooke's Wharf. Outside the window, an odd mix of well-dressed gentlemen and shabby merchants and seamen stood in attendance on an auction that, from the looks of things, was already well under way.

"At least give me the details of what you intend to do here, Lady Wentworth." Birch climbed out of the carriage first. Despite the biting wind off the Thames, the smells of the place—combined with the stink of the river's edge—were appalling.

"I read about the auction in the *Gazette* this morning. They are selling off the estate of a deceased physician by the name of Dombey. The ruined man moved back from Jamaica last month." She pulled the hood up on her woolen cloak and accepted his hand as she stepped out. "Before he could be put in debtor's prison, he succumbed to ill health some ten days ago."

Birch had to hurry to keep up with Millicent as she pushed her way through the crowd to the front row. "And what, may I ask, in Dr. Dombey's estate is of interest to you?"

She didn't answer, and the lawyer found his client's gray eyes searching anxiously past the personal articles that were laid out on a makeshift platform. "I hope I am not too late."

The lawyer did not ask any more questions as Millicent's attention turned sharply toward the set of wide doors that led into the building. The bailiff was dragging out a frail-looking African woman wrapped in a tattered blanket and wearing only a dirty shift under it. A crate was placed on the platform, and the old woman—her neck and hands and feet in shackles—was pushed roughly onto it.

Birch closed his eyes for a moment to control his disgust at this evidence of the barbaric and dishonorable trade that continued to curse the nation.

"Lookee, gennelmen. This here slave was Dr. Dombey's personal maid," the auctioneer shouted. "She's the only servant the medical bloke carried back with him from Jamaica. Aye, sure, she's a rum thing with her wrinkled face. And she's of an age to rival Methuselah. But gennelmen, she's said to be a weritable African queen, she is, and bright as crystal, they tell me. So e'en though she's worth a good thirty pounds, what say we start the bidding off at . . . at a pound."

There was loud jeering and laughter from the group.

"Look, now, gennelmen. 'Ow about ten shillings then?" the auctioneer announced over the roar of the crowd. "She's good teeth, she has." He pulled open the woman's mouth roughly. There were crusts of blood on the chapped lips. "Ten shillings? Who'll start the bidding at ten shillings?"

"What bloody good is she?" somebody shouted.

"Five, gennelmen. Who'll start us at five?"

"The woman is nothing more than a refuse slave," another responded. "If we were in Port Royal, she'd be left to die on the wharf."

Birch glanced worriedly at Millicent and found a look of pain etched on her face. Tears were glimmering on the edges of her eyelids.

"This is no place for you to be, m'lady," he whispered quietly. "It is not right for you to be witnessing this. Whatever you came for must be already gone."

"The advertisement said she was a fine African lass." A middle-aged clerk, sneering from his place at the edge of the platform, threw a crumpled *Gazette* at the old woman. "Why, she's too old to even be good for—"

"Five pounds," Millicent called out.

Every eye in the place turned to her, and silence gripped the throng. Even the auctioneer seemed lost for words for a moment. Birch saw the woman's wrinkled eyelids open a fraction and stare at Millicent.

"Aye, yer ladyship. Yer bid is in fer—"

"Six pounds." A second bid from someone deep in the crowd silenced the auctioneer again. All heads in unison turned to the back of the auction yard.

"Seven," Millicent responded.

"Eight."

On the platform the man's face broke out into a grin as the crowds parted, showing a nattily dressed clerk holding up a rolled newspaper. "Why, I see Mr. Hyde's clerk is in attendance. Thank ye fer yer bid, Harry."

"Ten pounds," Millicent said with great vehemence.

Birch scanned the number of carriages in the yard, wondering from which one of them Jasper Hyde was issuing his commands. A large plantation owner in the West Indies and supposedly a good friend to the late Squire Wentworth, the Englishman had wasted no time in taking over all of the squire's properties in the Caribbean after his death in payment for debts Wentworth had owed him. And if that were not enough, since arriving in England, Mr. Hyde had positioned himself as Lady Wentworth's chief nemesis, buying up the rest of the bills of exchange and promissory notes the squire had left behind.

"Twenty."

There was a loud gasp of disbelief and the crowd began to shift uncomfortably.

"Thirty."

The lawyer turned to Millicent. "He is playing with

you, m'lady," he said quietly. "I do not believe it would be wise—"

"Fifty pounds," the clerk called without a trace of emotion.

A group of sailors near the edge of the platform turned and scoffed loudly at the clerk for pushing up the price.

"I cannot let him do this. Dr. Dombey and this woman spent a great deal of time on Wentworth's plantations in Jamaica. From the stories I've heard from Jonah and some of the others at Melbury Hall, she became a person of some importance to them." She nodded to the auctioneer. "Sixty pounds."

Birch watched Jasper Hyde's clerk appear to squirm a little. The man turned and looked toward the line of carriages. The rolled newspaper rose in the air before the caller could repeat the last bid. "Seventy."

The rumbling in the crowd became more pronounced. There were sharp comments to the effect that he should let the woman have the slave. A couple of the sailors edged threateningly toward the clerk, muttering derisive obscenities.

"This is all a sick game to Mr. Hyde," Millicent whispered, turning away from the platform. "There are many stories of his brutality on the plantations. The stories about what he did after taking possession of my husband's land and slaves are even worse. He is answerable to no one and has no regard for what few laws are observed there. This woman has witnessed it all, though. He will hurt her. Kill her, perhaps." Her hands fisted. "Sir Oliver, I owe this to my people after all the suffering Wentworth caused. I cannot in good conscience turn my back when I can save this one. Not when I have failed all those others that Hyde took."

"That it, yer ladyship?" the auctioneer asked. "Ye're giving in?"

"Eighty," she replied, her voice quavering.

"You cannot afford this, m'lady," Birch put in firmly but quietly. "Think of the promissory notes Hyde still holds from your husband. You've extended the date of repayment once. But they will all come due next month, and you are personally liable, to the extent of every last thing you own. And this includes Melbury Hall. You just cannot add more fuel to his fire."

"One hundred pounds." The clerk's shout was instantly swallowed up by a loud response from the crowd. Birch watched the man take a few nervous steps toward the carriages as the same angry sailors moved closer to him.

"One ten, milady?" the auctioneer, grinning excitedly, called out from the platform.

"You cannot save every one, Millicent," Birch whispered sharply. When first asked by the Earl and the Countess of Stanmore to represent Lady Wentworth in her legal affairs a year ago, he'd also been informed of the woman's great compassion for the Africans whom her late husband had held as slaves. But his expectations had not come close to the fervor he'd witnessed since then.

"I know that, Sir Oliver."

"For all we know, he might already own this woman. In the same way that he has been acquiring all of the late squire's notes, he may have done the same with Dombey. This may just be Jasper Hyde's way of draining the last of your available funds."

As his words sank in, Millicent's shoulders sagged. Wiping a tear from her face, she turned and started pushing her way toward the carriage. Halfway out of the yard, though, she swung around and raised a hand.

"One hundred ten."

A round of exclamations erupted from the crowd. Gradually, people parted until she was facing the pale-faced clerk across the mud and dirt of the yard. Having already retreated to back edge of the crowd, the man shook his head at the auctioneer and looked back at Millicent.

"Lady Wentworth can have her Negro at the price of a hundred ten pounds."

The mocking tones of the man, accompanied by his sneer, caused the sailors to lose the last of their restraint, and two took off after him. The clerk turned and bolted from the yard. Watching him run, Birch felt the urge to go after the clerk himself. There was no doubt in the lawyer's mind that this ordeal had been arranged. In a moment, the sailors returned empty-handed.

She laid her hand gently on his arm. "Regardless of Mr. Hyde's actions, I had to save this woman's life, Sir Oliver."

Millicent Gregory Wentworth could not be considered a great beauty, nor could her sense of style be called *au courant* by the standards of London's *ton*. But what she lacked in those areas—and in the false pride so fashionable of late—she made up in dignity and humanity. And all of this despite a lifetime of oppression and bad luck.

Birch nodded respectfully to his client. "Why not wait in the carriage, m'lady. I would be happy to take care of the details here."

A small writing desk was being handed up and placed exactly where the slave woman had stood a moment earlier. Millicent watched several members of the crowd edge forward for a better look at the piece of furniture. They were far more interested in this item than in the human being who was auctioned off before it. Only the competition of the bidding had attracted their attention. She turned to watch the woman being led across the yard, with Sir Oliver trailing behind.

Appalled by the entire proceeding, Millicent pushed her way through the crowd to the carriage.

"She will be brought to my office this afternoon," Birch said as soon as he had climbed in some time later. "And, since you do not wish to have her delivered to your sister's home, I will arrange for a place for her to stay until you are ready to leave for Melbury Hall."

"Thank you. We shall be leaving tomorrow morning," Millicent replied.

"Rest assured, m'lady, everything shall be handled with the utmost discretion."

"I know it will," she said quietly, looking out the small window of the carriage at the door of the shed where the old woman had been taken. Millicent couldn't help

but worry about how much more pain these horrible
people would inflict on her before she was delivered to
the lawyer's office that afternoon.

As they rode along in silence through the city, she
thought of the money she'd just spent. A hundred ten
pounds was equivalent to seven month's worth of salaries of all twenty servants she employed at Melbury Hall,
not counting the field hands. It was true that the purchase of the black woman would cut deeply into her
rapidly diminishing funds. And she wasn't even considering the money that she needed to pay Jasper Hyde next
month. Millicent rubbed her fingers over a dull ache in
her temple and tried to think only of how much good it
would do, bringing this woman back to Hertfordshire.

"Lady Wentworth," the lawyer said finally, breaking
the silence as they drew near their destination, "we cannot put off discussing your appointment with the Dowager Countess Aytoun any longer. I am still completely
in the dark concerning why we are going there."

"That makes two of us, Sir Oliver," she replied
tiredly. "Her note summoning—or rather, inviting me—
to meet with her arrived three days ago at Melbury Hall,
and her groom stayed until I sent her an answer. I was
to arrive at the Earl of Aytoun's town house in Hanover
Square today at eleven this morning with my attorney.
Nothing more was said."

"This sounds very abrupt. Do you know the countess?"

Millicent shook her head. "I do not. But then again,
a year ago I didn't know Mr. Jasper Hyde, either. Nor
the other half-dozen creditors who have endeavored to
come after me from every quarter since Wentworth's
death." She pulled the cloak tighter around herself.
"One thing I've learned this past year and a half is that
there is no hiding from those to whom my husband owed
money. I have to face them—one by one—and try to
make some reasonable arrangement to pay them back."

"You know that I admire you greatly in your efforts,
but we both know you are encumbered almost beyond
the point of recovery already." He paused. "You have
some very generous friends, Lady Wentworth. If you

would allow me to reveal to them just a hint of your hardship—"

"No, sir," she said sharply. "I find no shame in being poor. But I find great dishonor in begging. Please, I do not care to hear any more."

"As you wish, m'lady."

Millicent nodded gratefully at her lawyer. Sir Oliver had already served her well, and she trusted that he would honor her request.

"To set your mind a little at ease, though," he continued, "you should know that the Dowager Countess Aytoun is socially situated far differently than Mr. Hyde, or your late husband. She is a woman of great wealth, but she is rumored to be exceedingly . . . well, careful with her money. Some say she is so tightfisted that her own servants must struggle to receive their wages. In short, I cannot see her lending any money to Squire Wentworth."

"I am relieved to hear that. I should have known that with your attention to detail we would not be walking into this meeting totally unprepared. What else have you learned about her, Sir Oliver?"

"She is Lady Archibald Pennington, Countess of Aytoun. Her given name is Beatrice. She's been a widow for over five years. She is Scottish by birth, with the blood of Highlanders in her veins. She comes from an ancient family, and she married well besides."

"She has children?"

"Three sons. All men now. Lyon Pennington is the fourth Earl of Aytoun. The second son, Pierce Pennington, has apparently been making a fortune in the American colonies despite the embargo. And David Pennington, the youngest, is an officer in His Majesty's army. The countess herself led a very quiet life until the scandal that tore her family apart occurred this past summer."

"Scandal?"

Sir Oliver nodded. "Indeed, m'lady. It involved a young lady named Emma Douglas. I understand all three brothers were fond of her. She ended up marrying the oldest brother and became the Countess of Aytoun two years ago."

That hardly sounded scandalous, but Millicent had no chance to ask any more questions as their carriage rolled to a stop in front of an elegant mansion facing Hanover Square. A footman in gold-trimmed livery greeted them as he opened the door of the carriage. Another servant escorted them up the wide marble steps to the front door.

Inside the mansion's entrance hall, yet another servant greeted them. As Millicent shed her cloak, her gaze took in the semicircular alcove at the far end of the hall and the ornate gilded scrolls and rosettes that decorated the high, patterned ceiling. In a receiving area beyond an open set of doors, she could see upholstered furniture of deep walnut by Sheraton and Chippendale tastefully arranged about the room, while handsome carpets covered the brightly polished floors.

A tall, elderly steward approached and informed them that the dowager was waiting.

"What was the nature of the scandal?" she managed to whisper as they followed the steward and another servant up the sweeping circular stairs to a drawing room.

"Just rumors, m'lady," Birch whispered, "to the effect that the earl murdered his wife."

"But that is—"

She stopped as the door to the drawing room was opened. Trying to contain her shock and curiosity, Millicent entered as they were announced.

There were four people in the cozy, well-appointed room: the dowager countess, a pale gentleman standing by a desk that had a ledger book open on it, and two lady's maids.

Lady Aytoun was an older woman, obviously in ill health. She was sitting on a sofa with pillows propped behind her and a blanket on her lap. Blue eyes studied the visitors from behind a pair of spectacles.

Millicent gave a small curtsy. "Our apologies, my lady, for being delayed."

"Did you win the auction?" The dowager's abruptness caused Millicent to look over in surprise at Sir Oliver. He appeared as baffled as she was. "The African woman. Did you win the auction?"

"I . . . I did," she managed to get out. "But how did you know about it?"

"How much?"

Millicent bristled at the inquiry, but at the same time she felt no shame for what she'd done. "One hundred ten pounds. Though I must tell you I don't know what business it is of—"

"Add it to the tally, Sir Richard." The dowager waved a hand at the gentleman still standing by the desk. "A worthy cause."

Sir Oliver stepped forward. "May I say, m'lady—"

"Pray, save the idle prattle, young man. Come and sit. Both of you."

Millicent's lawyer, who probably hadn't been addressed as "young man" in decades, stared openmouthed for a moment. Then, as he and Millicent did as they were instructed, the countess dismissed the servants with a wave of her hand.

"Very well. I know both of you, and you know me. That pasty-faced bag of bones over there is my lawyer, Sir Richard Maitland." The old woman arched an eyebrow in the direction of her attorney, who bowed stiffly and sat. "And now, the reason why I invited you here."

Millicent could not even hazard a guess as to what was coming next.

"People acting on my behalf have been reporting to me about you for some time now, Lady Wentworth. You have surpassed my expectations." Lady Aytoun removed her spectacles. "No reason for dallying. You are here because I have a business proposition."

"A business proposition?" Millicent murmured.

"Indeed. I want you to marry my son, the Earl of Aytoun. By a special license. Today."

Chapter 2

Faced with the threat of another life in hell, Millicent shot to her feet. In an instant, propriety and decorum were cast to the winds.

"You've made a grave mistake, Lady Aytoun."

"I do not think so."

"Your servant must have delivered the message to a wrong address."

"Sit down, Lady Wentworth."

"I am afraid I cannot." She glanced in the direction of her lawyer and found him standing as well.

"If you please, Lady Wentworth. There is no reason for panic." The dowager's tone was gentler. "I am well aware of your fears. I have been advised fully of the suffering you endured during your marriage. But what I am proposing to you now has no similarity to the situation you were forced to endure under the brutal tyranny of your first husband."

Millicent stared at the old woman, trying to understand how she could know any of that. The dowager was speaking of her life as if it were public knowledge, and a queasy feeling gripped her stomach. The urge to run for the door was strong. She wanted nothing more than to go out of the house and return to Melbury Hall.

To Millicent, marriage meant being owned by a man. She had felt the chains of that "blissful" state for five endless years. There was no protection for a married woman. Marriage was a state of mental and physical abuse. Period. The vows of matrimony were nothing more than a curse contrived by men to control women. And after Wentworth's death, she had sworn never to allow herself to be subjugated to that life again.

Millicent took a step toward the door.

"At least allow me to explain my purpose for this confusion." The dowager raised a hand to her. "I know at first I spoke in haste. I believe if you would be so kind as to allow me to explain the unpleasant situation in which I find my family, then you shall better understand the reason for the offer."

"Any explanation of your family's situation, m'lady, is completely unnecessary. If you know anything of my history, then you should also know that my revulsion to the very notion of marriage is unrelated to anything you might tell me of your own family. The topic is repugnant to me, Lady Aytoun, and under no circumstances am I willing to—"

"My son is a cripple, Lady Wentworth," the dowager interrupted. "After a horrible accident last summer, he has been left with no use of his legs. He has no strength in one arm. He has plunged into a state of melancholia from which he cannot lift himself. I thank God for the loyalty and persistence of his personal manservant and a half-dozen others who see to all of his needs, for without them I would have been lost. Indeed, without them I would have had no choice but to place him in a hospital for the insane. I do not mind telling you that such a situation would surely have killed me."

The distraught tone of the old woman's words tugged at Millicent's heartstrings. "You have my deepest sympathy, m'lady, but I fail to see what I could do."

The dowager's hands trembled as they absently straightened the blanket on her lap. "Despite all of my bravado, Lady Wentworth, I am quite ill. To be blunt, I am dying. And my physicians, the devil take them, are very happy to give me daily reminders that I might not see the next sunrise."

"Really, m'lady, I—"

"Don't take me wrong. I don't give a pin about myself. I've had a full life. Right now my greatest worry is

what shall happen to Lyon when I am gone. That is why
I have asked you here today."

"But . . . but surely there are other options. Family.
Friends. Other acquaintances who are not complete
strangers to you. Lord Aytoun is a peer of the realm.
You have so many venues available to you, so many
treatments."

"Please, Lady Wentworth. Please sit down. I shall
explain."

Millicent turned and found Birch standing attentively
a couple of steps away, awaiting her decision whether to
go or stay. She looked back at the aging countess. The
façade of strength she had encountered in the dowager
when first entering was completely gone. What Millicent
saw now was simply another woman. A dying woman.
A mother who was just trying to secure the future well-
being of her son.

She hesitantly sat down. The expression of relief on
the dowager's face was immediate.

"Thank you. You asked about family. Well, those remaining believe that if something were to happen to me,
then Lyon should be put in a madhouse." Temper
flashed in the old woman's blue eyes. "The Earl of Aytoun is not mad. He doesn't belong in Bedlam. I won't
have him tied and tortured, bled and purged, dosed with
opium and put on display for the rest of London's *ton*."

"But there must be other treatments for his condition.
Every day there seems to be a new cure for yet another ailment."

"I have tried every method and paid a great deal of
money, and seen no improvement in him. Just this past
week, there was an advertisement in the *Gazette* by a
Mr. Payne at the Angel and Crown in St. Paul's Church-
yard. It claimed that sufferers from 'loss of memory or
forgetfulness' for two shillings, six pence could buy a
pot of 'a grateful electuary' that would enable them to
'remember the minutest circumstances of their affairs to
a wonder.' I had Lyon try it, hoping to spur *some* response in him. Nothing." She gave a dismissive wave. "I
am tired of the charlatans and the Merry-Andrews who

eagerly endorse the claims of these quacks. I am tired
of giving my son highly colored pills that have no good
in them at all. You see, his legs and arm were broken,
but now they are healed, and yet he has no ability to
move them. He cannot walk. He cannot even lift his
right arm. So the so-called doctors say he must have a
secret disease. Those from the university have but one
answer: Bleed him and bleed him again. But it has no
effect."

"I am sorry, m'lady—"

"So am I," the dowager said, looking at her directly.
"But I'll have no more of that. And I'll have no madhouse for my son. And I'll definitely have no more of
these quacks with their dung tea, stewed owls, and
crushed worms. I am done with them all."

"I know there are many, many charlatans out there.
But there must be some reputable doctors, as well."

"Aye, there are. But the *reputable* ones, as you call
them, are also at their wit's end. Aside from bleeding
and purging, their only other suggestion is to keep him
sedated."

"Why? Is he violent?"

"Of course not," the dowager assured her. "But he
has been terribly unhappy at Baronsford, the Aytoun
family seat southeast of Edinburgh. That's where the
accident happened. In fact, this past fall he went so far
as to insist on transferring control of all his inherited
properties to his brother Pierce, my second son. Not that
his hasty decision did any good for anyone. Pierce is not
in England at present, and he has no interest whatsoever
in the family fortune. Besides, Lyon is the earl. He is
the one whom our dependents look up to and—" She
abruptly stopped and waved a dismissive hand. "But
Baronsford is the least of my problems right now. The
reason I brought it up is so you would know why I
needed to get him away from it. I need to find my son
a place where he shan't be reminded of his past and
what he has lost."

Millicent's nerves had once again settled. She was
calm enough to realize that no one could force her into

anything. The choices were hers; so were the consequences. "I still cannot see how your proposal could
improve the earl's life. I am no physician, and I am
hardly capable of—"

"He needs to be out of Scotland. He needs a home
with people who will care for him. Since your husband's
death, 'tis no secret that you have provided a safe haven
for the people Squire Wentworth enslaved." The dowager paused for a moment before continuing. "But you
should know that I intend to make this arrangement as
advantageous to you as 'tis for my son."

Without waiting for the younger woman's response,
she motioned to her lawyer to hand her a large sheet of
paper lined in the ledger style of banking clerks.

"My dear, this is a summary of all the loans and promissory notes that Squire Wentworth left you. We went
to a great deal of difficulty in gathering them together.
It may be that there are some that we have missed. Your
lawyer here can scan them at his leisure and let us know.
And as you know, there are a number of individuals
who take great enjoyment in revealing the painful layers
of your indebtedness just to watch you unravel."

Millicent reached for the proffered paper and glanced
down the list of debts. The totals at the bottom were
huge, but she would not allow her distress to show. She'd
known for some time that she was drowning. The depth
of the water made very little difference. The end result
was the same. She handed the paper to Sir Oliver.

"What is it exactly that you propose, Lady Aytoun?"
she asked dully.

"A marriage in name only. A business arrangement,
pure and simple. If you were to agree to the terms, the
Earl of Aytoun shall come to reside with you at Melbury
Hall. But he will arrive with his own manservant and
servants. We have a new doctor who can travel up from
London on a regular basis. All you need to do is arrange
for space for these people. In return, my lawyer Maitland here, will have all the debts listed on that paper—
and any others that are unfamiliar to us—paid in full. In
addition, these two gentlemen shall settle on a generous

amount that will be paid to you on a monthly basis to support the upkeep of Melbury Hall. It shall be more than enough for you to continue to pursue your causes."

Millicent's head reeled with all that the dowager had just proposed. She had spent endless nights awake, tossing and turning as she worried about her expenses. The last six months had been especially difficult. Lady Aytoun was offering her an opportunity to free herself of the shackles of her husband's debts once and for all. But the thought of the price she would have to pay kept pushing itself forward in her mind with terrifying clarity. Marriage again.

"What shall happen to our arrangement, m'lady, if the Earl of Aytoun recovers from this affliction?"

"I am afraid there is no hope. No doctor who has seen him recently believes . . ." The countess paused to quiet a quaver in her voice. "None of them believes there is any chance of him recovering."

"But he might."

"I envy your optimism."

"I want a provision in the agreement that, in the event of his recovery, a divorce will be uncontested."

The dowager glanced at her lawyer.

Sir Richard nodded curtly, rising from his chair. "Considering the nature of the marriage and the earl's present health, an annulment or a divorce could certainly be arranged."

Sir Oliver agreed. "His present state of mind makes it an arguable case for annulment."

Millicent couldn't believe how far she had been persuaded. In her mind, she was actually weighing the benefits versus the loss, and the scale was definitely tipping.

"Anything else? Any concerns that you have been left with?"

The dowager's question lifted Millicent's chin. "Aye, m'lady. Why me? I am a stranger to you. Why did you decide on me?"

"We did not settle on you without serious consideration. Faced with my requirements, my lawyer here had a great challenge laid at his door. His search has been painstaking. But I must tell you that your history and your reputation for goodness, combined with all that Sir Richard was able to gather about your present financial situation, made you the perfect candidate." The older woman nodded approvingly. "I hope you are not offended by the amount of poking and prodding that my people have been doing into your past and present affairs. When they concluded, there was very little about you that I did not know."

Millicent raised a curious brow. For all her life, she had maintained a very private lifestyle. She doubted there was much out there for anyone to dig into.

"This surprises me, m'lady, and I should like to hear a sample of what your people might have discovered about me."

"If you wish. You are Millicent Gregory Wentworth, twenty-nine years of age. You have been widowed for a year and a half. You were entered into an arranged marriage by your family."

"These are facts easily obtainable. They don't say anything about the person."

"That is true. But my meeting with you today has settled my mind about that. With the exception of an overnight stay at their residence now and then, as in the case of this trip to London, you are practically estranged from your kin. Not that I blame you. Your family consists of two older sisters and an uncle whom you do not trust, since he gave you to Wentworth without any inquiries into the man's character." The old woman's hand smoothed the blanket tightly over her lap. "There is little correspondence between any of your family. During your five years of marriage, you never once confided to any of them about the abuse you were receiving at the hands of your husband. You have very few close friends, but your pride does not allow you to ask for help, even when you are desperate. What else? Yes, you are involved in freeing your slaves—"

"My late husband's slaves."

"Indeed. Partly because of your efforts to correct that situation, however, you are on the verge of being crushed under the resulting financial burdens." The dowager's gaze swept over Millicent's face. "On a much more trivial level, you appear contented with your unadorned looks and your obvious disinterest in style. Actually, you have never been an active member of London's fashionable set and, since becoming a widow, have taken shelter within the walls of your country residence, Melbury Hall, at Hertfordshire."

"I have missed nothing important by staying in the country, m'lady."

"Quite true. And this attitude is one of the things that I find most advantageous. You shall not miss the parties in town during the Season nor hold a grudge against your husband for not escorting you to London, or Bath, or wherever the *ton* is running wild at the moment. In addition, you are a bright woman who is endowed with great compassion. You have finally discovered the value of independence, and you are now striving to wield the power that goes along with it. But to succeed, you could very well use the protection of a husband's name to keep the wolves from the door."

The battle inside Millicent raged. She did indeed need the protection of a husband's name in order to pursue her goals. Already she had found it nearly impossible to hire and keep a capable steward to manage Melbury Hall. Even in going to an auction by the Thames, she found that society demanded the presence of a male overseer, since obviously a man had such a higher level of intelligence than any woman.

Millicent did her best to control her temper and instead thought of her best friend's story of the ten years that she had spent in Philadelphia. Going under the assumed name of Mrs. Ford, Rebecca had used the ruse of having a husband to establish herself and a newborn in that city.

"What do you think of the offer, Lady Wentworth?"

Millicent shook off her struggle and met the dowager's direct gaze. "Why today? What is the significance of this marriage taking place today?"

"You don't stay away from Melbury Hall more than

a day or two at the most. My guess is that you are traveling back there tomorrow morning."

"I am."

"When I add that to my physicians' predictions about the scarcity of sunsets and sunrises in my future, I could not bring myself to tempt fate by waiting. There is too much at stake."

"How does his lordship feel about this great scheme you have been devising?"

The dowager drew a deep breath and released it before answering. "I did not know if I would be able to convince you, but I explained to my son that it would be out of your need for financial support and not out of charity that the marriage might be arranged. Once he heard that, he was resigned to it. He'll not be pitied. Whatever else might be stripped from Lyon, he will always have his pride."

Lyon Pennington, fourth Earl of Aytoun, remained motionless in the seat before the window. The muscles of the peer's gaunt face were drawn tight beneath the dark, untrimmed beard. His eyes were fixed on an invisible point somewhere out beyond the glass, out amid the dreary scenery of Hanover Square.

The earl's two valets had laid out a brocade coat, a silk waistcoat, a black cravat, breeches, stockings, and silver-buckled shoes for the wedding. Neither man dared to approach him, though, and they stood by the door, exchanging nervous looks.

"She's here," a young woman whispered, coming in with a tray of tea.

She hurried to put the tray down on a table near the earl. With a curtsy, she backed away and returned to where the men were standing.

"The dowager thinks," she whispered to one of them, "that the visitor'll be looking to meet with his lordship before the ceremony."

Another serving girl walked in carrying a tray of pastries. Following her, the earl's man, Gibbs, entered the chamber.

"What're ye waiting for?" he growled at the valets. "His lordship should be dressed by now."

As Gibbs took a step toward them, the two men moved to do his bidding. The earl's man was as tall and as broad as the great oaks in the deer park at Baronsford, and they both had felt the weight of his displeasure in the past. One of the valets reached for his master's buckskin breeches. He looked uneasily at his lanky fellow servant, who was picking up Lord Aytoun's shirt. They were both still hesitant to approach the master.

The one called John whispered warily to Gibbs, " 'Slordship was none too keen about dressin' this mornin'."

The two serving maids hurriedly escaped the chamber.

"Aye, Mr. Gibbs," the other valet put in quietly. "By 'slife, sir, Lord Aytoun near killed us both while we was tryin' to dress 'im. Not till we gave him the tonic the new doctor left for 'im did he settle down at all."

"His lordship had that already this morning!" Gibbs exploded, quickly lowering his voice to a fierce whisper. " 'Tis not to be given any bloody time ye fancy giving it to him."

"Aye, sir. But what he had weren't enough."

"If I had the time right now to wring your necks and kick ye from here to . . ." Gibbs tried to compose himself. "But the lack of time is going to save yer bloody arses. The company is already downstairs, and he's still not dressed."

" 'Tis only a minute or two that he's calmed 'imself."

Scowling at them, he motioned for the two men to follow him as he moved to the earl's chair. "M'lord?"

Lyon's gaze never wavered from the window. He was neither asleep nor awake. Gibbs closed the shutters and stepped in front of the sitting man again.

"We need to get you ready for company, m'lord."

The earl's face was blank as he looked up at the three men now standing before him.

"Lady Wentworth and her lawyer have arrived, sir," the earl's manservant said calmly, pulling the blanket off the man's unmoving legs. "The bishop has been waiting in the library an hour. Ye're expected, m'lord."

One of the valets reached down to undo the buttons of the double-breasted dressing gown. Perceiving the scowl being directed at him by his ailing master, he stopped and shrank back a step.

"Put me in the bed," Lyon growled in slurred tones.

"I cannot, m'lord. Her ladyship insisted that we should have ye ready."

With no thought for the legs that did not move—that had not supported him in months—the Earl of Aytoun pushed himself up from the chair. Before the hands of his panicked servants could reach him, he fell heavily to the floor.

"Bloody hell . . . !"

". . . landed on 'is right arm!"

"Help me roll him off it." Gibbs was down on his knees beside the earl in an instant.

"I 'eard the doctor say he'd have a surgeon amputate if that arm breaks again."

Gibbs flashed John a killing look for his comment and gently turned the earl over.

Lyon Pennington was as large a man as Gibbs. His months of confinement had detracted somewhat from his prior robustness, but moving him still required several men. Even more when he was not in the best of temperaments.

"M'lord, if I may remind ye . . ." Gibbs gingerly bent and straightened the earl's right arm. The bone didn't appear to be broken again. "Your lordship promised the dowager that ye would go through with this plan of hers."

"Put me back in bed." Anger was woven tightly into the words that escaped his lips. His good hand formed a fist and pounded once on the floor. "Now!"

"Your mother had another sick spell last night, m'lord. We had to send for the doctor." Gibbs crouched nearby, knowing better than to maneuver the earl when his anger was on the edge of exploding. The man's blue eyes were boring holes in the manservant's head. "The only thing pushing her from her sickbed this morning was your promise to abide by her wish. If she hears that ye have decided to throw it all down the well, then that could be the last straw. If ye please, m'lord, her ladyship has gone to a great deal of trouble to arrange this for ye. I'm thinking ye might give her a wee bit of peace for the few days she might have left in this world."

Whether it was the sedating medicine the valets had administered earlier or the realization on the earl's part that he had few choices left, Gibbs couldn't tell. Whatever it was, the servant was relieved when Lyon Pennington did not fight them when they lifted him again into the chair.

"And what of this woman, Gibbs?" he muttered. "Do you think this new bride of mine will ever have so much as a moment's peace?"

Chapter 3

Jasper Hyde pulled his pocket watch from his waistcoat and looked at it. It was nearly three in the afternoon, though there was no sign of his blasted clerk or Platt, either.

White's Club was crowded, as it was every day, and Hyde glanced around at the other gentlemen. He was beginning to recognize some of the faces of the players and the others who simply milled about drinking and being entertained by the sight of those intent on losing their fortunes. It didn't seem to matter what time of day it was here; the card and dice tables were nearly always full. Hyde knew, though, that the crowd would soon start to thin as some went off to the dinners and parties and the many other vices that London offered in abundance.

Hyde stared at the dice cup in the Earl of Winchelsea's hand. He himself had already lost more than he cared to, but he knew it was well worth it to be rubbing shoulders with such members of the *ton*. And it didn't hurt to lose money to them, either.

"All bets down," the periwigged croupier called in a bored voice.

Behind the man, by the large open hearth, a harpist and horn player were playing, and the director was upbraiding a servant for being slow with his delivery of a bottle of wine to a hazard table in the corner.

Lord Winchelsea rattled the dice once more for luck and rolled them out onto the table.

"Seven." The men crowded around the table responded with groans and shouts of victory, depending on their wagers, and Hyde watched Winchelsea smile arrogantly as the dice were passed back to him.

"Now *this* is what I call a celebration," Winchelsea said to the Earl of Carlisle, standing to his left. The other nobleman snorted in response, and Winchelsea smiled at Jasper Hyde. "Still betting with my erstwhile friend here, Hyde?"

The plantation owner glanced down at the quickly dwindling sum before him. Hyde knew the young earl had easily lost three thousand pounds this week. Winchelsea's luck, however, had definitely turned today.

"If you don't mind, m'lord, I believe I shall wager with you."

"Smart move, Hyde. By the way, I have reserved a private room at Clifton's Chophouse down by the Temple Bar before we go on to Drury Lane. Care to join us there for dinner?"

"I would be delighted." Extremely pleased at being included, Hyde doubled his initial wager on the table.

"Considering your good news today, you should invite everyone here for dinner," Lord Carlisle challenged.

"Damn me, but you're right about that, Carlisle. You can all come." Winchelsea started rattling the dice cup amid of the loud laughter and calls of approval by those gathered around the table.

"If I may be so bold as to ask, m'lord, what is the nature of your good news?"

Carlisle answered Hyde's question. "Rumor has it that our friend's chief nemesis is escaping to the country first thing in the morning."

"Aytoun is leaving London?" someone said from across the room.

"Carried away, to be more accurate," Lord Carlisle answered.

"Finally sending him to Bedlam, are they?" the same person asked.

"Despite my heartfelt recommendation, no." Winchelsea shook the cup more savagely. "But he is being sentenced to a lifetime of imprisonment all the same. We hear that he is getting married again this afternoon."

"All bets down," the croupier intoned.

"What simpleton would give their daughter to him?" another person asked. "Didn't he kill his first wife?"

"That was only an unsubstantiated rumor," Carlisle said in defense of the absent nobleman. "No truth to it whatsoever."

"I disagree with that," Winchelsea argued, putting the cup of dice on the table. "Having faced the man's brutal temperament, I find him perfectly capable of murdering his wife."

"You faced Aytoun's *brutal* temperament because you were dallying with his wife," Carlisle scoffed. "And you just say that now because he was the only man to best you in a duel. You've only just lately stopped complaining of the shoulder wound you sustained against him. If you'd beaten him, I say you would not be slandering him with such accusations."

"Are you accusing *me*?" Winchelsea challenged hotly.

"No . . . and you shan't convince me to face you in the park in the crack of dawn, either, my friend." Carlisle handed the cup of dice back to the earl. "I say we continue with our celebration and let Aytoun and his new wife just go to hell."

Voices rose in agreement around the table at that. Still scowling at his friend, Winchelsea grudgingly took the cup and rolled out the dice.

"Six," the croupier declared, handing back the dice.

Carlisle smiled smugly. "Hope this doesn't mean your luck has changed."

"Wishful thinking on your part."

"Next we'll be hearing that your tailor's at the door waiting to be paid."

"You are the devil himself, Carlisle, to wish such horrible things upon me."

Paying no regard to the give and take of the two men, Hyde closely followed the roll of the dice across the table again. *Seven.* Winchelsea's violent curse was mild compared to how Hyde felt at that moment. Losing five hundred guineas at a single throw might be insignificant among this group of gentry, but for Hyde it was another link in a lengthening chain of bad luck.

The plantation owner held his breath as a stabbing pain suddenly wracked his chest and shoulders. Hyde waited until the spasms subsided. He knew they would pass, and he did not want to draw any attention to them. Occurring with no warning and more and more frequently of late, the sharp pains came and went, but not before draining him of his vigor. He leaned on the table.

The dice cup passed on to Lord Carlisle, and once again wagers were being laid on the table. Turning his head, Hyde was relieved to see his lawyer finally appear at the doorway. He made his excuses at the table and made his way across the room to where Platt stood waiting. Without saying a word, the lawyer led him down the stairs to where the clerk, Harry, stood squirming just inside the front door.

A servant handed Hyde his cane and hat and gloves and helped him on with his overcoat. All the while, Hyde kept his gaze fixed on his servant. The pain in his chest had started to ease a little, but the air in his chest was scarce.

Hyde motioned to the two new arrivals to follow him into a small chamber beside the entryway. It was obvious that all had not gone as planned.

"Where is she?"

Platt closed the door of the chamber before breaking the news. "Harry was not able to buy the slave woman."

Rage, like a strong gust of wind, rushed through him in a single sweep. The clerk shrank back against the wall as the end of Hyde's cane jabbed him hard in the chest. "You had your instructions. All you had to do was to continue to bid on her until you won her."

"I did, sir. But the price kept climbing."

"Lady Wentworth showed up at the auction unexpectedly," Platt offered from a safe distance.

"I couldn't win the woman, sir, but I made her ladyship pay a fortune for her. She was a worthless refuse slave."

Jasper Hyde's fury boiled over, and he struck the man hard on the side of the head with the cane. "*You* are the worthless refuse. I should turn you out now. Did you hear nothing of what I told you before? Your specific instructions were to bid up and win that slave. What worry is it of yours about the price?"

"But she went for a hundred ten pounds, master," Harry blurted out, rubbing his head with one hand and ready to deflect the next blow with the other. "And the crowds were against me. They thought I was pushing the price up on Lady Wentworth and took her side, sir. I looked for yer carriage, but ye and Mr. Platt here were nowheres to be seen. I never thought ye'd be meaning to go anywhere above fifty pound. But I braced myself and went double, and—"

The cane flashed again, striking the clerk on his upraised wrist and causing him to howl in pain.

"This will solve nothing," Platt said nervously. "There are other ways of getting the slave back."

Jasper Hyde labored to breathe as he sank onto a nearby chair. He gripped his cane with both hands and tried to fight the pain that was once again raging through him.

"It is fortunate that Lady Wentworth was the one winning the slave," Platt offered reasonably. "She owes you a fortune in promissory notes. And she has no credit available to her at all. She bid five times the value of the slave woman and might not even have enough funds available to pay for the purchase. Either through Dombey's creditors or Lady Wentworth's lawyer, I could have the slave woman in your possession by the end of the week."

Hyde considered that for a moment, waiting for the pain to pass. When he stood up, the clerk, Harry, cowered against the wall. The plantation owner turned to Platt.

"You make certain of that," Jasper Hyde instructed his lawyer. "Time is running short."

The articles lay before her on the brick hearth of the small fireplace. They were no more than a few things

Ohenewaa had been able to hide in the sleeves of her ragged shift. A few stones, the crumbled broken bark of a tree, some dried leaves, a small satchel with a few strands of hair. The old woman poured a few drops of water onto the hearth and placed a small piece of bread as an offering next to the charms. She had much for which to give thanks, and she knew the spirits were listening as she knelt by the makeshift altar.

Reaching into the hearth, Ohenewaa took a fistful of warm ashes and spread them on her face and hands and arms. The ancient chant started low in her chest. Rocking back and forth where she sat, she thanked the Supreme Being, Onyame, for her deliverance from Jasper Hyde. She chanted her gratitude for having the shackles once again removed from her hands and feet and neck.

What was to become of her was still a mystery. She had been delivered to the office of the lawyer, Sir Oliver Birch, in the early afternoon. The tall Englishman had the name of a tree, she thought. Perhaps he had a soul, as well.

The lawyer had looked in on her a little later and had explained that the lady at the wharf had already signed the papers freeing her. A free woman, he had said. The words were difficult to comprehend fully. A free woman.

But the lawyer had also said that this same woman, Lady Wentworth, would be pleased if Ohenewaa would accompany her to her country estate in Hertfordshire. The lawyer had explained that there were many freed slaves who lived and worked at Melbury Hall, and Lady Wentworth thought that Ohenewaa might know some of them from her years in Jamaica.

Ohenewaa remembered the name Wentworth very well. She remembered clearly the people's celebration when news of Squire Wentworth's death reached the sugar plantations in Jamaica. But that was before Jasper Hyde's iron fist had closed around their throats.

At the sound of a knock on the door, she ceased her chanting. The door slowly opened, and a young woman's face appeared, peering in with uncertainty. "May I come in?"

The blue eyes were large and curious, taking in the articles on the hearth. They turned soft and the lips thinned when she looked at the ragged shift and the blanket covering Ohenewaa. Neither bit of cloth did much to hide the ugly bruises around her collar or her wrists.

"I'm Violet," the young woman said softly, opening the door a little. Ohenewaa could see the woman was holding a tray in her arms, but she did not enter immediately. "I'm Lady Wentworth's personal maid. She sent me here to see to your needs until we are ready to leave for Melbury Hall tomorrow morning. May I come in?"

Ohenewaa studied the young woman's pretty dress, no doubt a hand-me-down from her lady's wardrobe. The old woman nodded slowly, but did not rise.

"They told me there was some water and bread left here, but I brought you some hot food. My lady said that—good as he is—we shouldn't put too much faith in an old bachelor like Sir Oliver." She placed the tray she was carrying on the table beside the narrow bed and glanced around. A pitcher of water and a washbasin were on a small chest by the foot of the bed.

"I am sorry not to have thought of bringing you a dress to change into. But I'll leave you my cloak, and we'll be at Melbury Hall by tomorrow afternoon. Once we get there, Lady Wentworth—and Mrs. Page and Amina, of course—will see to it that you have everything you need."

The girl rubbed her hands up and down her arms. "Would you mind if I added some more wood to the fire? 'Tis really quite cold in here."

Ohenewaa was surprised that the servant asked. The girl was waiting for permission from an old slave.

"Do as you please."

Rubbing the chafed skin on her wrists, Ohenewaa pushed herself to her feet and went to sit on the edge of the bed. The young woman walked cautiously—perhaps even respectfully, she thought—around the items on the hearth before kneeling down and stacking more wood in the fireplace.

"You were praying," Violet said. Soft golden curls framed the woman's pale face when she glanced over her shoulder at Ohenewaa. "I admire that."

"As a Christian, that does not bother you?"

"No! I admire it. This is an altar, is it not? I know you see the altar as the threshold of heaven, as the 'face of God' . . . more or less."

"How is it that you know as much?"

"I have many African friends at Melbury Hall, and I have the opportunity of spending many hours with them, especially with the women. For some of them, their beliefs are much stronger than mine, even if they aren't . . . well, strictly Christian."

"Is that so?"

"I realized, for one thing, that they believe they are never alone, despite being taken away from their kin, as they were. They believe the spirits of their ancestors are always with them."

"You do not like to be alone."

"No. To be honest, I do not." Violet shook her head and stood up. "And I'm glad you're coming back with us. I'll be back in a moment. I need to find a tinderbox."

Ohenewaa watched the servant leave the room, and she stared at the open door. For the first time in her sixty years of living, she was free.

That knowledge alone, though, brought little joy. She knew how hard a place the world was. She knew what misery it could inflict. She might be free, as the lawyer said, but she had no place to go. No money to buy her bread. No job to earn money. She continued to be a slave in their society.

The one thing they had not asked her about was if she was willing to go with these people to the country. They assumed she would be grateful for the chance. Perhaps she should be. Ohenewaa went to the basin and washed her face and hands. She was finally a free woman, but the world remained the same.

As Violet came in again and bent to the task of lighting the fire, Ohenewaa considered Lady Wentworth's gesture. The woman had sent her own servant to see to the needs of a slave.

Perhaps going to Melbury Hall would be a new beginning. Or perhaps not. For a slave, nothing but death was a certainty.

Chapter 4

"I know this news is quite sudden, so please apologize to our people for the additional burden I am putting on them with all that must be done. But Lord Aytoun could be arriving at any time, and I truly need everyone's assistance in readying ourselves."

Millicent stood by the fire in the library, warming herself as she addressed the steward and the housekeeper. The journey up from London had been damp and cold. With her maidservant, Violet, and the old black woman riding in the carriage, Millicent and a groom had ridden behind, and a bitter winter wind had cut into her the entire way. But the physical discomfort of the trip had been nothing compared to the upheaval in her mind. Making a simple country house like Melbury Hall presentable enough to receive an earl was a challenge that Millicent had no confidence in facing. During her brief time in the dowager's company, she had heard a great deal about Baronsford, the Aytoun castle. She'd even seen a painting of it on one of the walls. And, having seen the magnificence of his town house in London, she could only imagine how grand her new husband's home was in the Borders of Scotland. Millicent's mind now reeled from her feelings of inadequacy.

"But really, m'lady!" The steward's protest cut through her thoughts. "Doing all of this today? What you ask is absolutely impossible. 'Tis already midafternoon. There is certainly not enough time to—"

"Mr. Draper," Millicent interrupted, already well ac-

quainted with the man's querulous nature and finding
herself short of patience. "We shall certainly have *less*
time if we dally here and argue over what can or cannot
be done. Now, kindly relay my instructions to the
grooms in the stables regarding the necessary space for
his lordship's carriage . . . or carriages . . . and horses.
Then relay the news to Jonah with my instructions for
the rest of the servants regarding the urgency of the
situation. Mrs. Page and I need to see to the immediate
need for living accommodations."

The tip of the steward's thin nose rose a few inches
in the air before he turned toward the door. Millicent
hoped the man was smart enough to realize that there
was also an immediate need for a change in his attitude
before he was introduced to Lord Aytoun. She saw
Draper pause by the door.

"What about the African woman? She refuses to
speak. Even her own people have not been able to convince her to take more than a step into the kitchens.
Why, the woman won't let go of that horrid rag she has
wrapped about her, either. Do you wish to have her
left where she has situated herself, blocking one of the
kitchen doors?"

Millicent silently reproached herself for not seeing
that the woman was immediately situated. Violet had
mentioned that she had refused the food last night and
even declined the offer of wearing a cloak over her rags.

"She is to be treated as a guest in this house, Mr.
Draper, but I will go and see to her needs myself as
soon as I am finished here with Mrs. Page."

"Before you uproot and offend everyone in the household, m'lady," the steward commented sharply, "you
should know that there is no space remaining whatsoever on the third floor. With so many of the field hands
who were formerly housed in the Grove now cluttering
up the household staff's quarters, there isn't a spare
place for her. Therefore, I recommend once again that
you reconsider your decision not to use the Grove
shacks. Any of those places would be a castle compared
to where she has been."

Along a bend in the river just beyond the glen lay the cluster of decrepit huts where Wentworth used to house many of the Africans he'd held as slaves at Melbury Hall. It was called the Grove. After his death, one of Millicent's first projects had been to move the people from that dark and dismal area of the manor land.

"I told you I will look after her myself, Mr. Draper. You may leave now."

Neither woman spoke until the steward had left the drawing room.

"You can always house her in one of Mr. Draper's rooms, m'lady. He is forever complaining that the two rooms he now occupies are unsatisfactory compared with what he was accustomed to with his previous employer."

"Do you think he would willingly surrender his sitting room to our new guest?"

There was mischief dancing in the housekeeper's eyes. "I think he'd quit at a mere suggestion of such a thing, m'lady."

Millicent shook her head. "I'm afraid I cannot allow that to happen right now, Mrs. Page. Though Mr. Draper maintains the record for anyone holding the steward's position since my husband's . . . my previous husband's death, this would not be a very good time to lose him. Finding and keeping a steward who believes in what we are attempting to do here is a daunting task, it seems."

"The problem is not with you, m'lady, but with these ignorant men who think that because you have no husband ordering you about, they should be taking over the job."

"Perhaps, Mary. But the real truth is that you are the one whom I really cannot do without." She touched the woman appreciatively on the arm. Millicent's previous worries edged again into her thoughts. "As to the rooms, how difficult would it be to prepare Squire Wentworth's old chambers for the earl?"

"The rooms have been kept clean. I had the bedding aired while you were in London, and with some fresh sheets and bedclothes, they'll be ready. I can go up and start right now."

"I should have arranged for some new furnishings in there before now."

"You haven't been in there for some time, m'lady. But they are just fine as they are."

"You should have a fire prepared to be lit if his lordship should arrive today," she said resignedly. "We also need to have the small guest room across the way ready for the earl's doctor. I am not really certain if he will be traveling with his lordship or how long he will be staying, but I want to be ready. Also, the other room by the servants' stairs. Hopefully, that would be suitable for the earl's manservant."

"It should, m'lady. He'll be able to hear his master call from there, I should think. As for the rest of them, I know that some of the field hands have put the loft in the dairy to rights for their own quarters. They could move out there anytime, now. Then, if need be, I can move two of the girls in with Vi and that will make space for . . ."

The housekeeper continued her planning, but Millicent's mind was caught up with the problem she'd been facing for some time now. After moving everyone out of the Grove, she had housed as many as she could in the few empty cottages in the outlying farms, and the rest in the servants' quarters in the house. But all of that had been temporary and very difficult during the hectic harvest days. With her limited funds, she had not even been able to think about any new buildings or renovations. But now, with her marriage, so many exciting possibilities presented themselves. Perhaps clearing more land along the river and building decent cottages for the field workers. Perhaps draining the marshy lowland and erecting a stone wall to contain the river during the spring. She paused, wondering if the Earl of Aytoun would consider staying at this crowded country manor long enough for her to start any of these projects.

"How many servants will be accompanying his lordship, m'lady?"

"Half a dozen, I should think. Perhaps more."

"And what should I instruct the kitchen staff as far as the earl's likes and dislikes?"

"I am not really certain. He is a Scot. What do Scots eat?"

"I'm sure I don't know, m'lady. Where would you think he'll be taking his meals?"

Millicent shook her head. "He is confined to a chair or a bed. We shall simply have to wait until he is here before we can make those decisions."

"And what about the furnishings in this room? Do you believe the earl will be spending his mornings here?"

Millicent glanced about at the old but comfortable chairs of the library and realized she wasn't sure how her new husband would be spending his days. There was a great deal she didn't know about him. She had never really thought of Melbury Hall as being small until now. Millicent's own bedchamber would be on the same floor as his. She would be within hearing if he should call, too. There would be no ignoring his presence.

Doubts about what she had done began to nag at her. "I am afraid he might find this place completely inadequate."

"You're worrying about too much right now, I think, m'lady. This is a fine home, and you're a perfect hostess. There is no use in upsetting yourself by guessing what he might think or do. The good Lord is sure to get everything working properly."

Mary's consoling words made Millicent nod in resignation. The two of them started for the door.

Beneath the vaulted ceiling of the entry foyer, four servants stood by the open front door, obviously agitated. At the sight of Millicent, the doorman ran toward her. "In the courtyard, m'lady. A carriage, two wagons, and a half-dozen serving men riding behind. He's here. His manservant said I should tell ye the Earl of Aytoun has arrived."

"Run, Mrs. Page! Get a couple of your people to ready the rooms. Also, find Mr. Draper. I need the two of you and everyone else in the yard to greet his lordship."

Receiving a quick nod from her before the house-keeper scurried off, Millicent rushed past the wide stair-case toward the front door. Before she reached it, though, a panicked voice from behind brought her to a sudden stop. Millicent whirled toward the young maid-servant hurrying toward her.

"What is it, Violet?"

"She's dead, m'lady! Ohenewaa! She just went down where she was standing in the kitchen. I don't think she's breathing."

Without hesitation, Millicent turned her steps toward the kitchen. She waved a hand at the doorman. "Tell his lordship's people I shall greet him in a mo—"

"M'lady!" a groom shouted as he ran in a doorway leading to the gardens. "They're killin' each other, for sure."

"Who is killing whom?"

"Mr. Draper and Jonah, ma'am. Something the stew-ard said. I saw old Moses headin' that way. Now, you know there's no stoppin' him if he thinks someone is hurtin' Jonah."

"Oh, no!" Millicent lifted the hem of her skirts and ran toward the door. "Go to the courtyard and help with the Earl of Aytoun's entourage."

As she went out, she prayed under her breath that the old woman was still alive and that the earl would not be offended by her tardiness in greeting him. Most of all, though, she prayed that Moses would not do anything that might cause irreparable harm to himself or to any-one else. Not again.

The dawn mists hung between the shadowy trees, the dew dripping from dark green leaves. The pistol, silver and pearl, looked to be but an extension of Lyon's hand. He glanced briefly in the direction of the two men in the distance, their images blurred by the mist enshroud-ing them.

A somber voice called out, the sound echoing and

then dying away. Lyon listened to the far-off burbling of the river, to the waking cry of a startled bird. He inhaled the damp, earthy smell of the park as if this were the last he might have the privilege to breathe.

As his foe raised his pistol, pointing the muzzle at the steel-gray sky, Lyon did the same. *How many men must die,* he thought. He watched the fop by the tree extend his hand. A kerchief dangled from his lily-colored fingers . . . and then fluttered to the ground.

Before Lyon could pull the trigger, the mist cleared around the ghostlike face of his opponent.

Pierce stood facing him. David, their youngest brother, stood as his second. And then the shot rang out.

Lyon awoke with a start, sweat drenching his face.

Only another dream, he told himself. *Just another nightmare.* He struggled to shake himself free. He had been sleeping for what felt like an eternity. They had given him one of those damned drinks again before they had set out on the road this morning.

The carriage was not moving, he realized. He looked about the confined space and found that his manservant, Gibbs, was not there, either.

The curtain on the far window of the carriage had been tied back. He stared out and all he could see were walls of brick and a high iron gate. He could not rise above the confusion clouding his mind. He could not think clearly. Then, though he fought to contain it, panic began to gnaw at him.

Bedlam. They had told him they were taking him to the woman's house in the country, but they had lied. He was at Bedlam.

Anger swept away his panic as quickly as a Highland storm sweeps away the sun. *One more bloody betrayal.* He tore the blanket off his lap with his good hand. He would not be a prisoner in an institution. He was not insane.

Lyon shoved himself away from the seat, away from the images of high iron gates. But even as he tried to escape, his body collapsed under him in a heap of twisted bones and flesh. Jammed painfully between the carriage seats, he stared out through a small opening between the curtains covering the opposite window. All he could see were the tall chimneys of a house.

At that moment, where they had taken him made no difference to Lyon. He was a lonely cripple, less than half a man. His real life was over, and he wanted release. If they would but give him a pistol, he would put a quick end to this accursed existence.

"You are dismissed, Mr. Draper."

Millicent's voice echoed against the garden walls that bordered the path leading down the hill toward the Grove. She'd heard the steward's shrill voice as soon as she left the house, proclaiming both her incompetence and her corrupted nature in bringing the infamous Scottish "Lord of Scandal" under her roof as husband. Jonah had stepped forward to defend her, and now violence was clearly imminent.

"You are fired. Dismissed." She stood short steps from the two men. The steward's contemptuous gaze never moved from Jonah's angry face. He didn't appear to be listening. "Now! You are to get your things and leave Melbury Hall immediately."

"This business has nothing to do with you, m'lady," he said, still glaring at Jonah. "This is between me and this insolent slave."

"There are no slaves at Melbury Hall, Mr. Draper. You are the insolent one here. I heard what you said just now. Jonah, as my servant, has every right to defend me against the disrespectful things you said about me."

Millicent glanced at old Moses and thanked the Lord that he had remained a bystander thus far. Beneath his hair of mottled gray, the man's face showed the scars of innumerable beatings by slavers and by owners like Wentworth. Millicent knew, though, that despite his size and the fierce look born of his mutilated features, Moses was one of the gentlest souls alive . . . so long as no one tried to hurt Jonah. She turned back to Draper.

"Now I tell you again, return to the house and pack your belongings this instant."

"Not until I am finished with him." The steward took a step toward Jonah.

Millicent quickly put herself in the path of Moses as the large black man moved toward the steward. She placed a hand on his arm and shook her head at him.

She shot a look toward the house, hoping that some of the servants would be coming. She feared that Jonah would not defend himself. After so many years of being beaten and abused as a slave, he could not be expected to assert his rights as a free man. Bright and competent as he was, Jonah was still struggling with his new job as bailiff. The freedman was extremely capable, but lacked confidence.

Someone was indeed coming down the path, though it took Millicent a moment to realize it was Gibbs, the earl's personal servant, whom she had met for the briefest of moments yesterday after the marriage service in London.

"The mistress told you to pack your bag, Mr. Draper," Jonah ordered.

"I'll teach you to open your ugly mouth to your betters."

Millicent turned in time to see Jonah being pushed backward off the path.

"Stop. This instant," she screamed at the steward as her hands clung desperately to Moses's arm to keep him from advancing. If Draper struck Jonah, Moses would kill the man. Of that Millicent was certain. She didn't know if she could hold him much longer. "I ordered you to leave these premises."

As the steward lifted his fist, Millicent was shocked to see Gibbs stride past her, grab the back of the attacker's coat, and throw him to the ground with no more effort than one might expend plucking a bad apple off a tree.

"Ye have a wee bit of trouble following the mistress's directions, sir?" He put his silver-buckled shoe on the back of Draper's neck and shoved the man's face hard against the frozen ground.

The earl's manservant was a tall, barrel-chested Scotsman with thick black hair tied at the collar. In addition to his menacing dark eyes and bushy eyebrows, it was impossible not to notice the size of Gibbs's huge fists. This was not a man to be trifled with, she realized. Obviously Draper thought so too. It was stunning to see the fight knocked out of the steward so quickly.

"I heard her ladyship tell ye to leave, ye bloated cur."

"I was about to. I am, sir. As soon as you release me."

Still not lessening the pressure of his boot, Gibbs nodded politely to Millicent. "If your ladyship would like to go in out of this cold, these men here can help me dispose of this ill-mannered dog on the road to St. Albans."

"I believe Jonah and Moses would be happy to assist you, Mr. Gibbs." She turned her attention to the man on the ground. "Your things will be sent to the Black Swan Inn at Knebworth Village."

The look on Draper's face, beneath the shoe of the Scotsman, was not that of a happy man.

Millicent glanced up toward the house. "Has his lordship been brought in, Mr. Gibbs?"

"Nay, m'lady. Lord Aytoun was sleeping, so I left him in the carriage. I thought ye might prefer to greet him yourself before we moved him."

"Of course," she whispered, knowing the importance of such protocol. But Vi's earlier news about the collapse of Ohenewaa in the kitchen preyed on her mind. Gibbs must have noticed her gaze in the direction of the house.

"If ye please, m'lady. As I came through the servants' hall, your wee housekeeper asked me to relay a word to ye about the African woman in the kitchen. The woman is fine and has come about."

"Thank you." Millicent was indeed grateful for Gibbs's intervention, and Jonah appeared much more at ease as well. She saw him grab Draper by the scruff of his neck and yank him roughly to his feet when the Scotsman removed his boot. "I think I shall go around the house to the courtyard and greet his lordship."

Not until she rounded the corner of the manor house did she feel the cold wind penetrating her dress. She started to shiver. For the first time since charging out, Millicent realized that she had on no cloak or shawl.

At a respectful distance from the carriage, a number of her servants had lined up in greeting. As she went past them, she saw Mrs. Page rush out of the front door and—with a curtsy to Millicent—take her place beside the assembled staff.

The earl's servants as well stood waiting by their horses and wagons in the courtyard. Intensely aware of the dozens of eyes on both sides watching her every move, Millicent tried her best to hide her nervousness and approached the carriage with confident steps.

From the outside, she could not see in clearly through the curtains, but there appeared to be no one sitting in the carriage. At her nod, the footman opened the door.

The earl was twisted, helpless, wedged between the seats in the most awkward position. She saw her new husband's eyes open as the light from behind her poured inside the carriage. Millicent hurriedly stepped over his sprawled boots and climbed in, pulling the door closed behind her. He didn't have to say anything. She knew this was not the way he would wish to be introduced to his new household.

"I am so very sorry, m'lord. You have fallen down from the seat." Trying clumsily to find solid footing in the cramped space, she tried to bend his knees and straighten his boots. "The roads traveling up from London are not in the best condition, and nothing is worse than enduring a long trip like that to a strange place and . . ."

Millicent knew she was jabbering, but her embarrassment at not greeting him immediately was compounded by the sharpness of the earl's glare. She crouched down in the cramped space between the seats and searched for his right arm. It was twisted behind him.

"If you would be kind enough to place your other arm around my neck, perhaps I could lift you a little, and we could free this arm."

The earl did not respond, and she glanced up at his bearded face. His expression was intimidating, but she decided the tenseness she saw in his blue eyes had to be caused in some part by pain. This made her all the more determined.

"Please, m'lord. If you could just—"

"Gibbs. Get him."

Millicent was relieved to get some response. "He is coming, but—"

"Get Gibbs," he said louder.

"I have no intention of moving you inside by myself. I just thought it would be more comfortable for you to be sitting on the seat, instead of where you are."

She stopped, feeling like a liar for not speaking the whole truth. For a moment, she vividly recalled a time when she herself had sat inside the carriage, battered by Wentworth, desperate to hide her face from the prying eyes outside the door. Hiding the truth had always been Millicent's way of avoiding the embarrassment of her husband's horrible treatment. But the Earl of Aytoun's condition was nothing like hers.

"I am sorry, m'lord. I was acting without thinking."

She drew back and sat on the edge of the seat. "Your steward was kind enough to get involved with a problem I had with one of my workers. He should be back momentarily."

"*Gibbs!*"

The man's shout in the confined space of the carriage was startling. A vision of Squire Wentworth with the veins bulging in his neck, with his clutching hands reaching for her face, flashed before Millicent's mind. She quickly buried the terrifying image in the recesses of her mind. With her heart pounding in her chest, Millicent quelled her impulse to fling open the door and leap out. Through the small window, she could see the curious glances of the servants in the courtyard.

"I told you that he would be coming back shortly, m'lord," she said, keeping her tone reasonable.

"*Gibbs!*"

The impotent fury that laced his shout drew Millicent off the edge of the seat. She crouched beside him again. "Tell me how I can help you. It is your arm, is it not?" This time she didn't bother to ask for his cooperation. Instead, looping an arm around his waist, she desperately tried to shift him enough to free the arm. She just could not muster the strength to move him. And the earl was doing nothing to help her. Nonetheless, she continued to try.

When Gibbs yanked open the carriage door a minute later, Millicent's hair had already escaped the tight bun on top of her head, her dress was crumpled and twisted, and her body was tangled on the floor with the Earl of Aytoun's. Out of breath, her face flushed, she looked up at the manservant, who stopped to stare with one eyebrow raised.

"Pardon me, m'lady, I didna know ye planned to start your honeymoon quite so soon."

Chapter 5

"There is no physician traveling with them," Millicent advised the housekeeper a few minutes later as they were heading toward the kitchen. "But Mr. Gibbs informed me that a Dr. Parker will be coming once a fortnight from London and will remain with us overnight. So for the moment, I should like to put Ohenewaa in the chamber you've prepared for the doctor."

To Mary's credit, she never even batted an eye at the suggestion of putting the woman in one of the guest bedchambers.

"She needs a bath, m'lady, and some clothes. Violet tells me that on the ride up from London, the woman scarcely spoke a word. One of the girls was able to spoon some broth into her when she was just coming around, but as soon as she knew which end was up, the poor dear went back to her place by the kitchen door. Curious thing, though, as quick as word went round that she was here, I've had more field hands poking their heads into that kitchen to see her. But still she continues to stare at the wall. If you don't mind my asking, m'lady, who is she?"

"I believe she is seen as someone very special. I don't know her entire history, but I do know she belonged to a physician named Dombey, who traveled on many slave ships and lived in Jamaica between his travels. Before I even went to London, I had heard numerous stories of this woman's courage. Even as Dr. Dombey's slave, she was well known for the many ways she helped people on the sugar plantations there, my late husband's included."

In the kitchen, Mrs. Page went off to organize her staff of workers. Millicent was relieved to see Amina already there and speaking quietly with the old woman. Married to Jonah last summer, the younger woman was quickly becoming Mary's right hand in running the house at Melbury Hall.

"All of us are grateful to you, m'lady, for bringing her here," Amina said quietly, joining her mistress in the middle of the kitchen.

"She looks hungry and weary." Millicent watched the tall, thin frame of Ohenewaa sway near the door. "Why is she refusing to come inside?"

"Her pride. Not knowing what is expected of her here."

Giving an understanding nod, Millicent walked toward the old woman. Ohenewaa's dark eyes remained fixed on the wall in front of her. Hers was a face lined by age and disappointment.

"We're happy you're here, Ohenewaa," Millicent said softly. "There is no need for you to stand by the door. Would you please come in?"

"I was told I am a free woman."

"You are."

"Then I do not wish to step inside a slaveholder's home." The old woman's gaze shifted to Millicent's face and then back to the wall again.

"I do not hold any slaves, Ohenewaa. I do not believe in owning or abusing innocent people. All the workers you see at Melbury Hall today, regardless of the color of their skin, or where they were born or came from, are here of their own will."

"I have seen how Wentworth treated his workers in Jamaica."

Millicent could hear the diamond edge of the woman's voice draw steadily across glass.

"That was my husband. Not I," Millicent replied passionately. "And I am trying, Ohenewaa. Since the death of the squire, I am doing my best to mend some of the injustices done to the people. I lost those plantations in Jamaica before anything could be done. But I am trying here."

The black woman's gaze once again moved away from the wall and rested on Millicent's face. "What do you wish from me? What do I have to do to earn my keep?"

Millicent paused to answer. The dark, penetrating gaze continued to look into her soul.

"It would be a lie if I said you have to do nothing. We need help of all kinds. The truth is that I don't know yet what you can do here." This time she was the one who fixed her gaze on the cracks running in every direction on the wall. "I came to the auction yesterday because I recognized Dr. Dombey's name in the notice in the newspaper. I came because I had failed to act effectively when Jasper Hyde took over Wentworth's plantations. There were so many lives that I did not save. Thoughts about if I were a stronger person, if I had acted quickly enough, continue to plague me. I wonder if, had I traveled there myself, I could have kept the plantations."

She turned to face the older woman. "In freeing you, I suppose I hope to lessen my guilt. And in bringing you here, I hoped to remind my people—and myself—that strength and courage like yours are to be aspired to."

"I am a healer. Nothing more."

"In Jamaica, you were the one person whom they knew they could trust. That was everything to them." Millicent noticed more than a few of the kitchen helpers and servants had paused in their work. Many eyes were on them, curious as to the outcome. She gentled her voice. "At least for now, until you have the opportunity for employment, will you please stay at Melbury Hall as my guest?"

"If I step across this threshold, it will not be to ease your conscience, but to ease my hunger."

Millicent smiled. "I respect that. We both have a reason. They do not conflict. And that is as good a place as any to start."

Ohenewaa looked about the room at the cluster of

hopeful faces before stepping through the door and into the house.

The air was frigid, the ground frozen. The night was dark, and the woods were threatening. Violet, however, scarcely gave the possible dangers a second thought. She had been passing through this deer park at least twice a week for over a month on her way to him. Lifting the hem of the quilted petticoats she'd been given by her mistress last month, she stepped over a fallen branch. Violet herself had embroidered the long apron she was wearing over the petticoats. And the pleated taffeta around her neck was a gift she'd bought herself when she and her mistress had been in London. She wanted to look pretty for Ned.

Ned Cranch—tall and broad with muscles as hard as rock—was a stonemason who had come in the fall to Knebworth Village to build the new grange. They had met outside church one Sunday morning. And after that, every time Vi had gone to the village, the handsome green-eyed giant had been there, tipping his hat or making some sweet remark about how good she looked or smelled.

Mrs. Page had witnessed Ned's sweet-talking a couple of times and had given Vi an earful about being careful, of course. But Violet was already eighteen, and she knew exactly what she was doing.

She was getting herself a husband.

Vi emerged from the woods and ran to the edge of the meadow above the village. He wasn't there, and Vi looked with concern at the lights in the windows of the cottages below. But before she could worry for long, powerful arms encircled her from behind, and she stifled a gasp as she was turned around in Ned's embrace.

He kissed her lips before she could whisper a greeting. His attentions were already becoming an obsession to her, and Vi dug her fingers into his thick, wavy blond hair and opened up to him so he could deepen the kiss the way he'd taught her. At last he tore his mouth away, but his hands continued to press her to him.

"I've missed you so much, Ned," she whispered while kissing the muscular column of his throat.

"Aye, lass, I know the feeling." He tossed his chin in the direction that she had come. "And with all the big doings at Melbury Hall, I didn't know if ye'd be getting away."

She looked at him in surprise. "You heard about it already?"

"Some. Ye know how village folk talk." His mouth dipped to her neck, and she shivered as his teeth nibbled and his lips brushed over her skin. "I've been looking forward to this since I saw ye last."

"You are the devil, Ned Cranch." She sighed.

"Who told ye?" he said with a laugh. "But tell me, Vi, is it true that yer lady has fetched herself a new husband?"

"As sure as I'm standing here," Violet managed to say, almost purring with pleasure as he kneaded her breast through the dress. Ned's caresses had become more and more intimate with each meeting. At the beginning, it had been only kisses. Over the past couple of weeks, though, Ned had begun touching her in places that made Violet shudder with excitement. But touching had been the extent of it. Vi knew that—in spite of Mrs. Page's words of warning buzzing in her head—not much could happen if they kept their pleasures at this.

"And they're saying she brought herself back a new slave as well." Ned's hand moved down over her stomach.

"An old woman." Vi closed her eyes and leaned into him as his hand reached the junction of her thighs. "Her name is Ohenewaa, and she is already freed."

"Ye can tell me all about it later." His lips took hers in a dizzying kiss. Suddenly he pulled away and wrapped his hand around her wrist. "Come with me."

"Where are we going?"

His eyes danced with mischief when he looked at her. "Back to my room at the Black Swan. We'll go in through the back door, lass. Nobody will see ye."

Violet hesitated. What he surely had in mind was the

one thing that she was hoping to avoid, at least until he asked her to marry him.

"What's wrong with staying here?"

Ned put his arms around her and placed his hands on her buttocks as he kissed her. She could feel the size of him as he rubbed himself hard against her. "What I want to do to ye, my sweet, means taking every stitch of your pretty clothes off and then kissing every inch of your skin. Now, we can do that here, if ye like, but 'twould be a mite cold, I should think."

Her body was on fire, but her brain was still working.

"Ned, I don't think we should." Vi was sorry the moment she voiced her objection, for a look of hurt came into his eyes. "You know I've never . . . well, never done this before. 'Tis just that I am nervous. Afraid, to be honest."

"Nothing to be afraid of. But I'm in no hurry, lass. We'll stay right here, if ye like." He smiled and led her to a fallen tree at the edge of the woods.

"You don't mind, Ned?" she said as he pulled her onto his lap. "Really?"

"Nay, my dream. And I know just how to get your mind off your worries." He caressed her thighs, sliding his hand slowly upward until she drew in a breath sharply. "Aye, ye just think of Melbury Hall and tell me whatever ye want about it. And I'll kiss your neck—this pretty little spot here below your ear—and ye can keep talking. How's that?"

"Are you sure—" She gasped as he rubbed harder. "Are you sure you're not put off?"

"Put off? Nay, lass." He lifted his head. "In fact, I wasn't going to say this now, but perhaps 'tis for the best."

"What is it?"

"I love ye, Vi."

"You do?"

"Aye," he said, turning his attentions back to her neck. "But tell me what's doing at the Hall."

Chapter 6

$\mathbf{I}$t seemed quite awkward to Millicent, retiring for the night without having seen or spoken with the Earl of Aytoun again. His man, Gibbs, and two of the valets had taken their master to his chambers after the ordeal in the courtyard. At his request, she'd had dinner sent upstairs. The earl's servants appeared quite proficient in seeing to all of his needs.

No complaints. No requests. Everything had been deathly quiet since dinner. But as she left Mary in the servants' hall, Millicent couldn't shake off the nagging feeling that merely giving Lord Aytoun a suite of rooms was not at all what the dowager countess had wanted when she asked Millicent to marry her son. She had clearly stated that she wanted someone with compassion.

To bring herself to the point of getting closer to her new husband, though, Millicent had to crush the seeds of anxiety inside of her. In the few short hours that she had spent in London after marrying him, she had heard a number of grim reports about Lyon Pennington. The man had a notorious temper. He had definitely fought at least four duels during the spring before his accident. There were rumors of others, too. And there was a general belief that he had killed his wife.

Wentworth had killed his first wife. And on more than a few occasions, he had nearly taken Millicent's life, too. She cringed, remembering the first time. In her mind's eye, she could still see him taking his riding crop and approaching her. She had stood disbelieving at what was happening. They had been married less than a month. It was a miracle that she had survived him, survived their marriage.

Still shivering, Millicent recalled the first time she had met the earl, a silent man with dark hair and an un-trimmed beard covering a pale face. His blue gaze had been restless, but not hostile. Even today, when she had been trying to help him in the carriage and he had be-come angry, fear of him had never entered her mind. Sympathy and worry perhaps, but not fear.

Different situation, she told herself. *A very different man.*

Climbing the wide stairwell from the entry foyer, Mil-licent moved down the hallway past her own bedcham-ber. She paused at the door to Ohenewaa's room. The old woman had confined herself to her room tonight. Millicent felt better about that situation, at least, know-ing that Amina had gone in a couple of times, directing servants who had brought in a tub and water for wash-ing, and later food and several changes of clothing for the woman.

There were so many things pulling at Millicent's mind. Things such as how to make the old woman feel safe at Melbury Hall. And how she was going to advertise for the position of steward to replace Mr. Draper. And where she should spend her new income. She told her-self that she needed to sit down and decide what should be done first.

Too tired to put her thoughts in any manageable order, she turned toward the earl's chambers and lifted her hand to knock.

She paused, recalling the misery she had endured when Wentworth was in possession of these rooms. At times she would break into a cold sweat just coming this near the door. Once again, she pushed the fears back and knocked softly.

Gibbs opened the door, and one brow arched in sur-prise. "Lady Aytoun."

Millicent stared at him for a moment. No one had called her that before, and she was not accustomed to

the name yet. Lady Aytoun. She managed, at least, not
to look behind her in search of the mystery woman.

"Is the earl sleeping, Mr. Gibbs?"

"Aye, m'lady." He stepped back, opening the door
wider.

Millicent could see part of the bed and the man sleeping on it. She didn't come into the room. "Did he have
any dinner?"

"I am afraid his lordship had no appetite after so
many hours on the road today. But he tried some of the
soup, thank ye."

"Does someone stay with him all the time?"

"We try to, m'lady, at least when he's awake."

She gave a nod of approval, remembering how helpless he had seemed today, wedged between the carriage seats.

"What is the earl fond of doing, Mr. Gibbs?" It was an
unexpected question, she realized, as the servant seemed
perplexed as to how to answer. "What I meant to say
was, how does he prefer to spend his days now?"

"Well, he spends most of it in bed or in his chair."

"No, what I want to know is whether he likes to read,
or does someone read to him? Does he have a favorite
newspaper that I should have delivered? Is he fond of
playing at cards?"

"Nay, m'lady, none of that. His lordship likes to stare
outside, and that is the extent of it, I'm sorry to say."

A twinge of sympathy pinched at Millicent. What kind
of life was that for anyone? she thought. She made a
silent vow to establish a better routine for her husband.
She gave a final glance toward the sleeping man on the
bed. He looked subdued, certainly not the hellion that
he was reputed to be. "Are your own sleeping arrangements satisfactory, Mr. Gibbs?"

"Aye, they are far better than I expected, m'lady. I
thank ye kindly."

"Very well. Good night, then." She turned toward her
own rooms.

"Lady Aytoun." Gibbs stepped into the hallway after

her. "Since I'm to be here, if you think of anything around Melbury Hall that I might be helping ye with, speak out, for I'm willing. I do not think his lordship would mind."

Millicent knew from the dowager countess that the Scotsman had been with Lord Aytoun for years.

"You saw me fire Mr. Draper today. Perhaps you can help me as I try to find a replacement for him."

"Aye, m'lady. Whatever I can do to help, I am here to oblige."

Millicent nodded gratefully and turned away. As she walked back toward her own bedchamber, though, she found herself thinking not of the relief of having extra help, but of the man she'd found wedged helplessly between the seats of a carriage, and seeing in her mind the defeated look in his eyes.

"Why in the devil's name would you accept payment from her?" Jasper Hyde hissed at the other man. "You know damn well once she got the slave, everything changed."

"My apologies, sir, but—"

"You and your deuced apologies can go to hell." He pounded a fist on the table. "Blasted lawyers."

Mr. Platt, a small man, folded his hands on his desk. "It was clear, Mr. Hyde, that our plans had been frustrated. I could find no way to refuse the cash payment. The amount covered all of Lady Wentworth's outstanding debts to you. Her lawyer did not even try to wheedle out of paying the interest for this month. The entire amount she owed you, correct to the last farthing, was included in the settlement sum."

The sharp pain slicing through his chest made Jasper Hyde refrain from hammering on the desk again. His hand clutched a spot just below his heart, where he felt a dagger burn and twist its way in. There were never any bruises. No symptoms that anyone could see. The few doctors he had spoken to about his ailment had told him, in so many words, that there was nothing wrong with him. The heart appeared strong, they said. He knew better. As always the pain came on sharply, then gradually eased.

"Are you unwell, Mr. Hyde?"

"Did you offer to take . . . ?" He was gradually recovering his breath. "To take the black woman as part of the settlement?"

"I did. But Sir Oliver would not consider it."

"Then you did not have to take the money."

"It was all done legally, you understand. I could not reject the payment."

"And since when do you stick to legalities, Platt?" Hyde planted both hands on the desk and glowered menacingly at the lawyer. "You seem to be having a hard time understanding me. You told me that she has no credit at all available. That she would not be able to pay for the woman."

"Mr. Hyde, there was no way of knowing that she would marry the Earl of Aytoun that very day."

Hyde cursed his damnable luck. Yesterday, hearing all the rumors about the fallen earl, he'd not once imagined the crippled bastard would be ruining his plans.

"We are *not* going to let anyone stop us. Do you understand me?"

Hyde's fist landed hard on the desk again, scattering a pile of papers and making the lawyer jump as the candle wobbled in its holder. Platt tried to straighten the documents before him.

"What is done we cannot und—"

With a sweep of his hand, Hyde cleared the lawyer's desk of all the papers, scattering them across the chamber. "I want the old slave, Platt. *Now.*"

Sweat beaded on the lawyer's brow and ran down his temple. Hyde knew Platt did not want to face his fury. Many words were left unsaid between them, but the intimation was clear. Hyde was certain the black witch had cursed him. The pains in his chest. The change in his luck. He did not need more proof than this.

"In a fortnight or so, sir, we may still be successful in making another offer for the slave."

"You said yourself that she doesn't need the blasted money. Besides, she'll never sell the woman to me."

"Perhaps you might present yourself in a different light. Perhaps you can tell her you have seen the error in your ways. That you wish to employ the woman to help with the health of the slaves in Jamaica. She did have the benefit of assisting Dr. Dombey, I understand."

"You are a fool!" Jasper exploded. "There is not a chance in the world that she'd fall for such a ruse. She'd see through it in a moment."

"I am simply suggesting, sir, that money is not the only method we have to persuade her. She is just a woman, and therefore weak. In addition, she now has a crippled husband added to her burden."

"And no debts with which to crush her."

"True, and her money might not run out in the near future, so we shall need a new weapon to use against her."

"What?"

Platt's bony fingers formed a steeple. "We need to continue keeping a close eye on her."

"We need to find a way to pry her fingers off the old woman." Hyde straightened up, remembering the last meeting he'd had with Dr. Dombey. With what was practically his last breath, the old fool had spoken of honor, of how he would not sell Ohenewaa to someone like him for any price. Fearing Dombey might do something as stupid as actually freeing the woman before he died, Hyde had then simply helped the good doctor toward his eternal reward.

But his damnable luck had been against him that day too, as the slave was not there. A bailiff, representing a number of Dombey's creditors, stood outside, though, as well as several others who were attending to the dying man. Hyde knew there was no way that he would get his hands on her. He even had a good idea that she was somewhere nearby, waiting for him to leave.

"Perhaps we can somehow reason with the lady through the earl's lawyer."

Hyde dismissed Platt's comment with a wave of his

hand as a brilliant idea presented itself to him. "The doctor. Find out for me the name of the doctor who is attending to Aytoun while he is at Melbury Hall. I want you to arrange a meeting with him."

Violet wasn't aware that her boots were wet. She paid no mind to the quilted petticoats and the white apron, all mud-stained and soaked through as well. She didn't even realize that she was shivering violently. As she fled along the path through the woods by the Grove, though, tears continued to roll down her cheeks. It was still dark when she emerged from the woods, and she quickly moved up the knoll toward the back of the house.

Vi had no complaints about Ned. He had not forced her to go back to the inn. When the cold rain had begun, she'd gone willingly, giggling like a little fool the whole way. Once there, he had not rushed her, either. He had taken his time, teasing and kissing her and saying such sweet things to her. And like a wanton hussy, she had cried out in ecstasy as he had been doing all those wicked things to her.

Once she'd left him and come out into the night, though, shame had washed through her like icy rain. She became more and more horrified as she ran home, thinking how she had simply spread her legs. What made it worst of all, though, was that he'd had his way with her without any definite commitment.

As she neared the gardens, she thought back over the things he'd said. He'd said he was her man. He'd said she was his true love. He'd said . . .

She stopped and leaned against the garden wall, covering her face with her hands. He'd never said he would marry her.

"Oh God," she said in a moan. What if she was with child now?

Her mother, long a widow, was no whore. She had always been poor, but they'd always lived decently in St. Albans. And her grandmother had always been so proud of her. Years ago, her grandmum had spoken almost boldly to Lady Wentworth about how Vi must be treated before allowing her to serve as maid to the mistress.

Vi stabbed away at her tears, remembering how her grandmum always referred to her as her own innocent thing. Where had that innocence gone? Before the squire had died, Violet had been ready to kill herself rather than let him touch her. She recalled how she had hidden in one of the slave huts in the Grove so he wouldn't find her. She had been terrified, but she had survived. She had kept her maidenhead. And now she had given it up like some slut.

She had to talk to Ned. She had to make sure he understood what kind of a girl she was. But perhaps 'twas too late? A sob caught in her throat.

The house loomed in the dreary predawn light. Pushing away from the wall, Violet ran toward it. As she reached the open garden gate, though, a tall, dark figure suddenly appeared in front of her, and she barreled straight into the man, who grabbed her arms to keep her from falling.

She gasped and looked up at the scarred face. "Moses!"

The man's hands dropped back to his sides.

"What are you doing out here at this hour of the morning?" she asked gently. She knew that Moses served as a watchman at night, but she had never returned this late and had not expected to run into him.

"Vi hurt?"

The gruff tone could not mask his concern, making her feel doubly guilty. She shook her head at him. "No, Moses. I'm not hurt."

"Why is Vi crying?"

" 'Tis nothing, Moses. I was just a little sad. But I'm better now. Truly." She touched his arm before going around him and heading quickly up the hill. When she reached the door to the house, she turned and looked back at Moses. Though she couldn't see his face, he was still standing where she'd left him, watching over her until she'd gone safely in.

Chapter 7

With the Chiltern Hills rising behind it, Solgrave sat on a ridge overlooking a long, narrow lake that stretched along a handsome valley. With its fine deer park and well-tended farms, the country house of the Earl and Countess of Stanmore was truly a beautiful place, one far superior to any of its neighboring country manor houses. But the mansion's grandeur did not diminish the value of its neighbors. Solgrave conferred on them greater status merely by having the good fortune of being located in the same vicinity. This added value had been reason enough for Squire Wentworth to purchase Melbury Hall.

Of course, Millicent thought, that was before Wentworth had married her to enhance his social status. How ironic that within a few years, Rebecca Neville would come back from the American colonies, marry Lord Stanmore, and provide Millicent with an ally who would help her fight for her liberty.

Despite the different roads that they had taken, fate had certainly brought the two school friends together again after nearly a decade apart. And Millicent would be forever grateful to Rebecca and Stanmore for helping her climb back onto her feet and manage to keep Melbury Hall after the squire's death.

Mrs. Trent, the housekeeper at Solgrave, was as friendly as ever when she led Millicent to the library. Inside, the young woman had only just managed to remove her hat and gloves before her friend rushed in to meet her.

"I was going to come to Melbury Hall to see you myself this afternoon."

Millicent returned Rebecca's embrace. "I couldn't risk not seeing you during the short time you were here. I heard you are only staying overnight."

"We are on our way to visit my mother-in-law in Scotland. Depending on the traveling conditions, we should only be gone for a month, but we had to stop here." Rebecca stepped back, holding Millicent at arm's length and studying her friend carefully. "Stanmore and I couldn't believe your news. You are *married* again."

"It is true."

"To the Earl of Aytoun."

Millicent nodded.

"But you didn't know him before, did you?"

"No, I didn't."

Seeing how puzzled her friend looked, Millicent sat down on the settee with her and told her about the dowager's letter. Short of getting into the exact details of their financial arrangement, she explained everything else.

Rebecca listened quietly and then chose her words carefully. "Did you know anything about the man? About his reputation?"

"Yes. Sir Oliver forewarned me, and I have heard a great deal since. But I consider much of it simply rumor and gossip."

"Then you know that some have openly accused him of pushing his wife off the cliffs at Baronsford."

"I believe she slipped and fell—as he did, trying to go down and help her. She died, but his fate has been almost as bad. He appears to be crippled, most likely for life." Millicent shook her head. "I spoke to the dowager at length about that accident, and about the other accusations. Lord Aytoun is a much different man now than he may have been a year ago. He is quite subdued in every sense."

Rebecca's hands clutched Millicent's tightly. "You know I am not one to meddle in anyone's life, but you have been married to him only a week, and already I see the strain in your face. You look tired."

She tried to smile. "I am the one to blame for that. Not him."

"And why is that?"

Millicent rose from the settee and walked to the large window overlooking the lake. This was the same question she had been asking of herself. "When I agreed to marry him, I convinced myself that I was simply offering his family a place where Lord Aytoun would be cared for." She turned to face her friend. "You know me, Rebecca. I have no illusions about love. They were crushed out long ago. But at the same time I know the importance of having a husband. This marriage to the Earl of Aytoun presented me with the most ideal situation I could ever have hoped for. By this union, I would have gained a husband without the fear that comes with having one. I am married without having to be a wife."

"Things are not going as you planned."

"No. I . . . I find that I feel sorry for him. He has no use of his legs, his arm. He spends most of the day in a silent stupor. He is as wretched as any beggar on the side of a London street. Yet I can see the pain in his eyes. He does not want this kind of existence."

"Is there no way you can help him? Perhaps different doctors. Or by finding ways of challenging his mind, at least. There are many ways you might be able to improve the quality of his life."

Rebecca would know about this. For ten years, she had lived on her own in the colonies and raised the earl's son, James. The boy had a misshapen hand and was partly deaf.

"But . . . but I fear I have married too far above my position," Millicent blurted out. "I am certain he sees how deficient I am, and what Melbury Hall lacks."

"Even without knowing him, I doubt that is true. I know you never give yourself the credit that is due." Rebecca's voice resonated with the passion of her belief. "You said yourself he spends his days in a stupor. So there is no way for you to know what he thinks or feels. Now, as far as improving on the condition of his life, I think you should be yourself. Do what your heart tells you to do and help him as far as he lets you. And there is no reason to worry about what happens beyond that. The future is as mysterious as the man you have married. But that is true for all of us. None of us can tell what awaits us down the road."

So true, Millicent admitted. She was worrying about forever, when tomorrow was the challenge that she had to face.

Through the mist and the gloom, he could catch only glimpses of Emma. She was holding up her skirts with one hand and running like a doe, weaving in and out between the stunted pines.

The wind-driven rain was on his face, in his eyes. Lyon wiped the wetness away, trying to see her. His legs were heavy, as if he were running in deep sand. The trees and brambles tore at his face and clothes, but he could not let her go. He glanced back at Baronsford, the walls rising gloomily in the gray of the gathering storm.

Turning, Lyon saw her again, her golden hair flying behind her as she disappeared in the mist by the cliffs. The rain was stinging his face, and he slipped and stumbled on the path.

Pierce's startling revelation was still clouding his mind. The hostile accusations of his brother continued to stab at his sense of honor. But how could he defend himself against something that he was ignorant of? Emma had the answers. She had to make Lyon understand. She had to come back with him and face the truth.

Lyon's chest was burning as he regained his balance and pushed himself to run harder.

The echo of Emma's scream filled the hills.

The break in the trees came quickly, and the path was slick where it turned at the cliff. Lyon could not see the far side of the river. All was bleak and gray. The path along the bluff was empty, except for the billowy mists.

And then he saw her—there at the bottom. Her

golden hair spread around her on the rocks. Her eyes stared up at him, unseeing.

Lyon awoke with a start and stared at the unfathomable darkness that surrounded him. He was dead. He had slipped and fallen down those same cliffs.

A shadow moved over him. Cold hands pressed against the fevered skin of his new face. He stared into the concerned face of his new wife. If he was dead, it was clear that he had not won heaven.

At best, this was only purgatory.

Millicent stared out the window of the Morning Room at the shining new chaise the physician had driven up from London. A groom and his manservant stood at the head of the handsome pair of geldings, talking and stamping their feet in the cold.

Though they had been out there an hour, when Millicent had sent out hot drinks and asked them to come in for something to eat, they had declined. Dr. Parker had told them to wait with the carriage, as they would be staying for only a few moments before going on to Lord Eglinton's estate near Chiswell Green today.

She continued to pace the room. Dr. Parker had been abrupt and dismissive when she'd greeted him upon his arrival, and the doctor and his assistant had gone directly upstairs to Lord Aytoun's chambers. Aside from asking that some food be sent up, the physician had declined with a wave of his hand her offer of spending the night at Melbury Hall. His other patients, who were "too lofty in London's social circles to name," needed him. And he must return to the city immediately.

The physician's comment did not sit well with Millicent, as she again found herself being reminded of her own social position. She would never have been in Lord Aytoun's company if it were not for his accident. But despite the slight, Millicent was quite happy that he'd made the trip out, for she had dozens of questions about the earl's condition, and they were becoming more pressing with each passing day.

Dr. Parker didn't keep her waiting much longer. While

the man's assistant went directly to the carriage, Gibbs showed the doctor to the Morning Room. Millicent gestured for him to sit down, but the man ignored her invitation and glanced at a watch he kept on a gleaming gold chain in his waistcoat pocket.

"All is well, m'lady," the physician said in a slightly hurried voice. "There will be no need for any new medicine, but I have directed Lord Aytoun's manservant to increase the frequency of the dosage that we began in London. So now, if you will forgive me, Lady Aytoun, I shall be on my way." He turned to the door. "I do not know when I shall return to Melbury Hall, but perhaps now that the earl is under such capable care, I could send out my very able assistant every fortnight or so, and I shall keep you advised as to his lordship's condition."

"I do have a few questions, Dr. Parker, which I was hoping you might answer for me." She took a step toward him, her voice shaking slightly with emotion. "They concern the earl's general health."

The physician paused and turned back to her. His bushy brows drew into a tight frown.

"I don't believe you need to be troubling yourself, m'lady. Lord Aytoun is in my care now, and I shall see to it that his lordship gets whatever care he needs."

"I am not doubting your abilities in the slightest, sir. I am certain that the dowager would have enlisted your services only if she had the greatest confidence in you."

"As I may have mentioned earlier," he began, puffing up with a pompous air, "my clients consist only of the most elite members of London's *ton*."

"I am certain that is true, and to have a physician of your stature journey all the way out to Hertfordshire is greatly appreciated."

Millicent watched as his attitude settled into one of benign condescension.

"Of course," he said slowly, smiling as if he had just learned something profound about her. "Your concern for your new husband is understandable, if not admirable. And I shall be certain to convey your concern to her ladyship, the dowager countess."

"That is hardly necessary, I assure you. But with regard to the earl's treatment—"

He raised a plump hand to stop her. "You do understand, m'lady, that I have never been involved with his lordship's external injuries."

"I understand that. But—"

"I have been informed that a Scotch surgeon from Edinburgh, named Wilkins or Wallace or something similar, set the bones after his lordship's . . . er, unfortunate fall from the cliff. Now, if that man's negligence has caused Lord Aytoun to continue having difficulty using his legs and his right arm, I cannot say one way or another. But after such a fall, I would tend to place the blame on the blow he received."

"My question has to do with my husband's treatment *now.*"

The physician looked at her as if she were a child intent on trying his patience.

"As I said, Dr. Parker, I appreciate your coming to Melbury Hall. I simply want to know your view of my husband's condition and what your plans are for treatment. What, for example, did you do today?"

"Very well, Lady Aytoun," the doctor said shortly. "If you insist on knowing every detail, I checked his lordship's pulse and had a sample of urine taken. Lord Aytoun's condition is unchanged from ten days ago, when I saw him last."

"Indeed, you've hit on it exactly, sir," she replied. "Since the second night of his stay at Melbury Hall, I have been sitting with him for several hours each night."

"Have you, m'lady?" he said, his eyebrows going up in surprise.

"I have. And what I found was that at night his lordship is unsettled. He does not sleep soundly, so far as I can tell, and when he is awake he is not completely aware of his surroundings." Millicent's fingers twisted together. "Initially, I thought that perhaps my perception was skewed because of the hour of my visit, so I questioned his man, Gibbs, as to the best time to come.

But I was told that during the daytime Lord Aytoun is particularly unfit for company."

"I do not know what you mean by these comments, Lady Aytoun," Parker said defensively. He looked at his watch again.

"Gibbs has confirmed that his lordship's sleep is fretful. Moreover, when he is awake, Lord Aytoun is far more agitated than he has been in the past. Added to that, I have been informed that he does not wish to eat. He does not drink. Any nourishment he takes at all is forced upon him. I simply cannot help but think that something serious might be wrong, and that his condition is getting worse."

Dr. Parker fixed her with a disapproving glare. "Lord Aytoun is being administered some very powerful medicine, m'lady. To be exact, he is presently being given a tincture of opium, the preferred treatment for someone in his condition. That is, the preferred treatment for someone in his mental state and whom the family insists on caring for at home. The opium functions to calm him, to control the melancholia and avoid the need for securing him or locking him away."

"Why should he be locked away?"

"To keep his lordship from injuring himself during the blackest moments."

"But he appears to be getting less—"

"Now, with regard to that medicine, I can assure you this has been tried and proven to be highly effective. Before he left London, I increased his dosage several drops per day, and I believe he is responding well to my treatment."

"With all deference to your knowledge and experience, Dr. Parker, I see no—"

"M'lady," the physician said, holding his hand up again. "You must trust in that medical knowledge and experience. His lordship's life is far more pleasant than the lives of many who are similarly afflicted with the same melancholia. And I am ministering to his affliction with the most effective treatment known to medicine."

"I'm certain you have Lord Aytoun's best interests at heart, sir, but—"

"Now, you can do your part by concerning yourself with his diet. You must have your people take great care to keep the stomach of the patient settled, furnishing him with light meals, and . . . well, I have directed his manservant as to the importance of regular digestive function. And in the meantime, I shall continue to advise you as to the state of his mind. Now, I must say good day to you, Lady Aytoun. I have tarried here far too long. Far too long."

Lyon clamped his mouth shut and turned his face away as John, his valet, tried to feed him a spoonful of soup.

" 'Od's truth, m'lord, ye might help me here. Yer losing too much weight, and Dr. Parker says we have to force ye to eat more."

The man continued to talk, but Lyon ignored him. He was growing so accustomed to the cramping in his stomach that it was becoming almost tolerable. The intense nausea, however, which he'd been feeling since early this morning, before the pompous physician arrived, was something new. Or was it yesterday morning? The days were beginning to blur in his mind. Lyon tried to focus on which day it was but soon gave up. What did it matter?

The bloody doctor. He was just another lily-handed, potbellied charlatan who practically jingled with coin when he walked.

Lyon glared at John and turned his face again at the proffered food.

While Parker examined him, Lyon had said nothing to the man. He had mentioned nothing of the spasms of strength that every now and then ran through the muscles of his right arm, causing his fingers to curl and straighten. He had made no mention of the pain in his joints and had not asked the question of why it was that sometimes he was capable of actually bending his knee and not other times. He'd had no desire to prolong the bugger's stay. He hated the doctors and their prodding and poking. He abhorred their all-knowing attitude.

More to the point, though, he admitted inwardly, he was tired of wondering which one of them would finally persuade his family to have him sent to Bedlam. Not that very much persuasion would be needed once the dowager passed away. Lyon tasted bile in his throat and felt cold sweat breaking out on his brow.

The spoon touched his lips again. He jerked his head away irritably and tried to focus on the chaise that he could see through the window. As he watched, the fat doctor appeared and stepped into the carriage.

"We're only asking for a wee bit of help, m'lord."

Lyon recognized Gibbs's voice. The man was back . . . finally.

"Bed." He closed his eyes, wishing for the oblivion that so often surrounded him these days.

"Aye, but not before we'll be getting some food into ye."

The spoon was again at his lips, and Lyon slapped the annoying object away with his left hand. "Put me back in bed. Now."

The room was too hot. He felt his chair being turned around. He tried to focus on the face of John, still shoving a spoon at him. Beyond the valet, Gibbs was approaching with a crystal glass. The medicine. There was someone else behind him. Long Will, no doubt.

"Give him this only after his lordship has some food in him," Gibbs ordered, placing the cup on a table near him. "I'll be coming back shortly, now, so ye two mind what I say."

Lyon watched Gibbs move across the chamber and go out the door. He wanted to scream after the man to take this pair of imbeciles with him. But the bitter taste was still in his mouth, and he could feel himself shaking uncontrollably.

"We'll make it quick, if ye please, yer lordship. Eat jist a wee bit o' this, m'lord, an' we'll have ye back in yer bed in no time."

This time Lyon successfully dashed the bowl out of the man's hand, sending it crashing to the floor.

"Bloody hell," Will said from behind him, realizing his error as soon as the words had left his mouth. "Beggin' yer lordship's pardon, sir."

"The medicine," he managed to say. Oblivion. This was the only thing left to him. Opium and brandy. Laudanum. He started pushing himself out of the chair with his one good arm. "The medicine."

He didn't know which of the valets brought the glass to his lips, but the taste of it managed to push down the bitter bile. His stomach, though, cramped fiercely as soon as the liquid reached it. Lyon felt himself fighting back the involuntary desire to retch. As he tried to breathe, though, one of the two morons was trying to push bread into his mouth while the other held his shoulders pressed against the back of the chair. He reached out desperately to push the food away.

"Do *not* force him," a woman said sharply.

Through a haze of illness and frustration, Lyon watched her cross the chamber from the open doorway.

" 'Slordship ain't eaten not a bite all day, m'lady," John explained, the bread in his hand.

"We give 'im the medicine already, Lady Aytoun," the other one explained. "But Dr. Parker himself told us to mix it with 'slordship's food."

He tried to focus on her face, but it was all a blur. Her fingers were icy cold when they touched his face and brow.

"Take the food away," she ordered. "And bring that washbasin quickly. Give it to me."

His gut twisted painfully again and bile rose into his mouth. Lyon felt her arm wrap around his shoulder and lean him forward at the very moment that everything inside of him spewed out.

It was sympathy and not revulsion that washed through Millicent as the harsh smell of his sickness surrounded them. She wrapped her arm tighter around him and tried to give him some of her own strength. His left hand desperately clutched the basin on his lap. Streams of sweat dripped down his brow and blended into his dark, matted beard. She saw him close his eyes, and she wished she could soothe his suffering somehow.

"Get a towel and a clean bowl of water," she ordered the short valet.

Aytoun's wide shoulders shook as he continued to retch spasmodically.

"You! Give me another basin," she said to the one called Will.

As she was replacing the basin on Lyon's lap with a clean one, Gibbs swept into the chamber.

"Och! By the . . ." The manservant was at her side in an instant. "Forgive me, m'lady. A minute ago when I left, his lordship wasn't in such straits."

"Just support his shoulders like this, Mr. Gibbs," Millicent directed. She took the towel and clean water from John. She knelt again beside the earl's hunched, shuddering body, and started wiping his face and the corners of his mouth with the towel. He continued to heave, though nothing but bile was left in his stomach.

"This is not really the place for ye, Lady Aytoun," Gibbs said. "We can be doing all this if ye wish to—"

"I'm staying." She did not look up but dipped the towel into the water again and wiped her husband's face. "Does this happen often, Mr. Gibbs?"

"Nay, m'lady. The laird has been sick to his stomach twice or thrice over the past few months, but never like this, mum."

"What has he eaten today?" Millicent saw Gibbs look up at John and followed his gaze. The man answered with a shake of his head. "And last night?"

"A wee morsel. If that, m'lady."

"What about the medicine?"

"His lordship had a healthy dose of it last night," Gibbs told her. "But none yet today."

Will cleared his throat uncomfortably, and John reluctantly spoke up.

"Beggin' yer pardon. We give him more this mornin', but only because 'slordship forced us," he admitted in a small voice. "And some more jist now. Only but a wee taste, though, an' not a minute before 'er ladyship come in."

Millicent fought back the urge to scold the men for their carelessness. The poor man could have been poisoned. She knew, though, that the fault lay not with them, but with her. She had freely married this man. She had signed papers, stood beside his chair before a bishop. She had accepted his family's generosity in paying her debts, and she had vowed to care for him. But other than providing him with a set of rooms, she had done nothing of what she had promised.

Aytoun appeared to be improving slightly. The heaving was subsiding. She gently unclasped his fingers from the basin and wiped his mouth and face with the towel as Gibbs leaned him back in the chair. His eyes remained closed. His face was pale.

"Would you be kind enough, Mr. Gibbs, to put his lordship into the bed?"

She stood back while the three men skillfully followed her direction. She waited until he was settled before turning to them.

"I am very grateful for the care that you have been giving his lordship. From now on, however, I should like to be kept abreast of everything that is given to him, and you will tell me *before* it is done." She met the men's gazes directly. "If his lordship does not feel well, I will be told. If he has no appetite and misses a meal, you will tell me. I shall make a change in my own routine from this point forward. I am planning to spend much more time here than I have previously. Nonetheless, if Lord Aytoun is ailing and I am not here, I want you to find me. It is my express wish that you interrupt whatever it is I am doing. Is that clear, gentlemen?"

The two valets exchanged a glance and then nodded.

"Thank you. Would you be kind enough to clear these things away?"

With a bow, they quickly gathered up the dirty dishes and basins and left the room.

"Ye do not know what ye are asking, m'lady." Gibbs's quiet comment drew Millicent's attention. " 'Tis not without reason that his lordship has gone through so many surgeons and doctors since the accident. The pain is unceasing, mum, and the requirements of his care constant."

Millicent recalled the Scotsman's firm hold on Aytoun's shoulders, the concern that he showed for his master. She looked at the earl. His eyes were closed. He appeared to be asleep. She stepped away from the bed while the steward went about closing the curtains.

"I am not being critical of you in any way, Mr. Gibbs. I understand what you have done. I understand the pressures you must have faced watching over him all these months. He trusts only you. When he needs something, he asks only for you. This would put a great deal of strain on anyone, no matter how dedicated they are."

"Ye shall not be hearing any complaints from me, m'lady."

"I am certain of that." The last thing Millicent wanted to do was to hurt this man's feelings and lessen the care that Aytoun was already getting. "I only wish to be of assistance. Perhaps I can ease your burden a little, and do some good, too. This is what I think the dowager had in mind for me. Perhaps it is what she would do if she were in my position and in good health."

He gave a noncommittal shrug. "Good health or not, m'lady, I think the dowager would have sent Dr. Parker running, with his tail between his legs, if she had seen him here today. Ye will have to excuse my way of talking, for I was reared in the Highlands, where we speak plainly."

"Thank you, Mr. Gibbs. I appreciate your candor." Aytoun stirred, mumbling in his sleep, and she looked across the chamber at him. "Why do you say that her ladyship would have been displeased?"

"The good doctor had more interest in his meal than in his patient. Why, he barely looked at the master, and when he did, the rogue even had the nerve to complain about his lordship being but half awake." He snatched the glass off the table, saying angrily, "And then he orders us to give him more of this poison."

"The solution to this is quite simple. I shall send a letter to London, telling him that we no longer require his services. It was clear to me that he had no interest in coming out here anyway."

Gibbs cocked a bushy eyebrow at her. "Would ye do that, to be sure?"

"Indeed I shall. But we must find another right away. Someone better."

"None of them are any good, m'lady." He sent a thoughtful glance in the direction of the sleeping earl. "Most of them will press ye to have him bled till he comes to his senses or dies. The others will tell ye to purge him till he has no strength to fight. And those are the good ones, m'lady. The rest of them are charlatans and only after the money."

"I suppose you would include Dr. Parker among the last sort."

Gibbs shook his head. "I've no mind to be deciding any such thing. But I can tell ye that ye would have no trouble at all forming a line of his type from here to Bath. All he wants is to be doing one thing: keep his lordship sedated from now till doomsday and send his bill on to the family bankers once a month."

"You've been with his lordship since before the accident. Do you think he would have been content to live this way?"

"Not for a minute," the steward said passionately. "I know if he could do it, he would have ended his life long before now. I think his refusing to eat is part of it. 'Tis the only thing he can control. If we let him, his lordship would starve himself to death as sure as we're standing here."

"We cannot let that happen."

Millicent's gaze drifted toward the door. The valets had left it open when they'd gone out. In the hallway, she saw Ohenewaa, standing silently, staring at the sleeping form of the earl. The old woman had kept her distance for the entire week, and Millicent had not pressed her. She had simply let her know that she was welcome.

Ohenewaa's gaze drifted from the bed and came to

rest on Millicent's face. A moment later, like an apparition, she disappeared from the doorway.

"And we shan't let him spend his life in a stupor,
either," Millicent whispered to the manservant. "There
must be other ways of dealing with this condition. We
just need to find the right kind of medicine and the right
kind of doctor."

Instead of going downstairs, Ohenewaa walked to her
own bedchamber and closed the door. The sight of a
person's suffering was nothing new to Ohenewaa. For
more years than she cared to count, pain and death had
been all that surrounded her. On board slave ships, on
the sun-scorched fields of the sugar islands, inside the
walls of the rat-infested shacks she had seen the un-
speakable; she had experienced the unimaginable.

Ohenewaa knew it was fate that she had been sold to
Dombey, a doctor of mediocre skill and the deepest self-
loathing. She had spent more than forty years with him,
until his death. In that time she had always been at his
side, assisting him in the islands and on the slave ships
as well. She had learned the Englishman's medicine,
what there was of it. But on those long, horrible trips
from Africa, she had seen the rituals of *okomfo* and
dunseni and the *Bonsam komfo* and had carried deep
within her the ways of the Ashanti priests, and the medicine man, and the witch doctor.

Ohenewaa had gathered this knowledge and kept it
safe, like the most precious gold, and with it she had
tried again and again to help her people.

Her people. The whites didn't trust her ways, and she
let them be. When Dombey himself had been sick—even
though he knew she had gifts—he had sent for his own
kind. Ohenewaa didn't know if she could have helped
him. Cures lay in the hands of the goddess. But he did
not want her, so she had let him be. Why bend her
ways? Why touch the ice?

But with this woman, Millicent, she could feel the ice
inside her melting. Since her arrival, Ohenewaa had
spent many nights visiting with the black families at Mel-

bury Hall. The stories they told of Squire Wentworth were horrifying. His brutal handling of the people here was much the same as what she had witnessed on the plantations in Jamaica. His bailiffs had obviously been the same brutes he brought back from there. While telling her all of this, however, every person's account had been filled with praise for the mistress. Though they had suffered terribly under Wentworth's cruelty, so had she—and often for her open support of them.

Ohenewaa had seen many white women of Millicent's station during her time on the islands. Whether they were a plantation owner's wife or a pampered mistress, the women there saw the slaves only when they were issuing a command or gathering for the entertainment of seeing a black man whipped, often by other blacks who had sold their souls to serve as overseers. In Jamaica, at a place called Worthy Plantation, she had seen a slave stripped and flogged while a group of white women stood with their children and stared openly at the man's genitals as he screamed in pain. And it was not the only time. In the islands, she had seen more than she ever wanted to see.

Ohenewaa walked to the table on which she had already collected bowls and bottles of seeds and herbs and liquids. Jonah had brought some of the ingredients back for her from his last trip to St. Albans. The black women of Melbury Hall who had brought seeds with them from Jamaica, or gathered them during past spring and summer months, gave other herbs to her. And even though it was winter, Ohenewaa had found other useful things as well in the kitchen and in the woods and fields around Melbury Hall.

Her collection was growing.

Tonight, instead of working with her herbs, Ohenewaa moved to the hearth and crouched before it. She spread some leaves from a nearby basket on the coals and picked up four stones.

There was a soft knock on her door.

Ohenewaa threw the stones on the floor before her and called to Lady Aytoun to enter.

*   *   *

Startled by the sight of the room, Millicent forgot to ask how it was that Ohenewaa had known it was she at the door. The simple guest room at Melbury Hall had been altered greatly. It was now a place somehow ancient and mysterious. Everything was changed. Jars of varying sizes sat on tables and on the floor. Dried herbs hung above the hearth. The closed draperies dimmed the chamber, which was lit only by the fire. Fascinating and exotic scents infused the air. But Millicent saw nothing menacing or frightening. In fact, the chamber had a calming, serene atmosphere.

Shaking off her surprise at the change, Millicent focused on her reason for coming. There would be time in the future for satisfying her curiosity about the woman and her ways.

"I am at the point of defying traditional English methods of medical treatment. I was wondering if there is any insight you might give me."

Ohenewaa continued to stare at the stones spread before her. Millicent quietly approached the hearth.

"Dr. Parker believes the only thing that can be done for Lord Aytoun is to keep him sedated with opium. My concern is that the drug is doing nothing for him. In fact, I wonder if it is doing him more harm than good." She sat down on the edge of a chair. "You worked with Dr. Dombey for a long time. If I were to cut back on the medicine, if I were to eliminate it completely, would I seriously hurt him? Could he die because of my meddling?"

Ohenewaa picked up a half-burned leaf from the hearth and waved it over the small stones. "He is drowning in a sea of mists. You have not seen him as he is." The dark eyes looked up and met Millicent's. "Are *you* prepared to see him and deal with him as a whole person? Do you have the courage to free his mind?"

Millicent remembered the rumors, the accusations, and the scandals. She had told her friend Rebecca that the Earl of Aytoun was not the man he had once been. Of course, the Aytoun she had seen had been a man continually sedated by drugs. Was she ready to face a changed man? She thought of the broken creature doubled over the washbasin.

"Yes."

Ohenewaa studied the stones for a long time and then seemed to smile to herself. "You can take away the laudanum," she said, gathering up the stones. "And no, 'twill not kill him. Your instincts are correct. Heal the mind first."

"But what of the pain? Is there anything else that I should give to him instead? I do not want him to suffer unnecessarily."

"We must wait and see."

Millicent looked about the room again, taking in the aroma, the bottles, the dance of the shadows over the smoke in the hearth. There was a presence in the room, a power that she could not explain. She turned her attention back to the old woman. "Your knowledge is not bound by the limits of English medicine, I believe. Is there anything you would recommend that I do to help improve his lordship's other ailments?"

"Wait until you have taken the first step. This will be a monumental one. We will talk again after that."

Reluctantly, Millicent rose to her feet. There were so many other questions that she had, but she understood Ohenewaa's concern. Nothing could be done for the earl until he had gained the full capacity of his mind. "Thank you."

Ohenewaa nodded slightly; her gaze was fixed on her fire again. Giving a last glance around the room, Millicent started for the door. Just outside in the hall, she was surprised to find two of the African women waiting.

Millicent stood aside and watched them enter. One was carrying a bowl and pitcher of water, another holding a folded linen cloth. The former slaves at Melbury Hall respected Ohenewaa. They treated her like a queen or priestess. And Millicent could see why. She had felt the power of the old woman, too.

Chapter 8

Not having a steward to run the affairs of Melbury Hall was taking its toll on Millicent's time. Jonah was a wonderful help, but with the planting season approaching, many decisions that would affect them all needed to be made. Millicent knew she needed to speed up the process of finding a suitably experienced steward. Sir Oliver Birch was already contacting potential applicants, but London was simply too far away from the farmlands of Hertfordshire.

Sitting in the small study that she used for estate business, Millicent glanced at the guttering candle as she finished writing her letter to Reverend Trimble at Knebworth Village. He knew much of what went on in the surrounding countryside, and she hoped he might offer some help or some advice.

Millicent glanced up when she saw Violet enter.

"Can I help you get ready for bed, m'lady?"

"I am too restless to go up yet." She sealed the letter in her hand. "But why don't you go up yourself? You look tired, Violet. You probably are not getting much sleep since we moved those two girls into your room. I am sorry."

"No, m'lady. We're settled in nicely. I enjoy having them with me."

It was so much like the young woman not to complain. Over Violet's shoulder, Millicent's gaze was drawn to the door as she saw one of her husband's valets appear, holding a lit taper.

"What's wrong, John?"

"Beggin' yer pardon, m'lady," he said. "I know ye left 'slordship not an hour ago, but he's awake now and cross as a one-legged rooster, he is. Now, 'fore we give him anything, ye said ye wanted to be told, and we're doin' as ye said, mum. So I come runnin'."

"Thank you." Millicent immediately rose from the desk. "Why don't you go on to bed, Violet."

The young servant curtsied and moved off. Millicent followed the man toward the stairs. "Where are Mr. Gibbs and Will?"

"Will went down to the kitchen for some soup, jist in case 'slordship would allow a wee mouthful, and Mr. Gibbs is up in the room with 'slordship."

This afternoon, after leaving Ohenewaa, Millicent had returned to Aytoun's room and had watched him sleep. While there, she had pondered the physical ailments that were plaguing him. He had broken his arm and both his legs over six months ago, and she had no idea why he still could not use them. Gibbs said that one of the doctors had blamed it on the fall, referring to it as a form of "palsy." The dowager had commented about the earl's melancholia, but had not related it to his injuries, only to the accident. Considering that Aytoun had lost his wife and his independence of movement in the same horrible fall, Millicent could well understand the thinking of her mother-in-law.

As she approached her husband's bedchamber, Millicent thought about melancholia. It was an ailment that she herself had struggled with during one of the lowest points in her marriage to Wentworth. She had lost a child in the first part of her pregnancy because of the squire's violent rage. Physically beaten and feeling utterly defeated, Millicent had been more than ready to take refuge in the oblivion of the illness for the rest of her life. But at that stage of their lives, Wentworth had not been ready to commit her to Bedlam. He had still needed her for his social climbing. It was only when her friend Rebecca had come to the neighboring estate with Lord Stanmore that she had started fighting the disorder.

At the earl's door, she could hear raised voices, and she lifted a hand to knock. Neither man paused or looked at her when Millicent and the valet entered.

"You will do as I order, you cankered piece of dung, or you can just carry your wretched carcass out of my sight. Do you hear, you miserable, disloyal, dog-faced . . ."

Millicent paused just inside the door with John right behind her. She stared as the vehemence poured out of her husband. The number of words he uttered surpassed the total he had spoken in nearly a fortnight.

"Curse me as ye wish, m'lord, but ye'll not be getting a drop of this poison until yer wife gives her blessing." Gibbs stood between the bed and the table that contained the medicine.

"You filthy, spineless cur," the earl spat out. "You take orders from me, not from that foul bitch. Do you hear me?"

Gibbs turned in that instant and saw her. He shook his head in disgust as his master continued cursing one and all with equal vigor. Walking away from the bed, he joined Millicent by the door. "Do not take anything of what he says to heart, m'lady. Believe me, this is not his lordship talking. I think 'tis best if ye left him to us for tonight. He looks to be no company for man or beast."

She stayed where she was, refusing to be intimidated again in her own house. "Why is he so angry, Mr. Gibbs?"

"He wants the medicine. Stubborn as a goat he is, mum. He says he'll take no food, but only the laudanum."

"Is he in any physical pain?"

"I do not think so, m'lady," Gibbs answered in a low voice. "Those bones of his are long healed. Not that he ever complained of pain whilst they were mending."

Millicent sent a sharp look at the bed as the raging maniac referred to her as a lump of stale, mouse-eaten cheese.

"His lordship wants the medicine," the servant repeated, "because he knows 'tis sure to calm his mind. It makes him sleep, if ye wish to call it that—fretful as 'tis—but at least he rests."

The earl grew quiet, and Millicent realized that he was trying to catch his breath. For a moment, genuine worry overshadowed her desire to teach her new husband a lesson in manners. "Is this the worst you have seen him?"

"Physically? Nay, m'lady. But as far as that viper's tongue of his, he's lashing out sharp enough to kill a company of Dutch mercenaries."

And as if to prove Gibbs correct, Aytoun unleashed another string of obscenities.

"What do *you* think would happen if we refrained from giving him any more opium?"

Gibbs was astonished. "I'm sure I wouldn't know, m'lady. I'm no doctor. But I can tell ye that his lordship wasn't sleeping after the fall. Before he started taking the laudanum, he was miserable as a starving hound, though, and always made certain that every poor creature around him was sure to be miserable, too."

Millicent made a quick study of the chamber. Her husband was propped up in bed. The curtains of the windows were tightly drawn, holding out the chill of the winter evening. The brandy and the bottle of opium sat on a table. As she looked back at Aytoun, Will came in behind her, mumbling an apology and leading a servant girl who was carrying a bowl of soup and some bread on a tray.

Millicent told herself that she could handle this.

"None of you need to suffer his lordship's wrath tonight." She motioned for the servant to put the tray down on a table. "I want you all to go and catch up on your sleep. I should like to keep my husband's company for the night."

After a year and a half, Mary Page still considered herself new to the place and the job. Widowed as a young woman when her husband had died in a carriage accident in London, she had worked for almost ten years as a housemaid, putting in long, backbreaking hours of work, and getting treated with minimum respect. Then she had seen Lady Wentworth's advertisement for a housekeeper.

Mary had been impressed with Sir Oliver, and even more so with the mistress since meeting her. And she was forever grateful for the position and the opportunity she was given in coming down to Hertfordshire. And being new at the job no longer bothered the house-keeper, for the help was very good. The freed slaves worked as well as or better than the native English workers, and Amina, Jonah's wife, had become a good friend to her as well as a trusted helpmate.

Indeed, Mary Page loved her position, and she found she quickly came to love Melbury Hall as well. The addi-tion of the Earl of Aytoun and his people was no hard-ship, either. In fact, she thought the mistress and the household had all adjusted to it quite readily.

Sitting in a settle by the fire in the servants' hall, her needlework on her lap, she raised an eyebrow as two of Lord Aytoun's personal servants trudged in from the master's bedchamber. When the tall Highlander ap-peared a few minutes later with a troubled expression in his eyes, Mary fought down the fluttering feeling she felt in her stomach whenever she saw him. She sensed, though, that something was amiss.

"Good evening, Mr. Gibbs. You and your lads are taking a holiday this evening?"

"Aye. Though 'tis not to our liking, I must say, Mrs. Page. Your mistress insists on staying alone with his lordship for the night. The lass does not know what she's getting herself into."

"Is that so?"

"Aye, mum." With a frown etched on his face, the Highlander sat on the settle beside her.

Mary spoke to him in a low voice. "Don't think I mean any disrespect, sir, for I have great affection for the mistress, but this is the second time she's been mar-ried. I'd say she knows her way about."

The dark brows of the Scotsman lifted in surprise. "She knows her way about *what*, Mrs. Page, if I might be asking ye?"

Mary felt a blush rise up in her cheeks. "I was simply jesting to ease your mind, Mr. Gibbs."

"Och, well. I'm delighted to know that ye care enough to be doing any such thing, Mrs. Page. I believe that in the course of this past sennight ye haven't seen fit even to return a lonely Highlander's morning greeting."

"I'm quite sure I have treated you with all due civility, sir."

"Ah, civility." He sighed dramatically. " 'Tis come to that, now?"

Mary felt herself growing warm. Despite his size and his fierce attitude to many around him, she found Mr. Gibbs to be quite attractive. Mary smiled as she remembered Vi's comment to a group of giggling serving maids when they were discussing the looks of the newcomers. *Handsome enough*, she'd said, *if you consider hairy monkeys attractive.*

"But now ye smile." His dark gaze lingered on her face. "Now, to what should I contribute this glimpse of heaven?"

"Surely, I don't know. It must have been something I ate for dinner," she answered flippantly. "But about your master. In spite of anything you have heard about her ladyship's circumstances during her first marriage, Lady Aytoun has worked hard to become a very capable individual. His lordship will do perfectly well in her care."

"To be honest, I was more worried about her. I doubt the lass has ever faced anyone with a temper as foul as he possesses this night."

"From everything I've heard, sir, she has survived a husband who was the devil incarnate. I think you can put your mind at ease." Mary patted his hand confidently. "She can handle him, Mr. Gibbs. She can handle him."

* * *

The heat of his fury was scorching the inside of his skull. He could feel it swelling in uncontrolled waves, burning the skin of his face, of his neck. His chest was a knot of anger, and if he could get his one good hand around her throat, he'd go whistling to the gallows.

Not much chance of having luck that good, though, Lyon thought as he continued to stare at the closed door. The stubborn woman was moving about far beyond his reach—sliding a chair here, straightening a table there, ambling about the room as if nothing were amiss. Why, the bloody woman was simply carrying on and pretending that she was not responsible in the slightest for turning those dogs he once thought of as loyal servants against their master. Like cattle at feeding time, the feebleminded cowards had dutifully lined up and marched from the room at her command.

He finally exploded. "Get Gibbs."

"You were looking for something?" she asked in a disgustingly cherubic voice.

He wanted to throw up again. "Aye. I said, get *Gibbs!*"

"I'm very sorry, m'lord, but Mr. Gibbs just left. And he won't be coming back for quite some time." She moved to the foot of his bed, a smile plastered on her face, behaving as if she were not bothered at all by his barking at her. "But I am here if there is something that you need."

He had been aware of her presence from the moment she'd arrived. Strange, he thought, that even in the midst of the haze and the anger, he was becoming aware of her. And how curious that even the horrible names that he called her seemed to have no effect on the woman. In becoming his wife, she had promised to take care of him, but Lyon knew that many a woman in her position might be thinking right now about how to rid herself of baggage as foul as he must seem to her. He prayed that she was thinking those exact thoughts. Poison would finish it all.

"Give me a drink."

She walked away from the table of medicines. He was

annoyed to see her pouring a glass of what he assumed was water. Lyon waited until she came back, glass in hand.

"Can you manage this yourself, m'lord, or do you need help drinking it?"

This close she didn't look quite so confident. When Lyon reached out with his hand, he saw the tremor in hers. He could make a grab for her throat now.

Almost against his wishes, he found his fingers closing around the glass. As soon as she released it, though, he let it fall.

The glass dropped onto the bed, spilling the clear liquid before tumbling off onto the floor. It didn't break, and he watched it roll away.

"I am sorry. I thought you had it," she said, immediately reaching for a towel and starting to soak the wetness from the blankets.

"Get me my drink. I'll have no more of whatever that was."

Her eyes snapped up to his. They narrowed as the realization flashed upon her that it wasn't an accident. She backed away quickly and picked the glass up from the floor.

Lyon waited, only vaguely pleased with the small victory. The weakness was back and the nausea as well. But he could only remain quiet for so long. He fully expected her to do as he commanded.

His mood soured even more than before when she sat down in a chair across the room. "You vile, inhuman wretch. Do you defy the doctor's o-orders to give me the med . . . medicine?" The struggle to form words smoothly increased Lyon's anxiety. He needed the medicine now. "If your p-plan is to kill me, then do it, by the devil. But don't t-torture me. Listen, damn you. I need it *now!*"

His plea must have penetrated her thick skull, for he saw her rise to her feet again.

"I shall give you that only if you eat something first."

"I have no desire for food," he snapped.

"You need to try, all the same." She started sitting down again.

"You are a hateful, withered hag," he said in a raspy voice. "I know now for certain that I d-died at the bottom of that fall, for this is hell. *You* are my eternal punishment."

"Say whatever you wish to me, but know that you shall receive the medicine only after we get some food into you."

"No. I'll have it before." Lyon wished he had throttled her when he had the chance. "You will give it to me now."

"Not before you eat," she responded without any further consideration. "That mistake was made today at noon. And last night. And God knows how many times before that. No one can remember when was the last time you had a meal."

"You are no woman. You have no warmth in you." He turned his face away. "Damn you. You can see that I cannot move. I have no appetite. Medicine, however, I need."

She went to stand by the tray of food, and he watched her. "Think of this as medicine, too."

Lyon cursed ferociously at the world, including in his verbal barrage Gibbs and Millicent and his damnable luck at being stuck with such a bloodless, unfeeling villain. When he leaned back to catch his breath, she approached with the tray of food. He considered upending it, grabbing the tray, scaling it across the chamber, and sending her scampering on her merry way. But already exhaustion was setting in. His body had begun to tremble badly, and his stomach was knotted with cramps and nausea. He just wanted the opium-laced brandy. He just wanted to forget.

"I should like you to feed yourself."

He turned his murderous glare on her. She was sitting on the edge of the bed, her fingers still clutching the tray tightly.

"You have one good hand. You feed yourself, and I

shall ready your medicine." She positioned the tray on his lap. "But I warn you. If you intentionally spill this food, then I shall need to go to the kitchen for some more. So keep in mind how much this will delay you from receiving your precious medicine . . . if that is what it is."

He continued to glare at her, making certain she saw the extent of his hostility. The damn woman, though, simply carried on as if nothing were wrong. She removed the cover from a bowl of broth. She put a spoon near his left hand and spread a napkin on his chest. Then she stood back, looking triumphant and watching him expectantly. He moved his hand over the spoon, and she turned to the table holding the tray with the bottles of brandy and opium.

If she wanted this to be a battle of wills, Lyon thought, then he could easily be the victor. She started counting the tincture of opium, drop by drop, into a small glass. He watched her add the brandy.

"I have done my part." She raised the glass to him. "Now let me see you do your part."

He waited for a long moment, but the desire for the laudanum overwhelmed his pride. Picking up the bowl of broth crudely, he brought it to his lips and—almost against his will—took a sip.

It was the smile of approval that crept across her face that killed him. Without a word, he flung the bowl away from him, soaking himself and the blankets with the broth. The bowl broke into a dozen pieces on the floor.

She didn't raise her voice or complain. She didn't even look startled, though the smile was gone from those lips.

Instead, calmly, she placed the glass on the tray and deliberately tipped it over.

"Oh, how clumsy of me. I have spilled your medication." Picking it up, she looked at the glass closely. "And only a couple of droplets are all that are left, it appears. I do hope this will suffice for the night."

He should have killed her. Next time he had the chance, he vowed, he would.

*   *   *

"So, ye vixen. Tell me what's new at Melbury Hall."

"Lady Aytoun spends a lot of time looking after her new husband. But other than that, nothing to speak of." Violet stretched leisurely on top of Ned's naked body. Her fingers played in the thick mat of blond hair on his chest. "She's sending me to St. Albans this Saturday to buy some woolens and other things. While I'm there, I might get a chance to stop and see my mother and my grandmum. Will you come with me?"

"Nay, lass. I'm far too busy a man to be traipsing around the country after ye."

"Then perhaps I can slip away some Sunday when you're free. I'm anxious to have you meet my family."

"What for?" Ned asked shortly. "Are ye so anxious to tell them ye've got yourself a good lover?"

"No. I just thought that since we've become so close," she said, blushing. "I just thought, now that you're my man—"

"What's this?" Ned rolled over on top of her. He smiled that devilish smile that made her quiver inside. She could feel his huge member was hard again. "Your man? And here ye've only come to my bed but twice."

"Aye, that's true, but now that you've said you love me—"

"To be sure, lass. But 'tis not a good thing, my wee Violet, making me wait more than a week before coming to see me."

He spread her legs with his knee and pushed his shaft deep into her. She was still sore from his rough handling of her when she'd first come to him tonight, but she bit her lip and didn't complain. Instead, she wrapped her arms around him tightly and hoped this time he would go slower.

"A man needs good reason 'fore meeting family, vixen."

"More reason than this?" she asked in a small voice.

"Aye. Much, much more," he said, beginning to slide within her. "But ye're a smart one. Ye're learnin' all the time."

An hour later, Violet felt somewhat queasy as she ran

back to Melbury Hall. He had done it to her again, and she'd let him. That was not the truth. She had gone to his bed willingly, only to walk away unhappy with the way he treated her. What was worse—and she hardly wanted to admit it, even to herself—she was already starting to doubt his words. He had said he loved her, but he was not interested in meeting her family. He told her how pretty she looked, but in the next breath he was asking the news of Melbury Hall. Why did he care about the place anyway? It was not like he worked there or even knew anyone there but her.

Violet was relieved that she had not said much about the place to him. Not that there was much to say these days that was any secret. But there were some things that no one could ever know. Secrets about the day that Squire Wentworth had died.

Violet saw Moses carrying a lantern at the end of a pole with his dog beside him when she broke out of the woods onto the curved drive. The watchman raised a hand and waved to her as the dog turned and wagged her tail. Two of a kind, Violet thought. As gentle as lambs. She turned her steps toward him.

"Your clothes are not dirty. You are not sad."

"No, I'm not sad." She smiled, leaning down and patting the dog on the head.

"No moon now, Violet. The nights are dark. You want someone to walk with at night?"

She shook her head and smiled up at the man. "I am fine, Moses. Thank you, but you have an important job here. You and your dog need to keep Melbury Hall safe."

He nodded slowly, then looked toward the stables. "I made a basket for you."

"Did you?"

He looked back at her. "I can go get it, if you wait. I soaked rushes I had from last summer and used a leather strap for a handle. Maybe you can wrap some of your pretty ribbons around it and use it when you go to the village, Violet. Wait until I get it?"

She nodded at him, feeling better. "I'll wait right here. I'll even hold the lantern until you get back."

Watching the old man go off to the stables, his dog on his heels, Violet took a deep breath of the night air. She would never reveal the secrets of Melbury Hall. Most of all, she thought, no one must ever know that Moses had been the one who really killed Squire Wentworth.

Chapter 9

She felt more like a soldier leaving a battlefield than a woman leaving her ailing husband's bedroom. When Gibbs arrived not long after dawn, Millicent gestured for him to follow her out into the corridor.

"Please help his lordship bathe and change once he is awake," she said in a weary voice. "Offer him breakfast, but give him no medicine until you fetch me. I shall have some sweet cider and some water sent up if he wants something to drink. Give him no spirits." She looked in past the partially closed door. "Oh. The bedding needs to be changed. And also a few spills on the rug need to be cleaned. I shall speak to Mrs. Page about that. And there might be a few pieces of broken dishes under and around the bed."

"Sounds like ye had quite a night, m'lady."

"Aye, Mr. Gibbs. Quite a night. Have you eaten anything this morning?"

"Aye, mum. Thank ye for asking."

"Very well," she said, turning to go.

"I hope ye are not already discouraged, mum."

The tall man's softly spoken words made Millicent pause. She turned to him. "No, Mr. Gibbs. I was asking a great deal of him for one night. I deserved what I received."

"No one deserves that trouble." He glanced over his shoulder. "But I want ye to know that his lordship was not *always* like this."

"I shouldn't think so." She spoke honestly, though

there had been moments last night when she might have seriously doubted it. "You have been with him a long time."

"I have, m'lady. And that's why I've not given up hope like the rest of them. His lordship has had his share of bad luck these past few years. But the way I see it, with him being here at Melbury Hall and with you looking after him, his luck might just be turning again . . . and for the better."

Millicent nodded, appreciating the man's confidence. "Please call me if you need me, Mr. Gibbs."

"Aye, m'lady."

As she moved off, her legs wobbled slightly, but Millicent paid no attention. She considered her own luck. Perhaps hers would change now as well, with Lord Aytoun as her husband. But first she had to learn to handle his temperament.

After what felt like a mile of walking, she made it to her own room. Inside, she eyed the bed, which looked like some heavenly cloud. Without removing her clothes, she simply stretched out on it.

Last night had truly been a test of her strength. Whatever assistance the dowager had offered her for marrying her son, there had been moments when Millicent had wished she had asked for double or triple the amount. Lyon Pennington was absolutely the most arrogant, difficult, and stubborn person she had ever crossed paths with in her life. And not having the use of his legs or his arm didn't hinder his virulent behavior in the slightest. On more than a few occasions during the night, she had wished he'd lost the use of his venomous tongue along the way as well. But then she remembered what Gibbs had said in the corridor. He had not always been like this. Perhaps there was hope.

Millicent pulled the covers on top of her and closed her eyes, hoping for a few hours of rest. Lyon had fallen asleep for the first time only moments before she had left the room. She was certain that he had to be even more exhausted than she.

When the knock on the door came, it took Millicent

a few moments to realize where she was and to rouse herself. Glancing at the clock on the fireplace mantel, she realized she had been sleeping for only half an hour. Will's voice was hesitant, but his message was clear: Mr. Gibbs wanted her ladyship to know that his lordship was fully awake and in as foul a mood as could be.

And he wanted his medicine now.

Ohenewaa sat quietly on a bench in the corner of the kitchen, listening to the worried conversation between the two servants. One was Violet, Millicent's personal maid, the other a young black servant named Bess. The two were about the same age, barely more than girls. They sat side by side on the settle close to the fire. She did not move—her eyes mere slits and her hands resting on the skirts of blue muslin Amina had given her. If anyone were to look at her, she knew, they would think she was an old woman sleeping contentedly.

"They say he's like a madman, cursing and shouting when he's awake, and fretting and feverish when he's asleep." The black woman's voice dropped low. "But she's still holding her ground about not giving him any of the medicine. Stubborn as can be."

" 'Tis not stubbornness but common sense, if you ask me," Violet answered. "I saw him same as you the first day that they brought him into the house. He didn't know who he was or where he was. This morning when I took a tray of food upstairs, his lordship was as mean as a starving dog, but he had no trouble recognizing anybody."

"I've been lucky not to be called up there myself, but I heard Mrs. Page say the mistress don't look too good."

"That's true," Violet agreed. "The mistress is starting to look more poorly than Lord Aytoun himself. And who'd blame her? She's spent nearly two nights and days now at his bedside with not a moment away."

The two women continued to talk, but Ohenewaa rose to her feet and moved away. The household was already accustomed to her quiet presence, to her silent comings and goings, and these two barely gave her a second glance as she got up to go. In the servants' hall she found Amina.

"Come to my room at the noon hour. I will have a tea ready for the angry man upstairs."

"He is not drinking tea, Ohenewaa. He is not taking any food. If 'twas not for the mistress forcing him to drink water drawn straight from the spring, I don't know how he could have survived this long."

"Very well. Then we will mix it with his drinking water. It has very little taste."

" 'Tis good that you have decided to help her." Amina nodded gratefully. "How much should I tell the mistress to give him?"

"You will take what he needs the first day. After that we will watch to see how he does and then give him less and less each day. In a week or two, he'll be needing no more of it."

Doubt clouded Amina's features. "What happens if someone else or the mistress by mistake drinks some of it herself?"

The old woman nearly smiled. "She'll have a couple of hours of peaceful rest."

"Her ladyship is very distrustful of medicine, even English medicine."

Ohenewaa nodded reassuringly. "I understand her distrust. She will accept this from me. She might even be expecting it."

The edge of the feather bed sank beneath her weight. Millicent used a small towel to wipe the beads of sweat from Lyon's forehead. He had fallen asleep about one o'clock, but here it was not even an hour later, and he was caught in some type of nightmare.

She pulled the towel away as he jerked his head from side to side on the pillow. The words he mumbled in his sleep were gibberish. More glistening beads of sweat ran down his face and disappeared into his dark beard. He called something aloud that resembled a shout of warning.

Millicent pressed a hand to the side of his neck, check-

ing for fever. As she started to draw back, he reached up
with his left hand and trapped her arm against his chest.

She sat motionless on the edge of the bed, considering
the battles this man constantly waged, even in his sleep.
Her fingers were splayed on his chest, and the feel of
his heart pounding within overwhelmed her.

"No!" His hand clutched tight, squeezing her arm
painfully. "*No!* You cannot!"

"It is only a dream, m'lord." She leaned over him,
caressing his face with her free hand, pushing the strands
of wet hair off his brow, and talking to him reassuringly.

"Do not ever—"

"Wake up, Lyon. You're having a dream."

"Emma . . . do not . . . no!"

Millicent drew her hand away as if burned. *Emma.*
On his face, tears were mixed with sweat. She pushed
away from the bed and found Will standing in the
doorway.

"Stay with his lordship," she whispered to the valet.
"Please come and get me when he awakens."

Leaving the bedroom and heading downstairs, Millicent tried to push Emma's name out of her mind. The
woman had been Aytoun's wife—perhaps the most
important person in his life. She could not allow the
name to become a nightmare to her.

Instead, Millicent thought of Ohenewaa's medicine.
The drink had worked. In less than an hour after giving
it to him, her husband was sleeping, albeit restlessly. She
had to watch this closely, make certain how his mood
was when he was awake.

Downstairs, a servant hurried to her, carrying a letter.
A messenger had just brought it from Jasper Hyde. Millicent felt every nerve in her body go taut as she tore
into the letter. Again it concerned Ohenewaa.

"Please ask Ohenewaa to come to me in the library,"
she told the servant.

Sitting by a window in the library, Millicent read the
contents of it again. It angered her that Hyde was not
giving up. There were no more liens, no promissory

notes, nothing to give him any control over her, but he continued to persist. She could not understand the man's obsession about getting hold of the old woman.

When Ohenewaa walked in few minutes later, Millicent decided to not let her own feelings affect the healer's decision.

"Mr. Jasper Hyde has written to me, requesting a meeting with you. He states that he writes with no dishonorable intentions. He would prefer a London location, but if that is not satisfactory, he would even consider coming down to Hertfordshire."

As Millicent put the letter down on her desk, Ohenewaa stared at it with contempt.

"This is a most unusual request," Millicent continued. "My first reaction was to answer it with an abrupt no. But then I realized that it is not completely my decision, since the correspondence concerns you."

The young woman's tired face and gray eyes were disturbed when they looked up. "Before you give me your reply, though, I also want you to know that Mr. Hyde's lawyer has been in contact with Sir Oliver Birch half a dozen times in the past fortnight. Each time his offers and discussions have had something to do with you."

Though Millicent didn't voice it, the unspoken question hung in the room: *Why does he want you?*

Ohenewaa walked to the window and stared out at the dreary day and the gray, hunchbacked Chiltern Hills. She had been on one of the slave ships with Dombey when the rebellion erupted on Jamaica in 1760. It had been bloody, though; that she knew. The slaves of several plantations, fed up with the brutality of the masters and fooled by some old men into believing certain spells could make them invulnerable, had risen up and killed anyone who got in their way.

The revolt had been put down quickly and brutally, and she had seen the bloody aftermath. The years of cruelty that followed, fueled by fear of further uprisings, had become even more repressive. Wentworth and Jasper Hyde and his father and others like them had a free rein then, and in their hands the whip was wielded more viciously than ever. For over ten years the lash continued to fall without mercy.

"Jasper Hyde wants me because I have seen the fruits of his labors. I saw his ways when he took over Wentworth's plantations. I saw his calm disdain for the suffering of human beings. I saw the scars grow like the branches of trees on the backs of innocent men and women from the lash and the cane. I saw the rape of those who could not fight back."

Droplets of rain began to beat hard against the window, spreading over the cold glass and blearing the view of the hills.

"I, too, am branded. I, too, have felt the whip's sting. And now I am like the old mother of days gone by, suspected of witchcraft. Jasper Hyde would burn me alive if he could. He wants me because he believes I cursed him for what he has done. He believes in punishing the body to break the spirit. And he believes I am punishing his body to achieve the same end."

Ohenewaa turned back to the room. Millicent's face showed the pain that she was feeling for the suffering of all those enslaved workers.

"Hyde says his intentions are not dishonorable. That is true, because he feels there is nothing dishonorable in burning a witch with dry wood while her own people look on. He believes there is no dishonor in vengeance. But before he sees me die, he wants me to undo the curse that plagues him and release him from his sins. But that I cannot do."

Jasper Hyde knew that the doctor could do nothing to help him. But that was not why he had asked Parker to come and look at him anyway. He knew the only cure for his condition lay in what they could accomplish together.

"You have an unusually loud palpitation of the heart, Mr. Hyde, though I can see nothing physically wrong with you." The physician motioned to his assistant to pack up the instruments and leave the room. "Nonetheless, it is critical that you should start taking a few necessary precautions. There is always the possibility that a certain disease might be in its early stages, and we shall try to be ready for it when it surfaces. So before my next visit, I would like you to avoid all sources of unnecessary excitement. The meals should be taken at regular intervals, and should be very light. No violent exercise, and we should begin a series of regular bleedings."

Hyde watched until the physician's servant had left the room before interrupting Parker. "I am grateful that you were able to see me on such short notice. When I heard you are the chosen physician of the Earl of Aytoun, I knew you were the man for me."

"I see. Are you a friend of his lordship?"

"Not exactly. Just one who was greatly disappointed to see him thrown into the clutches of such an opportunistic woman."

The man's bushy eyebrows went up. "Then you are acquainted with the new countess?"

" 'Tis somewhat indelicate to speak of it, but I was her creditor until the lady's marriage to his lordship."

Parker's interest showed. "She was deeply in debt to you, sir . . . if you don't mind my asking?"

"Her first husband owed me a great deal, and she owed me more. I would have been forced to take possession of Melbury Hall in a couple of months' time, if she hadn't married. Like all women, she is a victim of her own poor judgment and is quite frivolous in her spending. I feel truly sorry for Lord Aytoun, finding himself in such an unpleasant situation."

The physician removed the spectacles from his nose and folded them. "Well, perhaps you don't know, but the wretched man had little choice."

"So when, Dr. Parker, are you going back to visit his lordship again?"

"I . . . well . . ." He cleared his throat. "I may not be going back. I find that Melbury Hall is too far from London, and I have many clients who demand my time here."

"She did not dismiss you, did she?" Hyde asked,

feigning great surprise and concern. At least his infor-
mants in Hertfordshire had provided one useful piece
of information.

"Lady Aytoun sent a letter indicating that it might be
easier for everyone involved if she searched out a more
local doctor for his lordship."

Jasper Hyde pushed himself to his feet. "You cannot
believe that, sir. This is all part of her scheme. First she
buys that black witch who killed Dr. Dombey, and takes
her to Melbury Hall. Next, she marries into that fortune
and takes Lord Aytoun back to the country, away from
everyone he knows. Now I find that she has dismissed
you."

"Well, I shouldn't call it 'dismissed' exactly, Mr.
Hyde."

"How convenient! What an easy way to kill another
husband."

"Kill her husband?" Parker said, suddenly alarmed as
the words began to sink in. "What witch? Who is this
Dombey? You must clarify this business, sir."

"Indeed, Dr. Parker. I believe you are correct. Won't
you please sit down, and I shall tell you my fears. I
believe, sir, that you may be the only man who can stop
this whole affair."

"I . . . ?"

"First sit down, and I shall tell you what I know about
Lady Aytoun's lack of character. Then you must promise
me that you will refuse her request to resign the commission Lord Aytoun's family bestowed upon you. You
must save his lordship from this black widow's deadly
venom. I'm certain, sir, that his family will be entirely
grateful."

"Yes, yes!" The man was quick to take a seat. "But
what was it you said about a witch?"

Chapter 10

The curtains had been left open, and a soft blue light imbued the room with a pervading sense of serenity. A light blanket of snow covered the countryside outside, and the moon shone brightly through the scudding patches of clouds.

Lyon's mind was clear for the first time in days. There was no nausea, no headache, no confusion. He tore his gaze from the rustic view and stared at the sleeping figure of the woman who was responsible for this recent improvement in his state of mind. Millicent was curled up in the uncomfortable chair near the foot of the bed. This was her eighth night here, and the first time he had seen her actually drop off to sleep. Exhaustion had finally set in, but not before she had succeeded in forcing him to clear his mind of the laudanum.

But sobriety, too, was a curse.

Lyon stared at his limp right arm on top of the blankets and felt the empty ache inside of him. He would never walk, never ride. He'd never sit in a chair unless someone propped him up. He would never lie with a woman. In his mind's eye he saw Emma with her wild blond hair spread across his pillow, her blue eyes smiling up at him, her arms pulling his weight down onto her willing body. She had been so young when he had first married her. But he had been a fool to think he was at the center of her world.

Pierce had been right about everything from the start. He had warned Lyon about Emma's true interests. Baronsford was what she coveted, his brother had told him, not the man who owned it. Out of arrogance, though, Lyon had not believed him.

Of course, Lyon had always known that Emma had been closest to his youngest brother, David. From the time they were children, the two of them had played along the cliffs at Baronsford, and the vision of them together was etched in his—and everyone's—mind. David and Emma had been inseparable through the years. And yet, when Lyon had taken over Baronsford, Emma had come to him.

Selfish, vain, blind—he could think of a hundred names for his actions. But at the bottom of it all, Lyon had acted the fool, and his family had been torn apart because of it. There was no one to blame but himself.

Lyon threw his good arm over his face and wished he could free himself of the vision that was permanently imbedded in his mind. The wet rocks. Emma's broken body at the base of the cliff, staring up at him. She had paid the price for her mistakes, as he was paying now.

Anger surged in his veins again, and he wished for oblivion once more. Forcing his eyes open, Lyon stared at Millicent's simple dress, her pale face and tightly pulled-back hair. She was everything that he'd always imagined plainness to be. She murmured something in her sleep and then woke herself with a start. She stared at him, sleepy-eyed.

"You want something?"

"I want the medicine tonight."

"No," she whispered quietly. She tried to return his stare, but after a few moments started to nod off again.

Lyon wished he had enough use of his foot just to be able to tip her chair backward. He considered shouting an obscenity at her and making sure that she stayed awake. But she drew up her legs tighter on the chair and tried to get comfortable.

And Lyon found himself content just to stare at her. His wife.

Sir Richard Maitland sat down on an armchair across the way from his client, the Dowager Countess Aytoun.

" 'Twas a wise decision not to meet with Dr. Parker yourself, m'lady."

The old woman closed the book on her lap and stared at him over the tops of her spectacles. "That bad, was it?"

The lawyer nodded. "Dr. Parker accuses your new daughter-in-law of being a heretic. He believes she is deliberately endangering the earl's health and well-being by not following a single direction he gave to her a fortnight ago. He insists that Lord Aytoun is in dire peril and that you should remove your son immediately from Melbury Hall. And though 'twill be very difficult for him to manage, Dr. Parker assures me that he is willing to spend whatever time is necessary to restore the earl to where his lordship was before in his treatment."

"How generous of him! Did he mention a fee for this service?"

"Of course." Maitland glanced down at his notes. "The usual exorbitant amount was quoted."

The dowager picked up Millicent's letter from the table beside her. She read it once again. "And did Dr. Parker say a word about receiving a letter from my daughter-in-law, terminating his services at Melbury Hall?"

"It must have slipped his mind, m'lady, for he did not offer the information. Once I mentioned it, he made some excuses about being away from London and not receiving her notice until the day he was scheduled to go back to Hertfordshire. He felt the situation necessitated his return to Melbury Hall."

"He went anyway?"

"Aye. And the gentleman was quite eloquent about what he found. He felt compelled to report that the earl's condition is so severely worsened that if you do nothing about it immediately, his lordship's life is surely in jeopardy."

"And how is that?" she asked wryly. "Is Lyon any thinner? Does he suffer from excruciating pain? Has he broken any more bones?"

"Fortunately, you have in your hand, I am quite certain,

a more accurate report on Lord Aytoun's health than anything Dr. Parker might have related. Indeed, the messenger who carried Lady Aytoun's letter told me himself that
his lordship is apparently improving every day."

"Then what the devil is this charlatan talking about?"

"His concern now is with his lordship's temperament."
Maitland gave a small cough to hide his chuckle. "Upon
being taken to Lord Aytoun's chamber at Melbury Hall,
the physician was delivered a plateful of pastries, straight
to the face."

"By Lyon?"

Sir Richard nodded politely.

"Were they intended for Dr. Parker?"

"Difficult to say, m'lady, though the result is a fine
bruise to his well-padded cheekbone."

"How dreadful! But why is it difficult to say?"

"Well, apparently your son and your new daughter-
in-law are given to daily battles that have all the elements of the siege of Edinburgh. And I am happy to
report that she is far . . . well, hardier than we imagined
her to be."

The dowager sank back against the sofa and actually
smiled. "This is *most* encouraging news, Maitland. And
did you throw Dr. Parker out of the house?"

"I certainly did, m'lady."

"Excellent. Most decidedly excellent."

With Gibbs trailing behind her with an armload of
rejected books, Millicent entered the library and waved
at a table.

"Pray, leave them there, Mr. Gibbs," she said, scan-
ning the shelves and pulling out several volumes.

"Ye know his lordship is playing a game with ye,
m'lady," the manservant said respectfully. "Ye might as
well bring up a hundred more volumes. He'll be sure to
find something wrong with all of them. With his mind clear
Lord Aytoun is too capable of playing the devil with ye."

"Indeed, he is doing an excellent job at it, but I am
not about to give up."

"Aye, m'lady."

Tucking the new selections under both arms, Millicent left the library. This was her third trip. Each time, the villain had found fault with her choices. She was determined to find a book this morning that would interest him, but still be something to her liking as well. There had to be *something* that they could agree on.

In the hallway and on the stairs, servants cleared out of her path. She had a suspicion, though, that no one was moving too far out of earshot. It was not hard to see that her disagreements with Lyon were quickly becoming a source of entertainment for the household.

The valets had moved the earl onto his chair by the window by the time Millicent returned to her husband's apartments.

"Here I am," she announced with an air of triumph, dropping the books on the table beside her own chair. "You cannot possibly find anything wrong with these."

Her challenge was answered with a defiant flash of the man's blue eyes. Millicent ignored the strange flutter of excitement inside of her and sat down on her chair, reaching for the first volume. "Dr. Johnson's *Rasselas*."

"You might as well burn that blasted book, for I refuse to listen to anyone reading it."

"Why?" Millicent managed to keep her calm.

"The man insulted the entire Scottish people in his dictionary, equating us all with horses."

"With horses?"

"Indeed. Look at his definition of 'oats' sometime."

She glanced down at the book in her hand, not truly sure of the truth behind the assertion. Finally, she put the volume aside and reached for the next one.

"Well, here is one written by a Scot. *Ossian's Fingal,* an ancient epic poem. Very exciting, I'm told."

"Written by James Macpherson. He is a Scot, but the man is a fraud. He made the entire book up of old Gaelic poems. There is not a shred of truth to it being by any Ossian. What else do you have there?"

Scowling at Aytoun, Millicent put this volume aside as well. She picked up the next. "Laurence Sterne's *Tristram Shandy*."

"Never. Open that book. I defy you to find a page that is not blotted with rows of stars and dashes and hand-drawn diagrams and every other bit of nonsense the author could contrive. Totally unintelligible! You call that a story? A wandering plot—if you can find it—and most of the tale is in the character's block-shaped head. Give me laudanum or read that book. The effect is the same."

"Very well," she replied shortly, putting this book aside too. "But I am telling you right now, m'lord, that there is nothing you could possibly find wrong with this next book. *Nothing*."

He raised a brow, waiting.

"Mr. Pope's *Imitations of Horace*."

"You must be joking."

"What do you mean?"

"The man was a virulent, malicious dwarf."

"Pardon me?"

"I refuse to listen to anything written by a man of his disposition."

"And is it the man's stature or his temperament that . . ." She glared across the room and then rose to her feet. "Oh, never mind! I don't even want to know. Just tell me, are we trying to read to broaden our minds? Or must we demean ourselves with trifling concerns about the authors that have nothing whatsoever to do with what it is written between the covers?"

"I cannot understand why you are getting so upset over something as trivial as finding a readable book," he said calmly. "All you have to do is ask me what it is that I would like to read this morning."

"How could I have forgotten? Oh, pray tell, what would you like to read, m'lord?"

"I do not know a thing about your collection."

"Other than the dozens of books I have already carried up here."

"Other than those. What else do you have?"

She sank back down on the chair. This was exactly where they were two hours ago. She would name the books, and he would find some fault with each of them.

Millicent knew she had to find a way to occupy this man's mind before he drove her so insane that *she* would be the one in need of laudanum. She picked up *Rasselas* and started to read. If Aytoun was representative of the Scottish people, then she was beginning to see some merit in Dr. Johnson's definition. But she wondered if the man hadn't meant to say "mules" in his dictionary.

Chapter 11

As always, the morning routine dragged on interminably. Lyon muttered his customary curses at his two valets as they helped him wash and dress. John, the turtle-shaped, flap-jawed rapscallion, and his scarecrow of a partner, Will, had both been somewhat tongue-tied when he harangued them for appearing in his chambers in "country" clothing rather than their customary livery. The poor devils had barely been able to utter an explanation about decisions the mistress had made about dressing the combined households. And Lyon made certain that he grumbled incessantly at Gibbs over the breakfast of which he refused to eat more than a bite.

But he was saving the worst of his temper for Millicent, knowing full well that she would be walking into his room about ten o'clock. Already weary from rising early to attend to the pressing affairs of the estate, she would no doubt be quite irritable after a nearly sleepless night. He knew that she would also be ready to deliver as hard a verbal punch at him as he was ready to afflict her with.

As the serving women finally cleared away the dishes in front of him, Lyon considered his wife. He couldn't fully understand it, but those moments when she was here arguing with him and berating him for his continual transgressions were the only moments of the day that he felt truly alive.

Of course, those were also the most frustrating times as well, for she never did what he told her or even asked her to do. She insisted on reading aloud despite his objections to her selection of books, ignoring him and only reading louder. She had even suggested that he leave these rooms occasionally. He'd argued bitterly against it, of course, flatly refusing and telling her that as the resident cripple, he had no wish to be paraded about for a houseful of gawking rustics.

Then, three days ago, with no regard to his wishes, she had bribed his own weak-livered servants into carrying him down to her drawing room. Naturally, he had made enough noise and caused enough damage that she had ordered him to be brought back less than half an hour later. Lyon had won the battle that day, but he was convinced she would launch another assault any day now. Vigilance was called for, without a doubt.

Ten o'clock came and went, but today there was no sign of her. Lyon felt his irritation rise. Half an hour later, when Millicent still didn't appear, he began venting his wrath in other directions. A young serving girl coming in to tend the fireplace fled teary-eyed after he hurled only the mildest of insults at her. Both John and Will tried to tiptoe about the chambers as they saw to his clothing, but when he upended a tray next to him and then flung a bound edition of the *North Briton* at them, the turtle John ran off, only to appear a couple of minutes later with Gibbs in tow.

"Can I fetch anything from the armory for your lordship?" the Highlander asked dryly.

"Indeed. Bring me my dueling pistols. I'd like to use these two dolts for target practice."

"Begging your pardon, m'lord, but perhaps 'twould be easier if ye'd just ask me where she is."

Lyon snorted and stared at him as if he were the village idiot.

"Very well, sir," Gibbs continued when Lyon said nothing. "Since ye insist on my telling ye, Lady Aytoun has gone to Knebworth to visit with the Reverend and Mrs. Trimble. Mr. Trimble is the rector at the church there. Quite the friends of your wife, they are. Her ladyship has been delaying this visit for two weeks now, on account of seeing to your needs. But today, it being bonny and warm for a late winter's day, she decided to take a horse out and ride over."

Lyon glanced at the beautiful sunny day outside the window. Of course she would be tired of being trapped in here with him day in and day out.

"When she gets back, I'll tell Lady Aytoun ye were pining after her," Gibbs offered with an innocent expression.

Lyon glared at his man. "And I will have your head on a platter for dinner."

"Ye shall have to be up and about before doing anything like that, m'lord."

"I should have let those dog-faced Edinburgh drunks at that oyster house in St. James Close hang you, Gibbs."

"Aye, m'lord, but that still doesn't put my head on any platter."

"The truth is, though, that all I have to do is tell my wife that I'd be sure to find my appetite if she'd only hang your ugly skull on a pole over my fireplace." The dark beard hid the trace of a smile. "Tell her that, and I have no doubt that she would make any necessary arrangements."

Mrs. Trimble's limp from an old carriage accident appeared more pronounced this winter. But to Millicent's delight the older woman's lively wit and high spirits were unaffected by the old injury. The two women sat together in the parlor, sipping tea and waiting for the rector to return from the village. Millicent was told when she arrived that he was expected momentarily.

"Things are happening in the village, m'lady," the kindly woman said. "Reverend Trimble took a walk to speak with the stonemasons who are building the grange. He was hoping to employ one of them in their off-hours to work on two of the rectory chimneys that are cracked and drawing poorly. But I am so glad you were able to come by this morning. Despite my bad knee, we were ready to drop by for a visit at Melbury Hall earlier this week. After talking to Mrs. Page last Sunday, however, we decided you might not be ready for any company just yet. She mentioned that Lord Aytoun's health is still a concern for you. Has his lordship shown any improvement yet?"

"Indeed, he has. Thank you." Millicent told herself she was not exactly misrepresenting the situation. Lyon's health had certainly improved in recent days.

"We were not envious of your position, my dear, in being faced with what must have been a very difficult decision to make. Not envious at all." Mrs. Trimble took Millicent's hand in hers and lowered her voice confidentially. "Lord bless you to take on such a responsibility. Caring for anyone crippled so badly is a true test, I'm sure. Both legs and an arm, I hear."

Millicent nodded.

"And a severe case of melancholia, too?"

This time she shook her head emphatically. Now that she had spent two weeks constantly in his company, Millicent was certain that Lyon's present temperament was not severe enough to be considered melancholia.

"Whatever my husband was suffering from when he first arrived at Melbury Hall, I believe his condition was being aggravated by the medicines he was being given."

"So you changed his treatment?"

"I did, and I believe he is feeling much more himself at present." Loud. Obnoxious. Occasionally bizarre. Awake practically around the clock. And Millicent liked him much better this way.

"You do look quite tired, my dear. If I might be also so bold to ask, how are *you* faring with this new arrangement?"

"I am doing quite well," Millicent answered honestly. "The changes have required some adjustment on the part of everyone, mostly due to the increase in the size of the household. But a shortage of living space has been my greatest problem right along."

Mrs. Trimble poured Millicent some more tea. "And I was so sorry to hear that in the midst of all this, you had to let go of your steward."

"That was inevitable. Mr. Draper and I did not get along from the start, and with each passing day things just seemed to get worse."

"But finding a replacement has been difficult."

Millicent nodded and took a sip of her tea before putting the cup back on the table. "I have interviewed three people thus far, but none of them seems to be the right person for Melbury Hall."

"And spring shall be upon us quite soon." She shook her head. "So much of the day-to-day responsibilities of the steward, then, are squarely upon your shoulders."

"Indeed, there is a great deal to do."

"And you were planning to improve the cottages on the estate, as well as building more. How can you possibly be holding up, my dear?"

"Fortunately, nothing has fallen to pieces yet." Millicent smiled. "Lord Aytoun's personal manservant, a very capable Scotsman who has been with his lordship for years, has been seeing to those responsibilities vacated by Mr. Draper for the past few weeks. Selfishly, I suppose, I'm hoping that he might consider taking over the job of steward permanently. Of course, I still have to convince Lord Aytoun of that."

Millicent thought that just asking the question should be good for at least a half-dozen overturned dishes. Lyon was quite fond of doing that.

"Your description of everything is so much more pleasant than the rumors that were initially floating around the village." Mrs. Trimble squeezed Millicent's hand affectionately. "I am so happy for you. I do hope we get a chance to meet his lordship soon."

"Well, perhaps once the weather improves, I'll persuade him to come into the village with me." She would have to do this persuading on the same day that she asked his opinion of Gibbs becoming the new steward. And perhaps the same day that she asked him to stop destroying the household furnishings. And the same day she asked him to talk rather than shout. Perhaps that would be the day to ask him to shave off that hideous beard as well.

Millicent glanced at the handsome clock above the hearth. It was approaching the noon hour, and she began to worry. She sincerely hoped Lyon had eaten some breakfast. She wondered what his reaction had been this morning when she had not come to his room, or if he had even noticed her absence. If he had eaten nothing for breakfast, she wanted to be there to encourage him to have something now. Well, either encourage or bully him.

"I cannot imagine what is detaining Reverend Trimble." The rector's wife, following the direction of her visitor's gaze, pushed herself stiffly to her feet and went to the window. She was a tall woman, and Millicent could see her looking out past the garden at the village.

"Would you consider me terribly rude if I were to curtail our visit today?" Millicent asked. "I know it sounds silly, but suddenly I find myself concerned for my husband. I have not left him alone for so many hours, and he is still recovering."

"I understand perfectly," Mrs. Trimble answered, turning back to her with a smile. "I am very sorry that Reverend Trimble missed you. The builders at the grange must be interesting fellows."

Millicent stood up. "I'm certain they are. In fact, I was hoping to ask his assistance in hiring one of these same men for the renovations at Melbury Hall. Aside from the new cottages, I was also hoping to build a stone wall to stop the river from flooding into the Grove every spring. I have quite a bit of work that needs to be done at the Hall."

"I know he'd be delighted to help out with that, my dear. Perhaps I could have him stop out at Melbury Hall sometime this week. Perhaps while he is there, he could meet his lordship."

"That would be very nice," Millicent said in a small voice, already wondering what kind of bribe she could use with Lyon to make him behave for the few minutes Reverend Trimble would be in his company.

The door to the earl's bedchamber was open. A few minutes earlier, Ohenewaa had seen one of the servants cursing and grumbling as he passed her with a tray. She took a step toward the door and looked inside.

The man was alone, propped up in a chair near the window. She was surprised to see he had a newspaper on his lap. His attention appeared to be divided between the paper and the view outside the window.

"Instead of hiding in the shadows, why not come in?"

He never turned his head, and he caught her off guard. Ohenewaa considered ignoring the remark and moving down the hall. Instead, though, she entered the chamber. There was a marked difference between what she saw in the room now and what she recalled seeing her first night here. There were no vials of medication. No smell of sickness. No sense of gloom. She inspected the painting and rugs and tables, and then looked over the man, studying him like any of the other furnishings.

"Why do you roam around the halls like a ghost? You can walk. You can talk. Why not make more noise?" His questions were abrupt, and this time his eyes focused on her from across the room.

"You make enough noise for both of us. Since we have started asking questions, though . . ." She motioned to the open paper on his lap. "Why don't you admit this to her? You appear perfectly capable of entertaining yourself."

"Perhaps I enjoy her company."

"Perhaps you need someone to torment."

"I do not ask her to come. She agreed to the arrangement. What she does, she does of her own free will."

"You haven't told her that you've improved. You might tell her that there is no need for her to fret over you every minute of the day."

"You care about her," he said, staring incredulously.

"You do not." Ohenewaa matched his expression for a long moment before turning and starting toward the door.

"Come back again. I enjoyed our lengthy visit."

Instead of going downstairs, Ohenewaa walked to her own bedchamber and stood looking at her herbs and bottles.

She had helped the earl and his wife once already. But her excuse to herself then had been that she was tired of listening to the two of them shouting and breaking things at all hours of the day and night. Her involvement, she told herself, had been as much for her own sake as for theirs. But what she planned next was far more complicated.

In fact, before today she wasn't certain that it might be a wise thing to go through the entire process of decocting to extract the oils for a particular mixture that she wanted. The salve she had in mind would serve several purposes. Thinking about him now, Ohenewaa told herself that she was a healer. Besides, from the first day on, she had been looking for a way to thank Millicent for what she had done for her.

The question of whether *he* was deserving of the effort Ohenewaa would expend had been answered today. She had seen today that he had a spirit within him, and—whether he knew it or not—he was helping his young wife to heal.

And that was a good enough reason, Ohenewaa thought. She would help him.

The ride and the bracing winter air had a noticeable effect on her. She looked far more relaxed—almost cheerful—and completely undisturbed by the complaints that he started with the moment she walked into the room.

"A swarm of dung flies would not sit on this bread. And this soup must surely be the result of some mangy cur lifting his leg and pissing in the pot. Are you and your bloody cooks trying to poison me?"

"With images like that running unbridled through your mind, m'lord, I don't blame you for not wanting to eat it. Indeed, you must surely detest the food simply for being weary of it. I must have a talk with the cook. You are beyond the need for these watery broths and dry bread. There is no reason that you should not be served what the rest of us are eating."

As she took the untouched tray off his lap, the profanities that he was preparing to deliver withered on his tongue. For the mere seconds that Millicent had leaned close to him, he had smelled the scent of fresh air in her hair. He found himself admiring the touch of sun on her cheeks. He watched her deposit the tray on a table beside the door. *Bloody hell,* he thought, recovering his composure.

"I don't want to eat anything you bring up here," he barked shortly.

"I perfectly agree."

"By the devil, I think this is a first."

"I assure you, it is only the first of many agreements we shall have."

He scowled at her bright face suspiciously. "What is this all about?"

"You should not be served your meals here in this room at all. The surroundings are too restricted. The air is too stale. I also believe that an ill-tempered disposition tends to linger in a place. And I must say that with your temperament, this chamber already reeks of it."

"Well don't leave your own temperament out, as long as you're going on about it."

"Very well, m'lord. *Our* temperaments."

"And don't call me 'm'lord,' " he grumbled. "I won't have my wife calling me that. You'll call me Lyon when we're alone, and Aytoun when we're not."

"As you wish." Millicent held her hands folded before her and gave him a bright smile. "But starting tonight, you and I will have our meals in the dining room."

Lyon would have told her she was daft if he weren't momentarily arrested by her smile. She was damned bewitching with those soft dimples in her cheeks and the mischief dancing in her gray eyes.

"That settles it." She clapped her hands once and reached for the servant's bell.

"The devil it does!" he finally managed to get out. "I am no wooden puppet to be dragged up and down those damned stairs three times a day while jug-headed rogues stand by and ridicule me."

"You certainly are not, m'lo . . . Lyon. No puppet

I've ever seen could talk and curse with such fervor or frequency." She moved toward him. "But in spite of your many faults, I will promise you that—other than two of your own men who shall help me move you—no one will be standing about and watching."

"This shall *not* be." He spoke more forcefully.

"Indeed, it shall." She matched his tone.

"I am content to remain here."

"Before, you were content to remain unconscious and to starve. Right now, you are content to play the part of the angry bear and constantly flash those teeth at me."

"Come closer, my dear wife," Lyon threatened in a low voice, "and I'll show you how contented I am."

A soft blush spread evenly across her cheeks, but instead of backing away, she placed her hand on his shoulder and leaned toward him until they were face to face.

"Despite the tangled beard and uncombed hair that successfully give you a certain mad look, I don't believe you look very frightening from this distance. Maybe if I were to shave your face—"

His left arm darted out and took hold of her arm, toppling her onto his lap. She gasped in surprise and fell against him.

"No one touches my beard."

She seemed lost for words. This close he could tell her gray eyes had silver speckles in their depths. Her skin looked so soft. Lyon's gaze fell on her lips, and without another thought he found his mouth had captured hers in a rough kiss.

She did not pull away, but rather leaned into him and clutched his shoulders. Blood pounded in Lyon's body. Her lips were so soft and giving. He slanted his mouth over hers and was about to deepen the kiss when suddenly she dragged herself off him and away from the chair. She was blushing furiously, her hand over her mouth as she backed all the way to the far side of the room.

Lyon tried to calm his unsteady breathing as he watched her flushed face. She touched her brow, tucked loose tendrils of hair behind an ear. With trembling fingers she tried to straighten her dress. He followed the movement of her hands and told himself she was his wife. After three weeks of being in each other's company constantly, this was to be expected. Still, though, what had happened between them was totally inexplicable to him. What he felt was confusing as hell. She finally turned to him with a polite smile pasted onto her face. But he could see through the mask. She was visibly shaken.

"We cannot live the rest of our lives in this one room, m'lord."

His thoughts, however, were not in agreement with hers. He still wanted to be left alone here, with one small exception . . . Millicent. Surprising as it was, he wanted her here with him.

"I believe it would be good for both of us to get out of this chamber."

Us instead of *you*. Anger began to seep into Lyon's bones. Every time the door had opened this morning, he'd hoped to see her. And now she was playing games with him. He forced himself to look away from her lips, cursing himself for this additional layer of dependence on another.

"No one asked you to spend so much time in this room. I was content without you. *I* live here. You do *not*."

"You are mistaken." Once again her fire returned. "I am your wife. Where you are, *Lyon*, I shall be. Where you eat, I shall eat. Where you—"

She cut the words short, but Lyon knew what she was about to say. *Where you sleep* . . .

"Do as you please, and the devil take you," he barked irritably. "I do not care to discuss this further. I don't need you. I am tired of seeing your face. And I'm bored with your incessant chatter. Out."

Lyon turned his head away without waiting for her response. Staring out the window into the courtyard and the fields beyond was his only escape. Silently, he tried to convince himself that she deserved his sharp tongue. So what that they were man and wife? Kissing her had been an impulse—a mistake. He only wanted her to let him be.

There was no sound for a long time. She had not moved, but she said nothing, either. Lyon wondered if she was finally going to give up.

"Actually, there is another reason why I wish to drag you out of this room." Millicent had the matter-of-fact tone back in her voice. She was not ready to let him alone.

"Is there, madam?" He did not look at her.

"From what Gibbs tell me, before your accident you took an active interest in many of the Aytoun family business matters. He said you never felt it was beneath you to oversee the management of your estate in the Borders and your lands in the Highlands. You served as a most valuable resource to many of your less capable peers. You are educated and obviously quite shrewd when it comes to getting what you want. And you are here."

"Your skills at flattery need work. Shrewdness is not a noble quality."

Lyon turned his head and saw her run a nervous hand down the front of her dress to smooth an invisible wrinkle. He knew what she was doing. This new strategy of hers was nothing if not transparent.

"I should like to introduce you around Melbury Hall."

"No."

"This is not a social request, but one regarding . . . well, business. There have been a few matters having to do with the estate where I have needed guidance. I would very much appreciate it if I could occasionally ask your advice on these concerns."

"You have the income now. Hire a better lawyer."

"I already have an excellent one, thank you," she replied, continuing tenaciously. "But you know that the law considers women feeble, at best. You also know that, as my husband, you are wholly responsible for the actions of your wife."

He snorted.

"Therefore," she went on, "I am giving you the opportunity of being involved. But again, considering your reputation in the household as a tyrant, perhaps I need to rethink my suggestion. After all, only a fool would want to have you meddle in things that you quite possibly know nothing about. It would not be the first time people's perceptions of a man's abilities have been mistaken. Or Gibbs may simply have been speaking out of blind loyalty. Then again, I may have inferred more about your abilities from what he said than he intended. Never mind. I don't know what I was thinking."

"Nor do I. Your vexatious nagging almost stops my breath, madam. Almost."

Lyon let the weight of his gaze travel down the length of her body. Despite the somber face that tried to mask the woman's feelings, despite the plain cut of her dark blue dress, despite the simplicity of the way she piled her hair upon her head, he knew at that instant that being confined in one room with Millicent was having a disquieting effect on him.

"If leaving this room means you will no longer plague me with your constant mindless chatter, then I will do it . . . and gladly."

Chapter 12

Preparing a dinner for the royal family would not have rattled Millicent as much as planning this meal for her husband. She wanted everything to be perfect—the food, the wine, the dining room. She had questioned Gibbs endlessly about Lyon's likes and dislikes with regard to the menu, and she had made certain every detail was conveyed to the cook and to Mrs. Page. Now, shortly before she was scheduled to go to her husband's chamber to supervise Will and John in bringing him down to dinner, Millicent was overcome with yet another reason for uncertainty. What could she wear that was appropriate? Of course, she wanted to dress presentably, but she also knew that what she chose for this occasion could relay a specific message to the earl.

She'd not had any time this afternoon to dwell on what had happened earlier, but she was still rattled by his kiss and by her own response to it. Avoiding intimate contact with any man had simply become Millicent's way after the physical abuse she'd endured under Wentworth's cruel fist. This had been one of the reasons why she had found marrying Aytoun so unobjectionable. Because of his physical inabilities, there would be no possible way that any such demands would be put upon her. Her insistence on a clause allowing for an annulment had been spurred by that very problem. Of course, she told herself as she stared into her looking glass, a kiss should not necessarily constitute any change in her thinking on the matter.

Millicent forced the thoughts to shift and settle in her

mind as her maid Violet rushed about the room laying out petticoats and stockings and other pieces of clothing. It was a kiss and nothing more. Millicent silently vowed not to think about it again, and nodded at the blue embroidered dress Vi held up for her.

"If you're sure you'll not wear the wig, m'lady, I can work some matching ribbons in your hair and—"

"We have no time for that, Vi." Millicent stepped out of her dress and donned the petticoats. In a moment, she was pulling on the blue dress with Vi's help. "I cannot chance having the earl change his mind about leaving his chambers. I told him seven o'clock, and I need to be there on time."

"At least allow me to tie a ribbon at your neck, m'lady. The square neckline of this dress looks far too plain without jewelry."

A glance in the mirror at the low neckline and she agreed. Violet had a good eye for colors, for what was becoming and what wasn't. There were many times that Millicent had thought the young woman's talents were wasted staying here, but Vi seemed content.

"Too bad you no longer have that sapphire the squire gave you when you married. The blue stone always looked fetching with this dress."

"I like this simple ribbon much better."

Millicent felt no regret about having sold her jewelry after Wentworth's death. Regardless of whether they were his gifts or handed down from her own family, she had no use for them. They all had been sold to take care of her people.

"Thank you, Vi. I think I'm ready."

"Wait! You need to change your shoes." Violet fetched a pair of matching slippers from the wardrobe. "Perhaps this is not the time, m'lady, but I was wondering if you would mind if I were to spend two days away at the end of this week."

"Visiting with your family in St. Albans?"

"Yes, m'lady."

Violet crouched before Millicent as she stepped into

the slippers. She thought the young woman looked thinner.

"I don't see any problem with that at all. But are you feeling unwell?"

"No, m'lady. I am quite well."

"I think you have been working too hard, Vi. In fact, if you speak to Mrs. Page about it, perhaps she can arrange to have one of the grooms drop you off while he is running errands for the household and pick you up again on another return trip."

"Don't fret about any of that, m'lady. I'll take care of the arrangements." She rose to her feet. " 'Tis almost seven, I think."

Millicent looked at the mantel clock as it began to chime.

"Indeed, it is," she said, and hurried to the door.

Try as he might, Lyon couldn't find anything to object to about the evening. The light from a dozen candles cast a soft glow over the room. A small fire crackled on the hearth. The food had been exquisitely prepared; the wine was excellent. He let his gaze run appreciatively over the woman seated near him. The company was enchanting.

Instead of taking the chair at the far end of the table, Millicent had chosen to sit beside him. After the food had been taken away, she had dismissed the servants, including Gibbs, and the two of them sat together. Lyon could tell she was in good spirits. Not only had he followed through on his promise, allowing his men to carry him downstairs, but he had also consumed small portions of fish and venison.

He watched her graceful movements as she poured more wine into his crystal glass. He was glad she had not retired to the drawing room and left him to drink alone.

"Frankly, I'm surprised that you trust me with this." Lyon nodded toward the glass.

"Are you referring to drinking the wine or breaking the glass?" Millicent asked lightly.

"The wine. I understand your late husband had some difficulties in that regard."

A small furrow formed on her brow. She reached up to smooth it with the tips of her fingers, and Lyon noticed the redness of her ears and the blush that had crept into her cheeks. "He had many difficulties."

"I am sorry to hear that your life was less than ideal."

"Thank you. But you are full of surprises. Here I had been afraid that you've been spending every moment perfecting your gibes."

"I enjoy a change of pace every now and then." He sensed her distaste of the topic, but he decided to press her on it, anyway. "And what were his other faults?"

He watched the delicate column of her neck as she took a sip of her own wine. The soft curves and the ivory skin above the neckline of the dress glowed in the candlelight, and for an insane moment he wondered if she tasted as sweet as she looked. He forced his thoughts away.

"Your husband's faults?"

"I am afraid I don't consider that a topic for dinner conversation," she answered as brightly as she could. "And I should tell you that it is senseless to listen to household gossip here at Melbury Hall. With the exception of a trusted few, the rest of these people are fairly new in their positions."

"And why is that?"

"I suppose it is just the natural progression of life in a household like this."

"Is it? And what is that progression?" Lyon stared at her flushed face, awaiting an answer. There was no point in retreating now. She had used the business of the estate as a lure. He had every right, therefore, to know what had brought Melbury Hall—and Millicent—to this point.

"I should hate to repeat what you already know. So why not—"

"Start from the beginning."

"Beginning of what?"

"You are being evasive." He caught her wrist when

she started to rise. "Sit, Millicent. You wanted me down here. You asked for my help. I am here, but I need to know your situation. *Our* situation."

"Very well." She sat down again. "As long as we can keep my personal life and my first marriage out of the discussion, I have no objection to telling you what is happening at Melbury Hall."

His nod was a lie, and he knew it. Leave out her personal life? Not likely. The person inside was what interested him the most. The truth behind the lingering sadness in those gray eyes was a mystery that was beginning to nag at him. He'd been told so little by his mother and Maitland before agreeing to the marriage. The dowager had been looking for someone to provide some care for him. Millicent, a widow, had been in financial need. That had been all he cared to know at the time. But the situation was changing now. He was improving every day, and he wanted to know everything about her. To achieve that, Lyon knew he would have to summon up his patience—certainly the least exercised of his virtues.

She took another sip of wine. "Perhaps you have noticed that a large number of black men and women live and work at Melbury Hall."

"Freed slaves."

She nodded. "Over the period of five years that I was married to Squire Wentworth, these people were brought in from his plantations in Jamaica to work the land here. Most of them"—she shook her head—"no, all of them were severely abused by a score of brutal bailiffs who were also brought back from the islands to oversee them."

Lyon watched her closely as she pushed her glass away. The candlelight danced in her gray eyes, now glistening. He knew many men who had made or saved their fortunes by investing in sugar plantations in the West Indies. Even as stories about the barbarous conditions of the places trickled back, many excused the practice, saying that the slaves that were transported to the islands were all criminals and captives of war. Lyon knew the excuses were falsehoods, however, for he himself had seen young children on the ships tied up at Bristol's Long Quay.

"You freed them."

"After the squire's death, I tried to return a small portion of what had been taken from these people. While I let go those servants who were loyal to my last husband, I felt it only just to replace them with the freed slaves. As a result the household has continued to function, but the farms have suffered." She rubbed her temple absently. "I do not wish to bore you with details of what was then and what is now. What I am really in need of advice on regards how to balance the needs of both Melbury Hall and its farms."

"Did all the people you freed stay?"

"Most of them."

"And do you pay them all wages?"

"Of course! They do the same work as anyone else. They should earn the same wage."

"I am not being critical." He matched the tone of her voice. "You married me because you were approaching financial ruin. Was Melbury Hall the cause of it?"

Millicent paused to answer, and he could tell she was contemplating how much to reveal. "No. I was confronted by other debts passed on to me. Large sums beyond what my annual income could afford."

"Left by your husband."

"That is correct. But, having become the recipient of your gracious generosity, I can say that those debts are now paid, and I am even left with enough money make some desperately needed renovations."

"Renovations to this house?"

"No, to the cottages adjacent to it. But that is a project with a one-time expense and not the subject of my greatest concern. As I look over the books from previous years, I realize that Melbury Hall has never been able to sustain itself financially. During the years when Wentworth was alive, it seems that he used the profits from his plantations in Jamaica to support this place."

"Such things are not uncommon, depending on the

amount of land and the quality of the farms here. Are such funds still available to you?"

"No! I lost those lands to one of Wentworth's friends. A man to whom my husband was deeply indebted. But even if I still owned those plantations, I would never consider it," she responded passionately. "I could never have drawn any profit from them. Before I knew I had lost the Jamaican properties, my plans were to free the Africans there as well."

Lyon noted the rising color again in her face. He could see the passion of her beliefs in the flash of her eyes. She looked so incredibly alive. Almost beautiful.

"Also, I am not willing to place the burden of this place on you. I am determined, however, not to pursue any solution that would mean turning out anyone else or cutting wages to make things work here."

The high degree of intelligence and compassion in the woman was a rare mix that Lyon had not come across very often. He studied her with new interest. Another scrap of information he had learned since arriving here was that Millicent was almost thirty years old, and that she'd borne no children in her first marriage.

"You are fond of your large household," he said. "I respect you for wanting to keep it together. I also admire you for all that you are trying to do."

The trace of a smile on her lips washed over him like a warm breeze.

"Gibbs tells me that Melbury Hall has been cursed recently with a line of incompetent stewards. That alone could have been the reason for the poor management of its lands and crops. With capable stewards in charge, you might not have any problem at all."

"My mind would rest more easily if I could somehow be assured of that, but for too long I have felt myself buried beneath a mountain of debt. Now, thanks to you, I feel I finally have the opportunity to breathe fresh air. I cannot leave the future to chance, though. I will not allow things to continue on as they have been."

"I understand. I would be happy to go over the account ledgers and review the crop books. I would also like to see a map of your lands, if you have one."

"I do. It is in the library."

"Then, whatever they are worth, I shall share my thoughts with you."

"You will?" She placed her hand on his arm. "I am so impressed with this change in you. The truth is that in dealing with the financial areas of running an estate, I have often felt adrift in a rudderless boat. Would you mind greatly if I were to look over your shoulder and ask the hundreds of questions that I have?"

"Dozens I might be able to endure. But hundreds?"

Millicent's laughter danced around them and lifted his spirit. Lyon didn't know if it was the effect of the wine or her. This was the first time in months, he realized, that he had spent a couple of hours thinking about someone else, rather than drowning in his own misery. He glanced down at her hand still on his.

"I'll be content with whatever time you can give me, Lyon."

Her chair slid closer to his. The touch of her knee against his leg was warm. She leaned forward and picked up the napkin that had dropped off his lap to the floor. He admired the soft curves of her breast gently spilling over the neckline of the dress. She folded the cloth and put it back on his lap, beneath his right hand. The image of her pressed against his chest this afternoon rushed back to his mind. His gaze moved up to her lips.

"I hope this will not be too much asking for one night," she continued, obviously unaware of the direction of his thoughts. "Mr. Gibbs has been a great help to me, assisting me with so many of the daily business matters. Your valets tell me how involved he was with running the household at Baronsford and again at your town house in London. Would you object if I were to ask him to take over some of the steward's responsibilities here? I know he wouldn't even consider the job unless he had your blessing."

She continued to talk, but Lyon wasn't listening. With a shock, he realized that he was growing hard for the second time in one day. For over six months he had considered himself less than a man. No feelings, no desire, no thoughts of ever lying with a woman again. But after all this time, when he'd felt Millicent's body pressed against his this afternoon, as he'd ravished her mouth with his, he'd felt the stirring of desire. He had cast the feeling aside as his imagination. But to have it happen again now! He'd just been watching her talk, and the sensations had returned.

Instead of excitement, embarrassment drenched him in a cold sweat. The fact that his body responded physically to hers held out no relief to him. He was still not whole. He could not forget how little remained of him in body and soul. He was relieved that she was unaware of these changes.

"I am ready to be taken upstairs."

His sharp tone caused Millicent to look at him with alarm. "What's wrong?"

"I am tired. Ready to retire. I wish to be carried upstairs. Now."

"I shouldn't have brought up all that about Mr. Gibbs. I know how much you rely on him, and I have no intention of reducing the care—"

"I don't give a damn what you ask him to do. I'd be content not to see his ugly face ever again." Irritated, he shoved away the plate before him on the table. The glass next to it fell against the plate and the stem snapped. Before she could stop it, a piece tumbled off the table and onto Lyon's lap. She was at his side in a moment.

"Oh, my Lord! That cut you. I am so sorry. You're bleeding."

Lyon was already staring at the beads of blood forming on his right hand. It was nothing—only a nick caused by the falling shard—but he continued to stare.

His muscles had reacted of their own accord. Without consciously trying to move them, his hand and fingers had moved. But damn him if he could move them again now.

"Call John and Will and have me taken up," he

growled. "If you ever want me to leave that room again, you will have it done *now*."

Millicent hovered in the background while the two valets worked diligently by the light of a single candle, readying their master for bed. Everything about tonight had been special until something had happened. She couldn't understand what had caused the sudden change in Lyon's mood, and her uneasiness was undiminished as she considered the tense wall that had arisen between them. She knew it didn't have anything to do with her question about Gibbs becoming the next steward. Lyon hadn't even seemed to be listening to what she had been saying then.

John bowed his way out of the room first, and Will followed shortly after, closing the door behind him. This had become the nightly routine. The attendants would leave, and Millicent would spend the night dozing in a chair or pacing the room or staring out the window. She did not want Lyon left alone as yet. Then, as dawn was breaking, Gibbs generally came in to take her place.

"I do not want you to stay."

Millicent cringed at the roughness of his tone. Pushing her feelings aside, she reminded herself that despite the pleasant hours they had spent together tonight, he was still recovering from his illness. And she had already learned to expect the sharp alterations in his moods.

"Well, I am not going anywhere."

"Do as you bloody please." He closed his eyes, shutting her out.

Millicent realized she was more disturbed by his indifference than his rejection. Gathering her resolve, she moved close to him. The covers were tucked around him—the left arm lay on top, the right one beneath the blanket. She thought of the cut on his hand, but decided she would not disturb him to check it.

She stared at the dark beard and the long lashes that lay against his handsome cheeks. The memory of their kiss this afternoon came back into her mind and an unexpected warmth spread through her body. She stared

at his hard lips and, without thinking, smoothed the bedclothes. As she did, Millicent wondered if he would ever
kiss her again.

Bothered by her thoughts, she drew back and looked
about the shadowy room. During the last few nights he
had often been sleepless, but other than carrying an argument when he started one or responding to his gibes,
she really had not been needed.

She was tired and he didn't want her here, but Millicent couldn't think of anyplace at Melbury Hall that she
preferred to be than here in this room. She sank into
her chair by the foot of his bed and gazed at his pale
face, wondering what he had been like before.

Everyone in the servants' hall was rushing about, obviously concerned about Moses, who was standing in the
back door, wringing his hands. A black serving maid
hurried up the steps to an upper floor after Mrs. Page
whispered an order to her. Holding the large man's arm,
the housekeeper led him to a bench by the fire. There,
one of the cooks handed her a steaming cup of drink,
which she pressed into his huge hands as she continued
to talk to him in a low, reassuring voice.

Gibbs had entered in the midst of all this, but instead
of meddling he stood back and watched the scene unfold
before him. Moses was saying something in a broken
voice, and it looked to Gibbs as if there were tears standing in the old man's eyes. Someone appeared with a
blanket that Mrs. Page threw around his shoulders. All
the time speaking soothingly to him, she ran a comforting hand over his back.

The household at Melbury Hall was roughly half
black, half white, but what had struck Gibbs most im-
pressively since arriving here was the familial feeling that
held sway. Clearly Lady Aytoun's desire to treat all
fairly, regardless of skin color, was a manner embraced
by the people she employed.

The same servant who had been sent up the stairs
returned, followed by the old woman Ohenewaa. Words
passed between Moses and the woman. Almost immedi-

ately Moses stood up, shed the blanket, and the two of them went out through the back door.

Gibbs's gaze returned to the housekeeper. As she bustled about, he could not help but admire the efficiency with which she settled everything back to normal in just a few moments. He had to admit, though, that Mrs. Page's competence was not the only thing he had been finding fascinating lately. Inviting from a safe distance, but somewhat reserved whenever he came near, Mary Page had been drawing him in bit by bit. What was most interesting, though, was the fact that Gibbs wasn't even minding the feel of the hook she had in him.

"What was troubling Moses?" Gibbs managed to ask, once he was within arm's reach of her.

Mary's green gaze lifted, and she smiled tenderly. "One of the stable dogs that he has become fond of caught a leg in a poacher's snare tonight. Some of the grooms think the poor animal should be put down, but Moses wanted Ohenewaa to look at the injured dog first."

"So is this what Ohenewaa means to them? Is she a healer of some sort?"

Mary nodded. "Aye, but she is also seen as an elder and wise woman. Amina told me that Ohenewaa forms a sort of bridge for them to a part of their past."

"Ye mean Africa?"

"I believe so, Mr. Gibbs."

The Highlander followed Mrs. Page as she made her way out of the hall.

"Since the first day, I have not seen much of this Moses. But from all I can tell, the man appears to be well looked after."

"He deserves it." The same look of tenderness shone in her face. "Despite his scarred body and a weak mind, Moses is the gentlest person I have yet to meet in my life. I've heard stories of all that he regularly endured during the squire's time. The man cannot be blamed if he's a little slow when it comes to any complicated thinking. I think I would have lost my mind completely long ago if I were in his shoes. But Moses is devoted to the mistress and to those who were kind to him over the years."

Gibbs waited when the housekeeper paused at the bottom of the stairs to exchange a few words with Amina, who had just entered the hall. When they were finished and the young woman went off toward the kitchens, Gibbs gave Mary his most serious look.

"And if I were to confess my absolute devotion to ye, Mrs. Page, would ye treat me with the same affection as ye were treating Moses a few minutes ago?"

A blush crept into the woman's fair cheeks. "A cup of warm cider and a blanket around your cold shoulders, Mr. Gibbs?"

"A caressing hand on my back and soft words whispered in my ear."

Mary Page gave him a coy smile. "And why, sir, would someone with your looks and manners be wanting any such thing from an old widow like me?"

"Old, mum? I think not." He took her by the hand and pulled her into the shadow of the steps. "But ye know I'm going a wee bit daft trying to win yer affection, Mrs. Page."

"I don't know what you mean!"

"Don't ye now?" Gibbs dropped his head lower until he was looking into her eyes. "Ye wouldna ride back with me from Knebworth Village last Sunday. Ye have twice refused my offer of walking the grounds in the evening this week. Ye didna find the—"

"I should be honored to have tea with you tomorrow afternoon."

"Tea, did ye say?"

"Tea," she repeated with a smile.

He bowed, placing a kiss on the back of her hand.

"Tea! Well, I'll be dashed, mum, but I'm thinking ye'll be making me the gentleman yet."

"I would expect no less from the next steward of Melbury Hall." She withdrew her hand and fluttered past him. "You would be perfect for the position, Mr. Gibbs, and I do hope you are considering it."

*   *   *

Violet ran to keep up with Amina's longer strides. "How is Moses taking it?"

"He is very upset, Vi, and that is not helping anything," Amina replied. "Jonah wants to have Ohenewaa see to the dog's leg, but to do that, Moses has to keep the animal calm. We do not want the creature to bite anyone. But with Moses moaning and acting more wounded than the dog . . ." The young woman shook her head.

Inside the stables, a lantern was burning in one of the stalls, and at least a dozen people had gathered. Violet, followed by Amina, pushed through them to find Moses crouched on a pile of straw next to his dog. The animal's leg was a mess, and Violet could see what looked like bone sticking out of the bloody flesh.

"They should take off the leg," a groom said to her left.

"She won't make it," someone else commented. " 'Twould be better to cut her throat and put the poor beast out of her misery."

Violet shivered and looked at Ohenewaa, who was spreading out linen strips and some broken branches amid several bottles of salve a foot or two away from Moses and the dog. The old woman said something quietly to Jonah, and the bailiff bent over Moses and whispered to him.

Even from across the way, Violet could see that Moses's body was shaking and tears were running down his face when he stepped back and let Jonah take his place beside the dog as Ohenewaa approached.

When the healer touched the animal's head, Moses winced. When she reached for the paw, the man's whimper matched the dog's. The old man's suffering tore at Violet's heart, and she found herself pushing through the people and going to him.

"Moses." She tugged on his arm when she reached him. Eyes filled with anguish turned to her. "Will you please come and sit outside with me? I cannot watch this. It breaks my heart." When he hesitated, she held his arm. "Please, Moses. I need you."

The old man's feet slogged through the straw as they left the stables. Violet led him outside the open doors and sat down on a wall, pulling him down next to her.

"I took the basket you made me to the village this morning," she said, trying to tear his mind away from what was going on inside. "Will you show me sometime how you managed to weave all those pieces together? That was the best present."

"Do you think she can heal my dog, Vi?"

"Yes, Moses. I think she can heal her."

"M'lady gave her to me. My own."

"I know."

"Never had nothing of my own, Vi."

"I know, Moses." Violet looked into the face of the former slave. It didn't matter to her how hideous he looked. He was so kind and gentle. She held tight onto his arm and pressed her cheek against his shoulder.

"You shall always have at least one friend, Moses, as long as I live."

"I know that too, Vi. Friends."

Violet nodded, forcing down the knot in her throat. "Tell me about your dog, Moses."

It was past midnight when Millicent saw the shadowy figure of Ohenewaa trekking up from the stables. A couple of hours earlier, when she had gone to her own bedchamber to change out of her gown, Millicent had heard from Violet about Moses's injured dog.

Millicent's time had been so consumed with Lyon that she hadn't spent much time with the old woman. She had barely had the opportunity to thank Ohenewaa for the tea that she believed had helped Lyon through the first nights of going without the laudanum.

She thought back to the day that they'd spoken about the letter from Jasper Hyde. Millicent had listened to everything Ohenewaa said. She had already heard such horrors. And she had seen the same superstitious ignorance in others that might very well drive a man like Hyde to hold Ohenewaa responsible for his suffering.

Millicent's refusal to the plantation owner had been

clear and direct. Ohenewaa had no desire to meet with him, and neither did she.

The old woman was no witch, of that Millicent was certain. The fact that she obviously had a knowledge of herbs and medicines did not make her evil. No matter what others chose to think, Millicent felt deep inside that Ohenewaa could be trusted. She had felt it from the first day the old woman had entered Melbury Hall.

That was why Millicent had to see her again tonight. She needed her advice.

Turning away from the window, she watched Lyon breathing comfortably in his sleep for a moment. He had been correct in saying that he didn't need her. There were no more nightmares. No staying awake just to be difficult.

Millicent went to the door and quietly opened it. The hallway was immersed in darkness, and she stepped out of the bedchamber, pulling the door partially closed behind her. Almost immediately she saw Ohenewaa appear at the top of the stairs. The old woman's dark eyes shone like a cat as they fixed on her.

"How is Moses?" Millicent asked softly when the woman drew near.

"He was worried about the animal, but he is doing better."

"Did the dog live?"

"She has a broken leg, but Moses was taught how to tend it."

"We are fortunate to have you here. Thank you."

With a nod, Ohenewaa started past her.

"Would you consider, at some point in time, examining my husband?" Millicent paused when the older woman turned to look at her. "From what I can tell, none of the English doctors have seen any hope in him ever improving, in mind or in body. But we have already proven them half wrong. He is awake, aware, intelligent."

"And loud."

"That too." Millicent smiled. "This is why I cannot help but believe there might be something else—in his legs and arm—that they might be overlooking. So would you consider it? When the time is right, of course, and when I can convince him of it?"

The old woman studied her for a while and then nodded slowly. "When the time is right."

Chapter 13

⌒

Millicent was astounded.

No other word could describe her feelings at the flawless perfection of manner with which Lyon greeted and conversed with Reverend Trimble, despite the lengthiness of the visit.

Settling into a chair in the library as if he planned on spending the remainder of winter there, the minister touched upon one topic of discussion after another. Like a pair of old university friends, the two managed to engage themselves in occasionally heated discussions on everything from the political and social struggles in Ireland, to the changing face of industry under the visionary and exploitative influences (Reverend Trimble's phrase) of such people as Josiah Wedgwood, to Hugh Williamson's recent assertion that comets were positively inhabited. Having covered the rumors of land clearings in the Scottish Highlands, they moved easily into the latest news of the growing unrest in the American colonies. In someplace called the Carolinas, she heard Reverend Trimble say, British troops had recently been needed to suppress open rebellion there. And things did not look to be improving.

During the entire time, Millicent had remained attuned to Lyon's mood. She was ready to jump in at any time that her husband suddenly decided that it was time to be rid of the visitor. She did not want her old friend to be offended.

Despite the minister's customarily talkative nature,

Millicent maintained a great affection for him. Mr. Trimble had been a great ally to her and to the workers at Melbury Hall for a long time, even while Squire Wentworth held the whip over them all. It had been because of Reverend Trimble and Mr. Cunningham, the village schoolmaster, that a routine of tutoring the slaves had been established on the estate. Because of their perseverance and watchful intervention, more lives had not been lost to the brutality of the squire's bailiffs.

Mr. Cunningham.

Millicent's chin sank. A knot the size of a fist formed in her chest as she recalled for the thousandth time how the young teacher had lost his life while trying to protect her. She had asked him to come to Melbury Hall in the early hours of dawn to help free the frightened Violet of the lecherous advances of the squire. But Wentworth had thought the man was taking Millicent away with him. He had killed Mr. Cunningham that morning. And after all this time, she still could not free herself of the guilt.

She blinked back the sudden tears and tried not to think of the young man's affection—of how he had been her friend, her salvation during those horrible years. During his last days he had even thought that he was in love with her. But Millicent had discouraged his declarations. She had feared for her own life, but never guessed Cunningham would be the victim.

When Millicent looked across the room, she found Lyon's gaze focused on her face. The conversation between the two men appeared to have become one-sided. She realized they were talking about building construction—or rather, Reverend Trimble was. What had he just proposed? She had missed his point, and an awkward silence fell over the room.

"Would that be satisfactory to you, Lady Aytoun?" the clergyman asked.

Millicent had no idea *what* was satisfactory. She sent Lyon a silent plea.

"Has anyone checked this stonemason's references?" the earl asked, never taking his eyes off her.

"I believe so, m'lord," the minister replied. "He would not have been hired to work on the grange otherwise, and his work looks entirely satisfactory."

"And with the grange work nearing completion, you said he is willing to begin working here two days a week."

"That is correct."

"And after he is finished in the village, he can work a full schedule here?"

"That is what he says, m'lord."

"What do you think of hiring him then, Millicent? You have been anxious to start on your projects."

She gave a grateful nod to her husband and then turned to Reverend Trimble. "That would be wonderful. Thank you for seeing to this."

"My pleasure, m'lady. Well, I suppose I should be getting home, though I must say I have thoroughly enjoyed my visit."

The clergyman pushed himself reluctantly to his feet and said his farewells to the earl. Millicent escorted him out of the room.

"Once again, m'lady," he started as soon as they were heading down the hall toward the front foyer, "I must congratulate you on this union. Lord Aytoun hardly matches his reputation. I am so eager for Mrs. Trimble to meet him. What an intelligent man! So well-spoken and such wonderfully progressive views. Very edifying, indeed."

"He is a surprising man."

"And I understand that Lord and Lady Stanmore are returning to Solgrave in a fortnight. It will be such a happy occasion to have both your families here. Quite happy, indeed."

"Please send my regards to Mrs. Trimble," Millicent said before the clergyman could start in on another topic. A servant helped him into his coat and handed him his gloves and hat. "By the way, what is the name of this stonemason?"

"Ned Cranch. He is eager to start at this second job.

He told me confidentially that he could use the work and the extra wages."

"Could he?"

Reverend Trimble gave a nod. "I heard all about his two wee ones and his wife in Coventry. Says she's expecting their third child any day now. The man has mouths to feed."

"Tell him we shall have work ready for him as soon as next week, if he is free."

"I am certain he will be here."

Goldsmith's *The Vicar of Wakefield*, the book that Reverend Trimble had brought for Lyon, lay on the edge of the table before him. As he reached for it, though, the heavy volume slipped through Lyon's fingers and struck his leg. His left foot jerked along the carpet, and the volume landed on the floor. Lyon stared down in disbelief.

The sensations running up and down his leg were real. His leg had moved. He tried to move his foot again, but he could not repeat the movement. Then, as quickly as they had come, the feelings disappeared. No matter how hard he concentrated, he was not able to move his foot so much as an inch.

"Thank you for your courteous treatment of Reverend Trimble."

As Millicent came back into the room, the soft voice drew Lyon's attention away from his legs. Her smile dimmed a little, however, when she saw his face. He simply nodded curtly and looked down at the book at his feet.

"While I was watching you with him, I began to doubt that you were the same man I married. So I immediately became a student for the rest of his visit, trying my best to observe the techniques the good reverend employed to keep you in so agreeable a state." She crouched down beside Lyon's chair and fetched the book. "Did you wish to read this?"

"No."

At his sharp answer, Millicent put a hand on his arm. She continued to kneel beside his chair. "Is something wrong?"

"No."

After a moment of close scrutiny that he tried to ignore, she rose to her feet. "I am going to fetch Reverend Trimble before he leaves. I am going to ask him to stay and dine with us." She started for the door. "There must be something that I lack in—"

"Millicent!"

Lyon's call turned her around.

"Nothing is wrong. However, I want *you* to read this book to me."

Violet gasped as Ned shoved her hard, pinning her against the wall. His eyes were flashing with anger. She tried to get a hand between his forearm and her throat, but he pushed harder.

"I am sorry," she cried. "I am so sorry. But I heard you were going to St. Albans, and I thought you might want me to follow you here. Ned, we did plan to come together so you could meet with my—"

"*Ye* planned," he shouted into her face. "I did no plannin'. And by the de'il, woman, I should give ye a bloody lip for sneaking into this tavern and hiding in my room."

"I was just trying to make you happy, Ned," she whispered tearfully. "We're always sneaking off to your little room in the village. I thought here . . . well, I have two whole days off and—"

"Here I might just whistle and bring a few o' the lads up from the taproom and have ye play whore to all of us." He took his arm from her throat and grabbed her chin roughly in his hand. "Or maybe I'll just bind ye on that mattress there, with a gag for your mouth, and have my way with you a hundred different ways without never havin' to listen to your whinin' at all."

The young woman spoke through her sobs. "You are scaring me, Ned Cranch. You know you shouldn't say such things. You know I'm no whore. I only came be-

cause I thought you would be glad to have me here."
She gathered the front of her cloak tightly around her.
"I'll go. I am sorry to upset you like this. I was a fool
to think you meant all those sweet things you said. I
know now you only said them to find your way under
my skirts."

"Mind your bloody tongue or I'll . . ."

When Ned raised a threatening fist, Violet cringed
against the wall. She was relieved when he didn't hit her
and instead dropped his hand to his side.

"Get out o' here, ye brazen chit, before I change my
mind and decide to teach ye a hard lesson."

There was no doubting his words. The anger she saw
in those green eyes was sobering. It was as if he hated
her Violet moved away, circling around him and then
running for the door. Outside in the dark, foul-smelling
hallway of the inn, she let the tears fall.

What a wretched fool she had been, she thought, trying to get her bearings. She had believed every word he
had told her. She had believed him when he'd said he
loved her. Behind her, a woman laughed a drunken, sa-
lacious laugh, and Violet turned around in alarm. In the
murky light of a shuttered window at the far end of the
hall, she could see the woman bent over, while a trades-
man with his breeches around his knees held her hips
and slammed into her.

Violet felt her stomach rising into her throat. She was
no different, she thought. The tears came faster. She had
become a whore. She pulled the hood of the cloak over
her head and hurried down the hall.

At the stair landing, she ran into a small man coming
up. Kid gloves steadied her. She stared down at the
man's shiny boots.

"Pardon me, sir," she whispered.

One glove took hold of her chin and raised it. Violet
shivered as she glanced into the coldly amused eyes regarding her. There was no escaping him.

"Aren't you a pretty thing? And what a fortunate
wench," he exclaimed, glancing toward Ned's door.
"Come with me, girl. This will take just a minute."

On impulse Violet pulled her face away and backed up a step. He continued to hold her arm. "The stonemason just had me, sir. Perhaps you'd care to take me someplace else?"

His amusement changed to a look of mild distaste. "Very well. Wait here, then."

She was relieved when he let go of her and continued down the dark hall. As the man tapped on Ned's door, Vi turned and fled down the steps. Going down the stairs, she could hear Ned's greeting.

"Come in, Mr. Platt. Ye're early."

Chapter 14

Two maids were already scrubbing the wax and ash from the table. Another was washing the floor. The housekeeper had every window open and was waving the smoke out with her apron. Gibbs had the two hangdog valets in the corner and was lashing into them like a prosecutor at a murder trial.

"Leave them be, Gibbs. The bloody candle dropped on the table; that's all. You are all making too much of a fuss over nothing." Lyon glared at the unsmiling woman who was scissoring through the sleeve of his jacket and shirt. "You realize you've just committed a capital offense in cutting my coat. And ruined a perfectly good one, at that."

"A perfectly charred one. And you can afford another," Millicent whispered absently, crouching beside him. She peeled back the sleeve of the coat and laid his arm on the armrest of the chair.

Lyon leaned his head back and stared in disbelief at the commotion around him. He had been going over the estate's books in the library when he had inadvertently bumped the candelabra on the table, tipping it over and setting the papers on the table on fire. Millicent had left the room only seconds before, but Will had been in here and had pulled Lyon's chair away from the table before dousing the small fire. What he had not realized immediately was that his master's sleeve was on fire, too.

Lyon flinched at the sharp pain in his arm. He looked down at the burned shirtsleeve. The cloth appeared to be stuck to his flesh. She immediately stopped trying to pull it.

"Mrs. Page, have someone get Ohenewaa for me. Mr. Gibbs, I want his lordship taken back to his room. It is getting far too cold in here." Millicent turned her gray eyes toward Lyon. "You moved your arm."

It was not a question but a statement.

"No, you're mistaken."

She gave him a look that he could not comprehend, and then the chair was lifted by the valets. Whatever concern Lyon had a week ago about being paraded through the household with everyone around had been cast to the wind. Every servant in the place was racing about, but no one seemed to have a moment to stand and stare. Millicent stayed beside him all the way upstairs.

Inside his bedchamber, Ohenewaa was already waiting by the window.

"I didn't do it intentionally," he barked at the black woman.

The wrinkled eyelids were open only a fraction. The dark stare told him she was not convinced.

"You two have met?" Millicent asked, motioning for John and Will to move him to the bed.

"We're old acquaintances."

Lyon became suspicious when Millicent and Ohenewaa started whispering together. When his wife started for the door and the old woman came over to check on his arm, he voiced his complaint immediately.

"Where are you going? Bloody hell. You really don't intend to leave me alone with her now, do you? Millicent!"

Millicent hid her smile before giving him an exasperated look over her shoulder. "I'm going nowhere." She stopped at the door and whispered some directions to a servant who was hovering outside.

Ohenewaa waved John and Will away from the bed. The old woman then approached him and began checking the burn on his arm. After looking at it for a few moments, she retrieved some sharp shears from the table and cut most of the fabric away from around it. In the meantime, the servant Millicent had sent away returned with a large bowl of white liquid.

"I am not drinking this," he groused when Millicent brought it to the bed. "Whatever it is."

"It is only milk."

"All the same, I'll not have it."

"As you wish."

Millicent sat on the edge of the bed and, following Ohenewaa's quiet direction, draped Lyon's arm over the bowl. Using a small towel, she poured the liquid over his arm again and again.

"Bloody hell!" he growled, gripping the bed with his good hand.

After a few minutes of the treatment, the aching pain started to subside. Ohenewaa directed her to lay the soaked towel on the wound. After the second or third soaking, he saw the fabric of his sleeve had loosened. Carefully, the two women peeled the cloth off, exposing fully the ugly blisters and raw flesh.

A few minutes later, Gibbs came into the room to check on him. Millicent assured him that everything would be fine and sent the Highlander and the valets away.

With the burn cleaned, Lyon thought the ordeal was over, but Ohenewaa had other ideas. Using featherlight touches, she started to examine his right arm and hand in the places that were not burned. She felt and moved each finger, following the line of each bone through the hand to his wrist. She gently felt the bones and muscles up to the elbow, being especially careful around the burn, and then worked her way up beyond the elbow until the material of the coat and shirt stopped her.

"Remove his jacket and shirt."

"The hell she will."

"I shall be back in a few minutes."

As Ohenewaa left the room, Millicent picked up the shears, and Lyon turned sharply to her. "What is this woman doing?"

"Ohenewaa is going to examine you, as any physician would."

"Why?" He caught Millicent's hand.

"Because she knows medicine as well as or better than the doctors you have been seeing. And because I asked her to do this," she said softly. "She won't hurt you, Lyon. I will not move from your side. Please allow her to tend to you."

He couldn't refuse her. "Very well, then. But no more cutting. Help me out of these." With her help he shrugged out of the coat. "You don't believe just because she healed a dog last week, she can heal me, too."

"She *liked* that dog, and you clearly don't believe she likes you."

"The old hag told me so herself."

"This is not the time to be so disagreeable," Millicent whispered. "Please, Lyon. I think she knows things that those highly educated physicians you have been dealing with have been blind to."

"And what do you think she knows?"

"Perhaps she can make use of the feelings and sensations that have been coming and going. The ones you ignore or try to hide." She met his gaze when he looked up startled at her. "I have seen it. Last week, when the glass cut you, your hand moved. Three days ago, when John was helping you out of bed, I think your foot was twisted, and I believe you straightened it yourself. And then, last night you were having a nightmare, and I saw the muscles in your leg move."

There was no rhyme or reason to what his body did, it seemed. Lyon had no control over what he was capable of moving and when. But he didn't want to say any of this to Millicent. He didn't want to raise any false hopes in her. Instead, he admired the loose ringlets that had escaped their tight confines and were now framing her face. She looked so soft. This was the way she had awakened him last night from his nightmare, and Lyon remembered how much he'd wanted to draw her mouth down and kiss her.

He wanted to do the same thing now.

"The movements were involuntary. They don't mean a thing."

Ohenewaa returned, carrying bottles of different liquids that she proceeded to line up on the table.

Millicent leaned closer, tantalizing him with her nearness. "I should like to grasp at every chance, no matter how small. Many people here believe in her, Lyon. I am not saying that she can heal you completely, but we would be fools not to give her a chance to help as much as she can."

"Do as you please." He let go of her hand. "But I think you are wasting your time."

Beneath his long, dark hair, his neck was strong and powerful. His shoulders were wide and his chest muscular. Lyon was thin, though, and his ribs showed through the skin, reflecting the weeks of refusing food and nourishment.

Millicent's throat was dry by the time she finished removing his shirt. They had been married nearly a month. She had spent her nights at his bedside. She had been present during the changing of his clothes and even during sponge baths by his servants. But none of those moments had felt as intimate as removing his shirt herself.

Ohenewaa came back to his bedside with a bottle of ointment and a few clean cloths. "Spread this gently over the burn on his arm and then wrap it loosely with this."

Millicent brought the jar to her nose. "It smells familiar."

" 'Tis a decoction of the bark of the elm tree. 'Twill dry the pus that will soon be forming, and help the healing process."

Millicent was grateful for having something to do, and she went to work while the healer started examining Lyon's body.

"You are too tense. Relax," Ohenewaa said softly to him. The woman's palm was pressed flat against the skin of his chest, moving in slow circles. "Let your body talk to me."

"You accused me of talking too much," Lyon retorted, moving his gaze momentarily from the ceiling.

"Close your eyes. Let your mind float away from here to a peaceful time in your life. Then your body will tell me where there is pain."

Millicent was surprised when he didn't protest or argue. She saw him close his eyes and give himself up to the touch of the old woman. She went back to her own task of dressing his wound. After she finished, Ohenewaa motioned to her to remain at the bedside.

It was soothing to watch her. Following the movements of the wrinkled hands over his chest and shoulders and arms, Millicent felt the calming effect of them on her as well. After a time Ohenewaa paused.

"Now I need to check his legs. You must remove his shoes, stockings, and breeches."

Heat rushed into Millicent's face. "I shall go and get one of the valets." She rose quickly to her feet.

"No." Lyon's eyes opened slightly. "I don't want any new rumors circulating in this house. You can manage it."

She took a deep breath. She had been sexually aroused simply taking the man's shirt off. Now his breeches!

Ohenewaa walked back to her table of medicines. Suddenly the room felt too hot. Lyon was lying on top of the bedclothes. Millicent took a folded blanket from the bottom of the bed and spread it across his middle. To make matters worse, he was watching her every movement.

"In case you're considering using those shears," he said in a low voice, "you can put that thought out of your mind. My stockings and breeches don't trust them . . . and the same thing goes for any parts of my body that you might encounter."

"Why don't you close your eyes and let your body talk to me?" she asked quietly, trying to inject some humor.

She moved to the foot of the bed and removed his shoes and peeled off the stockings. Without thinking, she ran her hands down one calf. Lack of exercise had shrunk the muscles somewhat. Her fingers moved up to the buckles below the knee on his breeches. Millicent's hands shook as she started undoing them. The skin beneath her touch was so warm.

"Keep this up, and you'll see very soon that my body

does indeed have something to tell you. That doesn't trouble you, does it?"

He was mocking her, teasing her. But his voice was beginning to sound a little strained. Steeling herself, Millicent held her breath and moved up to stand beside the blanket that covered his middle. The pulsing of her blood rang in her ears. She was thankful for the dimness of the chamber, for she could feel her face and ears burning. Her gaze remained focused on the weave of the blanket, and her hands brushed against his stomach as she reached under the covering.

"Get Gibbs."

At his curt direction, she leaped back from the bed and ran for the door.

"The news from the Borders is quite disturbing, m'lady. The Earl of Dumfries has begun to clear the farms to the west, raising the crofters' rents to exorbitant rates. As of the writing of this letter, it appears that some two hundred tenants have taken refuge at Baronsford since Michaelmas. My man says he's been told that perhaps five hundred more went to Glasgow with the hope of moving on to the American colonies." Sir Richard put down the letter that he had received from the Borders. "The earl should be told."

"No," the dowager asserted stubbornly. "He is not ready for this."

"As you wish, m'lady, but his lengthy absence is only adding more meat to the stew of rumor bubbling amongst the tenants. Many fear that with the earl's injury and the marriage to an Englishwoman—along with the fact that he signed the lands over to Pierce— Baronsford's farms will be next to go. They are already talking of him never coming back."

The dowager closed the book on her lap with a snap and glared at her old lawyer. "Under Millicent's care, Lyon is making great improvement. Relaying any such news to him now would only add strain and hinder further progress."

"You think she would not accompany him to Baronsford if he were to decide to make the journey?"

"I don't think it, Sir Richard. I am certain of it. And I do not believe anything of value will be accomplished if he were to go right now—for Lyon or for the people at Baronsford. Find some other way to put the tenants at ease. Pass on the news of the earl's progress. Write to Walter and have him lower the rents. Move every sheep off the farms, if that'll calm them. Whatever needs to be done, get their minds off such foolishness. Tell them I'm gasping for my last breaths, and they should begin mourning for me."

"That they shan't do, m'lady. The tenants at Baronsford are more wary of your tactics than your sons are. They all believe you'll outlive the entire family. But about the earl, you do realize that we can delay passing on this news for only so long. 'Tis his right to know if he is improving. And knowing your son, he'll be wanting to go back to Baronsford before the planting season anyway. How can we not tell him what he'll find there?"

"You are talking about the man he once was. You and I both know that Baronsford is no longer his responsibility. He might still simply tell us to notify his brother Pierce of all these problems. Have you forgotten his anger the last time he left Baronsford? He wanted never to return."

"I've not forgotten, m'lady. But that was the pain of the moment talking. Signing those papers was an act of frustration and nothing else. The tenants, Pierce, you, and I all know that he is the one who can save Baronsford. We all want to remember him as the man he once was, and *I* believe he will be that man again in time."

"I want to believe that, too," the dowager responded quietly. "But we have to give him time. We cannot push him into things that he is not ready for. He is coming along, it appears, but I do not want to set him back even a day."

Chapter 15

Lyon threw his napkin on the tray, hiding what he hadn't eaten of his breakfast. "What torture have you devised for me today, Madame de Sade?"

"Something very painful."

He noticed the dark circles beneath her eyes when Millicent leaned over him to pick up the tray. She was beginning to look paler and more drawn every day. "Excellent. When do we start?"

"Don't be impatient. Soon enough." She handed the tray to John to take out. "A few hours of uninterrupted sleep seem to have done you some good."

"You again spent the night here in this room, did you not?"

"I did."

"Why? I told you I have no need of a watcher, especially when I am knocked unconscious by the dark magic the witch is using to subdue me. I should ask her to use the same thing on you." He caught her wrist when she bent to pick up a cup and saucer that had been left on the table next to his chair. Her gaze flew to his in surprise. "You don't look very well."

"Thank you. But my health is fine."

"You look pale."

"I was born with this look, and there is not much I can do to change it."

"What I meant to say is that you look tired." She tried to pull herself free, but he tightened his hold. "We cannot allow you to become sick."

"Why?"

"Because then I would be left with no one to torment."

Gibbs cleared his throat at the door.

"Do not think it or say it," Lyon growled at his man-servant. He let go of his wife's hand. As Gibbs went wordlessly to the hearth and began poking at the fire, Millicent went about quickly tidying up the room. Lyon watched her carefully. She had lost weight, too. Even her dress was hanging off her.

"The scheduled torture for today is to expose you to the ghastly out-of-doors. Sunshine, winter air." She took a woolen blanket from a chest in the corner. "We have selected a delightfully protected spot within the walls of the gardens and—"

"I am not going outside, nor I am going downstairs today."

She whirled on him, hands on her hips. "Why? I know you are too stubborn to admit it, but you have been enjoying—"

"Because you are getting ill."

"I am not."

"You will if you don't get a few good hours of sleep yourself—and in a real bed." He didn't give her a chance to voice a protest. "I'll tell you what I shall do. If you promise to retire to your bedroom this instant and settle into your bed for a few hours, I will pursue whatever bloody routine you have managed to plan out for me."

"It is only half past ten on a very beautiful morning. I promise to go to bed tonight."

"No." He shook his head. "You go now."

"There are other things that I need to see to today. The new stonemason will be—"

"Gibbs."

"Aye, m'lord?"

"Tell the man we shall pay him his day's wages and then send him away until tomorrow." Lyon turned back to her. "Anything else can wait or be handled by others."

She stood for a moment, looking at him. She must

have been genuinely tired, he thought, for no argument rose to her lips. At that instant, his physical shortcomings once again stabbed at him. What he wouldn't give to be able to walk Millicent to her bedroom right now, to be able to care for her a little as she had been caring for him.

Violet's heart climbed into her throat at the sight of Ned talking to Mr. Gibbs by the door to the servants' hall.

He was holding his hat in one hand. He had made an attempt to comb his blond hair and bind it at his neck. His woolen coat was open and his broad chest was visible beneath it. She saw two of the scullery maids giggle and cast flirtatious looks his way as they passed him heading to the kitchen. In spite of herself, Vi felt her claws emerge.

While the Scotsman continued to talk, Ned's eyes scanned the room and paused when he saw her. Vi held her breath, waiting for his reaction. She had cried her heart out last Saturday on her way back from St. Albans. She had promised herself that she would not go alone to Knebworth Village as long as he was still working there. She did not want to see him or be left alone with him for a minute. She had learned an ugly lesson, and she knew she was fortunate to have a respectable job and a bed to sleep in after such a huge mistake. But now, with that engaging smile appearing at the corners of his mouth, with those eyes seeing only her, Violet nearly forgot her name, never mind the promises she had made to herself.

Mr. Gibbs looked over his shoulder, following the direction of Ned's gaze, and Violet hurriedly moved on through the room. No one had made any announcement, but everyone at Melbury Hall knew that the Highlander was to be the next steward. And this suited just about everyone, including Vi. Mr. Gibbs was strict, but he had a sense of humor. He was also obviously sweet on Mrs. Page, a feeling that the housekeeper appeared to share. That in itself was a good sign that he was going to stay.

* * *

Millicent rolled over in the bed and stared at the half-light that surrounded her. For a few moments she was totally confused. The day, the hour, even how she had ended up in bed were a mystery to her. And then she remembered: She had come to her room before noon to rest for a couple of hours.

Whoever had lit the fire had obviously done it hours ago, for the embers on the hearth held only a faint reddish glow. She climbed out of bed, and the feel of the cold floor beneath her bare feet awakened her completely. Lighting a taper from the embers, she looked at the clock on the mantel. It was almost twelve. Midnight. But how could that be?

Millicent stood in the darkness, listening. The house was quiet. It appeared that everyone was asleep. A sudden thought made her reach for her wrap. Had anyone changed the dressing on the burn on Lyon's arm this afternoon?

As she washed her face and rinsed out her mouth, she glanced at her reflection in the looking glass. With her tousled hair hanging loose around her shoulders, she looked terrifying enough to frighten a ghost. She ran a hand impatiently through the mess and headed for the door.

The corridor was dark. She would just take a quick peek inside Lyon's room to make certain he was asleep. Passing Ohenewaa's door, she recalled promising the older woman the night before that she would stop to see her today for some ointments she was preparing for Lyon. Millicent could not believe she had wasted an entire day in bed.

She didn't knock. Quietly pushing the door open, she slipped inside Lyon's room. By the light of the dying fire, he looked to be asleep. She closed the door behind her and padded silently across the floor.

"Did you sleep well?"

She was startled to hear his voice and find his eyes open. He was watching her.

"Too well. I cannot believe how long I slept. I had

specifically asked Mrs. Page to send someone to awaken me by early afternoon."

"I ordered Mrs. Page not to allow a single person to disturb you."

"I see then that I was outranked." She smiled at him and looked down at his arm. "Thank you. I didn't realize how tired I was until I crawled between those sheets. Did anyone change the dressing on your arm this afternoon?"

"No, I wouldn't let them near me."

"I see." Millicent retrieved some clean dressings and the bottle of ointment Ohenewaa had placed on the bedside table last night. She sat carefully on the bed beside him. "So this means I have not worn out my usefulness."

"There is little chance of that."

Perhaps it was the words or maybe the way he said them, but Millicent felt a subtle warmth wash through her. She gently lifted his arm from under the blankets and laid it on her lap. His nightshirt had a wide sleeve. She started inspecting the wound.

"Does it still hurt?"

"Nothing to speak of."

Her feet were bare and cold, so she tucked them under her. The serenity of being here, of doing this for him, filled her with a feeling she had never experienced. Perhaps it was the privacy of the two of them as they were, while the quiet of the night surrounded them. Millicent couldn't explain it, but she felt happy and content. The blisters on his arm looked clean, despite a couple of them having burst. She gently applied some more of the ointment and started wrapping it again. "I expected you to be asleep."

"I tried, but I couldn't. The witch brought her potions in earlier tonight." He motioned with his good hand toward the window. Millicent saw the half-dozen bottles crowding the tabletop.

"Did she give you any instructions?"

"Of course. Don't eat them or inhale them. Only apply them. They are all the same thing. A new jar for each night, she said."

"Did you have someone apply them for you tonight?"

He gave her an incredulous look. "The . . . whatever it is . . . is to be rubbed onto my skin. Just the idea of Gibbs or Will or John spreading the stuff on me is revolting. Besides, I think Ohenewaa is a fake anyway."

"Why should you think that?"

"What kind of physician refuses to say what is wrong with you and whether she can heal you or not? The woman spent hours inspecting every mole on my body and still says nothing."

Millicent rose from the bed and walked over to the bottles of ointments. "She was not inspecting moles, and you know it. And even if it was only for one night, you had some uninterrupted rest."

She picked up one of the bottles and smelled it. There was something familiar and earthy about the scent. It was like something she might have smelled in the woods.

"Did she tell you anything else?"

"Are you actually going to use it?"

She carried one of the bottles back to him. "You don't have to look so horrified. I am going to try some on this same arm." Before he could object, she resumed her previous position on the bed and started rolling the nightshirt up as far as it could go.

She dipped her fingers in the bottle. It was oily but not unpleasant.

"It feels cold." She started rubbing it gently on his arm, above and below the burn. Beneath her touch, as she continued to spread the ointment, she could feel his skin begin to warm. "But it changes quickly. Do you feel it?"

He didn't respond. She carefully worked it into the skin, up to the shoulder.

Millicent looked into his face. "I'm using only my fingertips, but I feel the heat of it seeping into my hands, moving up my arms and through my body." To prove her point, she dipped her fingers into the jar again, but this time instead of his arm, she rubbed it on the narrow span of his chest showing through the open collar of the nightshirt. The muscles flexed and moved beneath her touch. "Do you feel it now?"

"I do."

Leaning against him, she dipped her hand into the jar again, but as she was going to return it to his arm, Lyon's left hand reached across and took hold of her wrist.

"I want to feel it here," he said, bringing her fingers back to his chest.

Between the dancing shadows of the room and the beard covering his features, she could see little of his expression. His hand remained on top of hers, though, guiding her as she rubbed his chest in wider circles. His skin continued to warm beneath her touch, but Millicent's body began to burn. This was more than the fleeting sensuality of touching his body. There was an intimacy and a silent awareness between them. Feeling him react to the gentle caress of her fingers thrilled her.

"Why not close your eyes and let this have its effect?"

"I prefer to watch you."

Their gazes locked. Millicent didn't know what was happening to her, but she found herself being drawn uncontrollably to him. She leaned on his chest, her fingers working a slow path up his neck. The memory of the kiss they had shared before filled her mind. Wordlessly, she brushed her lips against his—once, softly, gently, and then again. His lips were warm, inviting. Summoning her courage, she let her mouth linger a bit longer. Her tongue hesitantly teased the seam of his lips.

His good hand slipped around the back of her head. Millicent felt his mouth open up beneath hers, drawing her in. Enthralled with her position of control and by the curiosity of the heat that was spreading through her, limb by limb, she deepened the kiss. Their tongues danced and mated.

A hungry groan escaped Lyon's lips, and his fingers delved and fisted in her hair. She answered and matched his urgency with hers. She moved on top of him. Her hands held his face, she threaded her fingers through his hair, and she was lost in the play of their lips and tongues and the power of a kiss that continued on and on.

Though she had been married for five years, she had never been kissed or ever kissed anyone like this. Millicent realized that the joy of this one act exceeded by far the horrid sexual encounters she had experienced with Wentworth.

Her head angled to deepen the kiss, and Lyon's passion surged. She reveled in his taste and scent, and her body moved restlessly on him, unconsciously seeking a better fit. Suddenly his arm tightened around her, and he groaned in frustration. Breathless and mortified, she tore her mouth away.

"I am so sorry." She tried to scramble off him, but his grip only tightened more. "What have I done? Lyon, I am so sorry."

"Wait! Don't go." His breathing was as uneven as hers.

Millicent was too embarrassed to look into his face. She had practically attacked him. Tears of confusion rushed into her eyes. She remembered so vividly how helplessly she had lain beneath Wentworth's body, time and time again, while he had his way with her. And now she had become the monster, a predator.

"Get beneath these blankets."

With her heart in her throat, she looked at him in confusion. Lyon's hand moved from her back, and he gently wiped off the wetness on her face.

"You are shivering. Get beneath the blankets with me and stay."

It would have been so much easier to run away, to hide in her own bedchamber. But she could not run. This was different. The brutality and the sadness of her past forced her to open her eyes and face these unfamiliar sensations. She wanted better, and she was not running away. She was not going to be frightened.

Without another word, Millicent slipped beneath the covers and nestled against his warm body. Taking her hand, he pressed it against his heart.

*　　　*　　　*

The black child's heart was pounding hard. Jasper Hyde could see the vein at his temple pulsing relentlessly. On his face and neck and throat, there were more than a dozen dark pimples. The boy had passed a wretched night of fever and pain. Hyde had been told everything, but he could see for himself what was afflicting the slave. It was smallpox.

"Take him to the forecastle. Keep him away from the rest," Hyde said to the ship's master, who stood ready to pass on the order. "I want a general inspection of the slaves. The crew needs to be made aware, too. I want to know if there are any more cases."

He was pacing the quarterdeck when the answer came. It was a single case, but it could imperil the entire ship. He could lose his entire cargo of slaves. He called to the ship's master.

"Kill the boy. And the two who were nearest to him. Over the side with them all."

Jasper Hyde awoke with a gasp. His body was burning. Sweat dripped from his face, and he pulled off his periwig. Afternoon sunlight poured into the room from the large windows of his study. He must have fallen asleep in his chair after the late breakfast.

Suddenly panicking, he touched his chest, his neck, his face, checking for the rashes. None. He didn't have smallpox. There was nothing wrong with him.

As if to contradict his thought, a burning pain sliced through his heart. He grabbed his chest and leaned his head back. It was like the twist of a knife, the heat of a poker. He pressed his chest, trying to rid himself of the pain.

"Damn you, Ohenewaa," he cursed, trying to breathe.

The witch was everywhere, digging her withered hands into him and steadily tearing the life out of him, out of his fortune. The news had reached him this morning: A slave ship Hyde had invested over twenty thousand pounds in less than three months ago had been deliberately run aground on a beach near Accra on the coast of Africa. The slaves had mutinied and taken over the ship, murdering the captain and crew. Two hundred seventeen slaves had disappeared back into the bush. The ship was lost, all gone, and due entirely to the curses of a filthy black witch.

Hyde barked at the door when he heard the knock. The pain in his chest was easing, but he didn't dare move when Harry's face appeared.

"Mr. Boarham is here to see you, sir."

"Who the hell is he?"

Harry's eyes motioned to someone standing behind him. "The surgeon who bled Dr. Dombey before his death. You sent for him."

Hyde realized his hand was shaking when he removed it from his chest. "Send him in."

Boarham entered the chamber cautiously, and Hyde watched the man's eyes darting from side to side, taking in the whole room. Whether he was assessing the value of every item in sight or making sure that a trap was not waiting for him, Hyde had no way of telling. The man had kept his hat, a greasy tricornered affair too small for his head, and it was propped on top of an old bagwig he was wearing. His face was badly pocked, and for a small-shouldered man Boarham had a suspiciously large belly. Hyde decided he probably carried his entire fortune in a satchel beneath his coarse woolen coat and matching waistcoat.

Boarham approached and doffed the hat with a nervous bow.

"Yer servant, sir. Ye're needin' to be bled, sir?"

"No."

"I've the finest leeches in London, sir. And I've served the finest. Even the Lord Mayor's butler's cousin, sir."

"No." Hyde answered sharply. "You were with Dr. Dombey when he died, weren't you?"

"Dr. Dombey? Oh, I know who ye mean. Nay, sir, not when he died, but I visited him the night before. He was good at taking his salts, he was. I had his slave woman make some rice milk for him for supper. O' course, I was astonished when she put an egg in it. But he was right as rain when I went away, sir. As I recall the next morning was market day. And 'twas sleeting.

Aye, the ground was ankle-deep with muck and mire when I went to the sheep pens. I didn't get back to Dombey until the old gent had passed on. You see I never like to miss market day, sir, and—"

"Dr. Dombey owed you money, didn't he?"

"Well . . ." The leech stuck his finger in one ear, took out a ball of wax, and examined it absently before flicking it across the room. "He had all kinds of creditors knockin' on his door, and I wasn't chargin' him much. But now that ye mention it—"

"I was hoping I might make good on his debt, Mr. Boarham. He left some money with his slave to give to you. I have it."

"That's mighty Christian of ye, sir." The drool practically hung from the man's lip.

Hyde leaned forward in his chair. "You are not the first one that she cheated—the slave woman—and that is why, being a good friend of Dombey, I have taken it on myself to set the wrongs to right." He opened a small wooden casket from the table beside his chair and took a bag of coins from it. "Now, how much did he owe you?"

Boarham's hands clutched the edges of his hat, and he held it to his chest. "I . . . I believe 'twas two guineas, sir."

Hyde drew a handful of coins from the bag and watched his visitor's eyes light up at the sight of gold. "And I thought he owed you so much more. I have fifty pounds here, Mr. Boarham."

"Maybe he owed me more, and I couldn't remember?" he blurted quickly.

"Perhaps he did. But I think your memory is very important, Mr. Boarham. Perhaps you might even remember that Dr. Dombey's death was caused by the greedy slave who is holding on to all his money."

"That old slave woman, sir?"

"The same one, Mr. Boarham." Hyde started stacking the gold coins next to him.

"I remember her well, sir." His gaze locked on the coins. "She looked to be a low-down poisoner, sir, if ever I seen one."

"Did you know she is a witch?"

The surgeon looked up startled and quickly crossed himself. "Is she, now?"

"Aye, my good fellow. And you are going to help me prove it."

Chapter 16

"The day is wasting away, man. Where the blazes is she?" Lyon bellowed as Gibbs entered the library with John in tow.

"Your wife is just finishing her interview with the stonemason. She said she will meet you in the gardens."

"When? Next bloody week?" he grumbled in annoyance.

Lyon's irritation had begun this morning when he had awakened to find Millicent gone. After that, while his valets were getting him ready for the day, she had poked her head in only fleetingly, mumbling excuses about the tasks she had to see to that morning. And she had not come back to see him even once, not even during breakfast. Now it was eleven o'clock in the morning, and Lyon was at the end of his damned patience.

" 'Tis a wee bit brisk out there, m'lord, though nothing we've not seen rounding the Cape of Good Hope on our way to India, I'd say. That aside, Lady Aytoun has insisted that ye should be wearing a hat."

Lyon took the hat Gibbs placed on his knee and fired it across the floor. "Tell her if she is so bloody worried, then she can come and see to it herself."

The valets lined themselves up on either side of his chair and carefully lifted him. As they tipped him ever so slightly, he blasted them all for their incompetence. With the air of a true martyr, Gibbs retrieved the hat and led the entourage out the door and through the house.

It was difficult for Lyon to understand, but last night had provided a fulfillment he'd not felt in months. The explosive reaction of his body to her kiss was stunning. And the warmth that had spread through him every time he'd stirred during the night and found Millicent still at his side had been remarkable. In the past, he had always felt the urge to leave a woman's bed when the evening's lovemaking was complete, but the feel of this woman against him last night had changed his mind.

Lyon knew he was starting to depend on Millicent. Perhaps he was just substituting her for the comfort that the opium drops had brought him. But hell, he thought, even if he was, the woman was flesh and bone, and he'd be dashed if it wasn't more interesting to lose himself in her kisses than to spend his time in a daze.

Outside, the winter air was indeed bracing, and Lyon took a few breaths, trying to adjust his lungs to the cold. They carried him down toward the old-fashioned formal gardens. Over the wall he could see trellises and arbors arranged amid symmetrically organized squares of herbs and flowers and paths of greensward. Beyond the lower wall of the garden, a landscape of fields and woods and evergreens stretched away from the house. Lyon glanced about him critically. The property needed some work, to be sure. But having glanced quickly at Melbury Hall's ledgers from recent years, Lyon already knew that renovation and upkeep of pleasure gardens and vistas were the last of Millicent's priorities.

He ducked slightly as they conveyed him through the gated and arched entry to the formal garden. Carefully they lowered the chair and positioned him next to a stone bench to the left of the gate. It was a place protected by trellises and stone walls that blocked most of the wind and yet captured the sun. A pair of cardinals flitted from branch to branch of a vine on the wall nearby. The male was more brightly colored than the female, and the birds went after the few bright orange berries still left on the vine.

"I am here. So where is she?"

"Here!" Millicent called breathlessly, walking briskly

down the path. She was holding his hat in one hand and some newspapers and a blanket tucked under an arm. Lyon stared at the well-worn woolen cloak. Its hood and lace edging framed her flushed face prettily. Wisps of steam escaped her lips.

"Leave us," he ordered his valets as soon as she arrived at his side.

"Thank you. I shall call you when his lordship is ready to come inside." She smiled at the men, and they bowed and took their leave. She dropped the papers and his hat on the bench and began unfolding the blanket. "We cannot have you catch a chill on your first day out, now, can we?"

"Don't *you* have something warmer to wear?" he asked irritably, watching her tuck the blanket around his legs. "Your servants dress better than you do."

"This cloak is quite sufficient, thank you, and you can put a stop to your peevishness. This is a beautiful day, and I plan for both of us to enjoy it." Picking up his hat, she placed it on his head and leaned down before him—cocking her head critically from one side to the other—checking the fit. "Your head must be growing, for that hat seems too small. Of course, the long hair and the shaggy growth on your face might have something to do with the fit."

"I do not wear the hat over my beard."

"If you gave any thought to hiding your brooding disposition, perhaps you would."

"And the logistics of that?"

"Quite simple, really." She trailed her fingers down one side of his face. "I can attach two long bits of ribbon to the hat to loop about each of your ears."

"Very stylish."

"Of course, we shall have to be clever about it and make them long enough to cross again over the front, thereby fastening the hat securely over your mouth before the ribbons are tied in a handsome bow above your head."

He couldn't stop a smile from forming on his lips. "So very clever."

"I thought so." She returned his smile. "And thank you, this is far more pleasant."

She reached up to settle the hat one more time, but he caught the ribbons at the neck of her cloak and pulled her toward him until their lips brushed, lingering for a moment before pulling apart.

"I think *this* is better," he said in a low voice.

Lyon was hungry for more. He had been fantasizing about her mouth all too often of late. She kissed with a fervor that was unmatched in any woman he had ever met. Her mouth was an instrument of desire, and she gave and took with more passion than most were able to summon even in the very act of lovemaking. But he sensed Millicent's hesitancy this morning as she drew back and sat down on the bench, just out of his reach.

"Why did you leave me in the middle of the night?"

"The dawn was already upon us when I left." A deep blush was coloring her cheeks. "And with your valets sure to come in to check on you, I just didn't know how appropriate—"

"We are husband and wife, Millicent. Though I do not recall the ceremony all that clearly, I have seen the documents." He hoped to see her smile a little, but her face retained its seriousness. "Therefore, not that I give a damn what my servants think, I do not believe they would think it odd finding you in my bed. Certainly it would be no stranger than finding you asleep in a chair, as they have seen you often enough this past month."

She was avoiding looking up at him. Something else was bothering her.

"Unless you find lying next to a cripple so demeaning that—"

"On the contrary . . . I find sharing your bed to be quite pleasing."

Her words fluttered shyly in the air between them, like butterflies testing their wings for the first time. Lyon was willing to wager she had never in her life spoken of such things openly.

"Then why did you slip away like some thief in the night?"

"I am not accustomed to it," she continued, blushing fiercely. "How am I to know what is appropriate behavior? I thought I was expected to leave at some point during the night."

"Is that how things were between your husband and you? You made love, and then each of you retired to your respective bedrooms?"

"Made love?" The color washed out of her face. "I don't care to talk of my first marriage."

Turning slightly to hide her face from him, Millicent spread the newspaper on her lap and turned her attention fully to it. "What can I read to you this morning, m'lord? News of the colonies or the continent?"

"Whatever suits you." That was a lie. He wanted to hear about her life. He wanted to know that she had been as eager this morning to see him as he was to see her.

As he listened to her clear voice, he realized what he would like to know was the story of the woman herself. Nothing would interest him more than to hear the reasons for her insistence on keeping the doors of her personal past so tightly shut. But Lyon knew he desired the same privacy regarding his own past life. There were limits as to just how far he would push her for answers.

They were two strange birds, he thought. Both of them were still drawn to the same brightly colored berry that they had each found so bitter in the past. And yet they were unable to pass it by completely.

"I do not wish to hear any news of the outside world," he barked, cutting her off when a news article she read referred to the regiment of his youngest brother, David. How many times during his months of being confined to a chair or a bed had he thought of him? Lyon supposed David thought him guilty of pushing Emma over the cliffs. He would naturally think the worst. Lyon had ruined David's dreams by marrying Emma. But it was another thing entirely to murder her.

Lyon pushed the disturbing thoughts away and tried to focus on the moment. He softened his tone. "Put that aside, if you will. Tell me instead about your interview with the stonemason. Or tell me about the village, or the mess that deuced Gibbs is creating while he decides if he can lower himself to take on the position of bloody steward."

She glanced worriedly from his face to the paper and back to his face again. Annoyed, Lyon wondered if she had guessed the connection. She folded the newspaper and put it with the others beside her on the bench.

"Very well." She thought a moment. "I received another letter from your mother, the dowager, with the packet of newspapers this morning. She is considering my invitation of coming to Melbury Hall for a visit."

"Since when have you been corresponding with that crafty old woman? And why would you do such a mean-spirited thing as to invite her here?"

"Twice a week from the first week of our marriage, and because I love tormenting you. Are these answers satisfactory?"

Lyon snorted.

"Very well, then we are ready to move on." Millicent clasped her hands in her lap. "Perhaps you would like to tell me what you have found in those ledger books regarding the Melbury Hall farms. Then I can interrupt you and tear you to pieces for no reason."

The ridiculousness of her challenge was comical, and her words caught him off guard.

Lyon Pennington had always been serious to the point of surliness from the day he was born. He had maintained the reputation throughout his school years, during his years of service in India, and later among his peers. And then, after marrying Emma, he had added the fine quality of being vile-tempered on top of it. As a result, most people avoided confrontation with him at any cost. And those who didn't soon felt—quite painfully—the error of their ways. Indeed, from early on in his marriage, his enemies' only means of attacking him had been by way of rumor and innuendo. There were some who had gone to great lengths to connect scandal with his name.

"Are you ready for the inquisition, m'lord?"

"I will tell you what I perceive, and then you may do your worst, Madame Torquemada."

Lyon looked at Millicent's straight back and couldn't help but smile. She had courage and spirit, and he wondered how his mother and the family lawyer could possibly have possessed such foresight.

Chapter 17

Ohenewaa's examination of Lyon had not been limited to the time she spent with him after his arm had been burned. The next day, Millicent learned that the old woman had spoken with Gibbs extensively about his master. And when she was finished with him, she had tracked down John and Will and the other servants who had helped with the earl's care after his accident.

Finding Ohenewaa in the kitchen—in a quiet corner that had become one of her usual haunts—Millicent sat down beside her. She wanted to know what the old woman had learned and what she still needed to know.

The couple of hours she and Lyon had spent outside this morning had done a world of good for him. His coloring had improved; his appetite had grown. Of course, his temperament could still be as foul as ever, but she now found it flecked with silvery touches of humor. After they had come in—while Millicent had been busy working with Mrs. Page—Ohenewaa and Lyon had spent some time together. And now, with him lost in the books again in the library—this time with Gibbs—Millicent was impatient to learn what she could of his condition.

"The only information I lack comes from not having seen the surgeon set the bones." Ohenewaa paused thoughtfully. "You know that any English doctor would either laugh at you or commit you to Bedlam for putting your husband's care into an old slave's hands."

"That matters very little to me." Millicent smiled gently. "Will you share with me what you have discovered thus far?"

Ohenewaa nodded. "Aye. And you should know that whatever I tell you your husband already knows. I even asked him if I might relay it all to you."

"Was his response, 'Do as you bloody please'?"

"Not quite so polite as that, but he said something similar."

"Why does that not surprise me?"

Ohenewaa's eyes opened more than usual, and one gray eyebrow arched expressively. "Despite his bad temperament, he does not suffer from madness."

"I never thought so."

"I believe he suffers from what old Dombey would have called partial palsy."

This confirmed what Gibbs had said of the first surgeon's opinion. Millicent kept her silence, though, waiting for Ohenewaa to offer more.

"The earl had a great injury inflicted upon his head when he fell from those cliffs last summer. I have talked to those in his service. At the time the greatest worries were the breaks in his legs and arms. No one wanted to amputate his limbs. While they worked on him, his lordship spent two full days lying unconscious. Of course, that was good, too, for it saved him much pain."

Pain of all types, Millicent thought. She already knew that these same cliffs, on the same day, had claimed the life of his wife. And how ruthless the gossips were to proclaim that Lyon had been the cause of that fall, when he had nearly died himself.

"His manservant tells me that once your husband regained consciousness, it took another fortnight before he was able to control his muscles or feel anything from his shoulders down. He even had difficulty breathing. His condition remained so severe that the family considered what arrangements needed to be made for a funeral."

His brothers were content to bury him rather than nurture him to health, Millicent thought cynically. When his siblings would do nothing, the dowager had taken responsibility for him, in spite of her own infirmity and advanced age.

"But the feeling and movement gradually began to return. A month after the accident, the earl could sit up. In another month, when the splints were off both arms, he had gained the full use of his left hand and arm. But then another fall—this time from a chair—and he broke the right arm again. I am told the splints from this second break were not removed until a few days before your marriage."

Millicent rose to her feet and walked to the window. From here she could see just the corner of the garden where she and Lyon had spent the morning. She had heard him laugh once this morning. The vibrant sound of it, like music, continued to play in her mind. No matter where she would go and what else might be on her mind, Lyon was now a part of her daily existence.

"You are saying they were gradual improvements for the first couple of months, but nothing after that?" She turned around to face Ohenewaa.

"So it appears. I think his impatience with the confinement, added to a constant melancholy that plagued him, inhibited the progress. He is a man whose spirit cannot be fettered or shut in. Instead of improving, Gibbs told me, he became worse, and the various medicines from the physicians did nothing to make him better." Ohenewaa could not hide her disgust. "There was no effort made to exercise and strengthen the limbs, but only to keep him confined in a bed or a chair. There was no one to clear and challenge his mind. Instead, he was kept subdued and out of the way. If you tie the legs of the great lion and keep him in a dark hole, he will soon refuse to eat. And then he will die. Kill the spirit, and the noblest of creatures will die."

Having lived with Lyon for over a month, Millicent understood more than ever how a situation like that would have killed him. The dowager's plea to her that first day to marry him made so much sense to her now. The old woman knew what was happening to her son.

"True, they managed to save his limbs, but in the process they were cutting off the sustenance he needed to live."

"What can be done for him now?" Millicent asked.

"He does not want to believe it, but there is no saying that he shan't be able to regain more movement in his limbs. Considering the extent of his injuries, the length of time he has been healing is short."

"One thing my husband lacks is patience. Is there anything that might help his body and not dull his mind?"

"I already have given him an ointment I call Matthiolus salve. 'Tis good for all pains in the joints. Something better than that would be an ointment of leopard's bane, but I do not have all that I need to mix that here. Jonah tells me, though, that the apothecary shop in St. Albans might have what is required."

"Leopard's bane. Even the name sounds fitting," Millicent said wryly. "I shall send someone for it today. And if you need anything else, that can be purchased as well."

"Another way of helping him is to force him to move those joints."

"Do you mean having someone else move them for him?"

She shrugged. "I already know no one could force him to sit through any exercise like that unless he himself is willing. But if he can be persuaded, he may heal more quickly."

"What do you mean?"

"All the ointments will do is help to warm and stimulate the joints. For him to walk again, though, he needs to ignore the voice in his head that says he cannot. Your husband's body is healing, but he does not believe it."

Millicent's head reeled with all this information. This was not at all what she had been expecting a month ago. Everything was changing so quickly, but this was not the time to confuse herself with the thoughts of that.

"Do you really believe that he has a chance to recover fully?"

Ohenewaa nodded her head. "You are the only one

who can persuade him to do things that he resists doing. 'Tis in your hands to nurture his spirit to health, too."

The afternoon's sun was still bright and warm through the single window of the steward's office, and Lyon stretched with pleasure at the feel of it. The farms' books lay open in front of him. He looked up as Gibbs and the bailiff, Jonah, entered the room.

Lyon looked at the young bailiff. He was not a big man, but he looked strong and his eyes were clear and intelligent. From what Lyon had heard from Millicent, Jonah had been outspoken and somewhat rebellious during his servitude to Wentworth, and he had suffered greatly for it. Still, he had managed to establish himself as a leader among the workers at Melbury Hall, and Millicent had apparently trusted him. Since being made bailiff, though, he had not yet shown the confidence that the position required. It must be difficult, Lyon thought, to go from the depths of slavery to a position of authority. Who could blame the man if he took a while to feel comfortable in his new role?

Lyon noticed the amity that already existed between Gibbs and Jonah. *A good thing,* he thought.

"Gibbs and her ladyship both speak highly of you, Jonah," Lyon said after the initial introductions. "What do you say we put our heads together about these properties?"

Together, the three of them discussed Melbury Hall's farms and lack of income. Throughout, he encouraged the two men to be open in their thoughts on ways of improving things. Before long, the ex-slave was expressing himself without hesitation.

Jonah's detailed assessment of the present situation was clearly based on close scrutiny and thoughtful analysis. Lyon listened carefully as the bailiff spoke at length.

"There are tracts of land in the east farms, m'lord," he concluded, "that are surely capable of yielding many good crops. But they lie fallow, and the farm buildings are tumbling down from lack of use. The land is used only for sheep grazing. Even the dairy farm. Makes no sense to me, begging your pardon. Wool prices are down. The squire was partial to his horses, too, so we have too much grazing land here at the home farm. Solgrave, the estate to the west of us, plants barley, rye, some oats, and acres of wheat."

When Jonah paused, Gibbs asked what was stopping them from doing the same here. The bailiff told them of the lack of people in the outer farms. All the Africans had previously lived in the Grove, and it was not practical for workers to travel daily to work those farms. But now, with Lady Aytoun's project of building new cottages, the hope was to plant those fields in the spring.

Lyon told them what he had heard of new methods that were being used throughout the countryside. Agricultural methods were changing, with progress being made using crop rotation, forage crops, and new field design. For an hour and a half, they discussed better uses of the soil and the land.

Finally, talk turned to the idea of reorganizing the outer farms, leasing the land to families, and helping them restore or build whatever dwellings or outbuildings were needed. By the time Jonah left the room, Lyon was confident that the man would do well. He also found himself looking at Gibbs differently.

"I am quite impressed with how suited you appear to be for the position of steward. Who would have thought that such a dog could rise to such heights?"

The giant man scowled at the earl.

"I am serious, Gibbs. You have established a workable relationship with this bailiff, who will be a great help to you. You know the household. Already you have had enough time here to learn your way around and get to know everyone. And as far as doing the job of steward, you have helped Campbell enough times at Baronsford to handle anything here."

"Och, I wish I could say for sure, m'lord. Men are born into these sorts of positions, I'm thinking. Perhaps yer wife should be looking someplace else to fill the position. Do ye think she might just be asking too much of me?"

"You are a muscle-brained ox, to be certain, Gibbs," Lyon snapped at him. "You have no more faith in yourself than a stewed prune has. She is not asking you to sell your soul to the devil, man. She is only offering you a position in the household. A position in which you will excel. Speak up, you Highland ape. What is stopping you? Out with it."

Lyon knew what his man was thinking. For ten years they'd been inseparable. Where Lyon had gone, Gibbs had gone as well. When he had taken a commission, Gibbs had joined to serve with him. When his regiment had been dispatched to India to fight the Dutch, Gibbs had been at his side. When he'd fought duels against any number of scoundrels, Gibbs had faithfully served as his man. Now the Highlander was being offered a position that would give him a place of his own, in a sense.

Gibbs's dark brows were a straight line when he finally looked up. "It has to do with responsibilities, m'lord—responsibilities and loyalties. After all these years together, I just cannot have ye thinking that I have forgotten what ye did for me."

"I dragged your arse out of an oyster house. That's all." Lyon shook his head in disbelief, but he remembered the day very well. Wandering into an Edinburgh establishment on High Street on King George's birthday, Lyon had found a tall, slightly inebriated Highlander refusing to drink to the monarch's health unless the rest of the drunken mob would drink to Bonny Prince Charlie's. They'd been ready to stuff his rebellious carcass into Mons Meg and fire him from the ramparts of Edinburgh Castle. "And that was over a decade ago. Do you know how many times you have repaid me over the years for that day?"

"Nay, m'lord. 'Tis been a very fine thing, serving in your house over the years. But I've ne'er had the chance to repay ye. For as many years as I have been serving ye, I've been the envy of every manservant from Baronsford to Bath. Ye have always treated me no less than as an equal, and I have much to be grateful for on that score alone."

Lyon expelled his breath in frustration. "You are not leaving me, you deuced son of a horse thief. You shall be put in charge of things and making a bloody difference."

"Och, by the devil. If ye are thinking—"

"I'm thinking that I shall be a great deal harder on you if you don't take yourself out of here right now and tell my wife that you shall take the position she has offered you."

Gibbs glanced at the door and back at Lyon. "If ye are certain, m'lord."

"Get out."

Lyon watched him go to the door and open it. Before going, the Highlander threw a glance over his shoulder. "Thank ye, m'lord. I'll do ye and yer bride proud."

"I know you will."

With the door to the bedchamber left open and a dozen candles burning brightly on every table and shelf, Millicent tried to dispel all appearances of intimacy in the room as she prepared herself for the task ahead. Following her instructions, the valets had dressed Lyon in a nightshirt with wide sleeves and deposited him on the bed.

While John was still in the room, Millicent applied the ointments to her husband's right arm and changed the dressing on his burn, which was healing beautifully. But the short, stocky servant then asked to be dismissed, and Millicent was left alone to apply Ohenewaa's ointments to the rest of Lyon's partially dressed body.

By the time she was finished spreading the healer's ointment on one of Lyon's legs, her face was on fire, and she was drenched with sweat.

"Why not just call in the bloody household to chaperon us while you are doing this?"

She gave him a startled look. "I don't know what you mean."

"Really?" He lifted his chin challengingly. "You have

been nervous since dinner when you thanked me for
Gibbs's deciding to accept your offer to make him
steward."

"You took me on your lap and kissed me."

"What is wrong with that?" he asked with a wry smile.

"There were at least half a dozen servants around,
still serving the meal."

"And?"

Millicent had been excited and embarrassed and confused. He had simply ignored all of the shocked glances
and unsuccessfully hidden grins of the servers. Of course,
the fact that she had practically melted into him hadn't
helped either.

"And nothing!" she whispered, dipping her fingers
into the ointment and spreading it on his other leg.

Her long talk with Ohenewaa this afternoon had opened
Millicent's eyes to the short-lived nature of her present
situation. On the first day of meeting with the dowager,
she had demanded that in the event of the earl's recovery,
a divorce would be uncontested. Now it appeared that he
would indeed recover, and perhaps speedily.

Millicent was no fool. She knew she would never be
an accepted member of the *ton*. As a young woman of
average looks with a fairly respectable lineage, she had
been barely attractive enough to suitors to secure a marriage to an abusive sugar plantation owner with social
aspirations. And in the years since, her looks and her
luck had only deteriorated. She didn't want to imagine
how objectionable Lyon would find her as a wife once
he was completely healed.

"You don't need to do this if it makes you uncomfortable."

"I am not uncomfortable," she replied, meeting his
amused gaze. She had made a bargain, and she was
going to fulfill her part of it. "This is only the beginning
of these treatments. The groom I sent to St. Albans was
able to find several herbs Ohenewaa was looking for.
She has already promised to prepare another ointment
for you tomorrow. And I shall need to have John or
Will help me every day to exercise—"

"This is all a waste of time. I have no bloody control of those limbs."

"Today you have no control. But tomorrow . . ." She paused, having finished rubbing the ointment on his leg; she pulled the blankets over him. "Tomorrow is a new day, with new surprises and greater promises."

He caught her wrist when she was about to tuck the blanket around his chest. "That is what I have been doing for all these months. Thinking of tomorrow. Knowing that nothing would change. Certain as a man can be that I shall continue to be a pathetic cripple, stuck in a chair for ten thousand tomorrows."

"Well, I am determined to change your mind on that, m'lord."

"How? By becoming distant? By running away?"

"No, I am here." She would help him, but she had to protect herself—and her heart. But how could she admit this to him? "I shall be here whenever you need me."

"Very well. Then spend the night here with me. In my bed, beside me."

"I don't see that—"

"Last night was the only restful night I have had in months. I want you here. I need you here."

He had tipped his hat to her and whispered good morning. He had smiled at her when he'd entered the servants' hall tonight. Violet didn't see anything wrong with serving Ned Cranch the late supper. Clearly he had found his manners once again, and Vi liked the way he was treating her.

Violet topped his cup of ale and sat across the table, watching his large, callused hands handle the food on his plate. As much as she hated to admit it, she missed the feel of those hands on her body. She looked up at his wide chest and thought of the crisp, curly hairs and the feel of them rubbing against her breasts. And that mouth biting and suckling her. She must have made a sound, for Ned's green eyes lifted from his food and met hers.

"Don't let yer thinking wander too far south, lassie,

or I'll be taking you down by the stables. If we make it that far."

Violet blushed with embarrassment and stared down at the deep grooves in the dining table. He was handsome and charming and the only lover she had ever had. But at the same time she needed to force herself to remember that he was mean and rough and had not thought twice about kicking her out of his room at that tavern in St. Albans. Violet knew she had to force herself to behave coyly, to remain cool and reserved, the way Mrs. Page did with Mr. Gibbs. It definitely would not do to drool after Ned whenever he came near her.

"Who's that one think she is, the bloody Queen of Sheba?"

Immediately annoyed with his tone, Violet followed the direction of Ned's gaze and saw Will, the lanky valet to the earl, holding a door open while Ohenewaa carried in a tray. The woman definitely had the look of a queen.

"She is a great healer."

"What the de'il does that mean? She's a witch?"

"No," she snapped at him. "That's Ohenewaa. She's quite knowledgeable about herbs and medicines. She was a slave to an English doctor for some forty years before Lady Aytoun brought her here. The women here at the Hall say she probably taught that doctor more about healing than she learned."

Violet watched with great admiration as the old woman glided through the room and disappeared into the kitchens with Long Will on her heels.

"The stories they tell about her ability to heal things are so impressive. Most of the black folk here knew her from the—"

"Ain't your mistress afraid of letting her near the food? I've heard stories about them witch doctors in the sugar islands. When they're not stirring up trouble with the slaves, they're poisoning the masters." He shoved his half-eaten meal away from him. "What if this one decides to poison us all with one of her brews?"

"That's a horrible thing to say." Violet frowned at

him. "Everyone trusts Ohenewaa. She wouldn't do anything like that. And that includes my mistress."

He snorted in disbelief and stabbed at a big chunk of meat on the plate.

Feeling compelled to defend Ohenewaa, Violet leaned toward him and lowered her voice. "Lady Aytoun bought her at an auction. That old woman was brought here in nothing more than rags."

"Aye? So what?"

"Well, her ladyship values Ohenewaa's opinion more than those of all those fancy doctors that have seen to his lordship since his accident. More than that doctor who came out from London. That's what I call trust."

"How's that? That woman is looking after the earl?"

Vi nodded exultantly. "None of those other physicians is even allowed to come here anymore. Her medicines are the only thing the earl takes. What she says goes. The mistress has put her husband's life in this woman's hands. That should tell you how much she values Ohenewaa."

Chapter 18

⌐The mattress shifted slightly beneath their weight, and
⌐Millicent awoke with a start. Lying on her stomach
at the very edge of the bed, she pushed up on her elbows
and watched him. While still asleep, Lyon was trying to
roll onto his side. She considered how she could help
without waking him up. Before her sluggish mind could
sort out a plan, though, he whispered something under
his breath and rolled successfully onto his right side.

Millicent had given in to his request of spending the
night in his bed. As odd as it felt, she was his wife, after
all. And last night had been special for her, too. What
harm could possibly come of it if she were to crawl beneath the sheets after he was asleep? She could keep a
safe distance between them.

Looking at how close they were now, Millicent realized that her assumptions had been wrong. She intentionally had slept on the right side of the bed so that his
good arm would not inadvertently brush against her
body. But he had rolled toward her and, as she watched,
his left arm reached out and came to rest across her
back.

His regular breathing told her that Lyon was sound
asleep, and Millicent laid her head back down on the
pillow. She could not sleep, though. She had never spent
the entire night in a man's bed. She lay there as the
dawn's light slowly brightened the chamber, studying her
husband's face.

He had a high, intelligent forehead and a straight

nose. The closed lids and long, dark lashes hid the eyes that turned a dozen different shades of blue, depending on his mood. Millicent wondered what the man looked like without his beard. There was no doubt in her mind, though, that Lyon Pennington would be the handsomest man she'd ever seen. Like some lowly mortal facing a god, Millicent knew she would probably just want to run away and hide.

And that would only be right. Then he would not need to face the humiliation of introducing her as his wife.

Millicent knew very well the ways of the social world Lyon inhabited. She had been an eager eighteen-year-old when she was introduced into the marital meat market of the London *ton*, but that eagerness had soon worn off. Suitors had barely looked at her. She had been too plain. She had been too thin. She had been too quiet. She had been too clever. She had been too everything but special. Gentlemen like Lyon Pennington—those whose fortunes and accomplishments and looks and manners placed them in airy realms far above the rest— did not even notice her. The ones who did were penniless boors who saw only the size of her dowry as an enticement.

The years of healthy living and a suitable education and a good family name were not enough. Millicent's self-confidence quickly drained away. Soon relegated to that wall of aging spinsters, she had suffered through five London Seasons of mortification. Then, at the advanced age of twenty-three, she had watched her uncle step in. He would have sold Millicent to the very devil just to get her off his hands. In fact, that was exactly what he did.

Millicent closed her eyes to halt the welling tears. She couldn't live with herself if Lyon should wake up now and see her like this. She was finished with self-pity. After Wentworth's death, she had found surprising strength by standing on her own two feet. This was how she wanted the Earl of Aytoun to remember her when they parted ways. Let him remember her strength, she thought.

She rolled slowly until her back was to him. Before she could slip out of the bed, however, his arm curled around her waist. Gently, he pulled her slowly back against his chest. Millicent didn't protest. She didn't make a sound but simply waited. Looking over her shoulder, she found him still asleep.

He whispered something again in his sleep and then— to her utter surprise—one of his legs moved, sliding over the top of hers. Her shift had ridden up in the night, and she could feel his warm skin touching her thigh. Millicent rolled toward him, not believing what had just happened. Perhaps this was all a dream. But he continued to move until she found herself lying flat on her back with half of her husband's sleeping body draped over her.

He had moved his leg. She did not dare to breathe. Stunned by the discovery, Millicent felt her mind reeling with thoughts of how she was going to awaken him— how she was going to tell him. The impact of his ability to move his leg—and what his reaction would be—had her spirits soaring. Ohenewaa had been correct. She'd said that the decision to heal lay with Lyon himself.

Her heart pounded with excitement, and she turned her head on the pillow to awaken him. His face was only inches away from hers. She could tell he was caught in the middle of a dream. His brow was furrowed and he was whispering again, words that she could make no sense of.

"Lyon," she whispered softly against his lips.

His body jerked once in his sleep, and the arm that was curled around her stomach moved. Millicent felt his hand drop to the edge of her shift. Lyon's leg moved again, rubbing against the sensitive skin of her bare thigh.

Millicent felt her throat go dry. Her voice was barely audible when she whispered his name again. He didn't awaken, but his hand slipped beneath her nightgown and moved upward with maddening slowness, along her thigh, her hip, the curves and hollows of her stomach, until he was cupping her breast.

A dozen times along that slow journey, she nearly grasped his hand, stopped him. A dozen times, though, she held back, unable to decide what she wanted more— to be touched by this man or to be free of any man's touch.

Her heart was hammering fiercely at the walls of her chest. A tight knot of fire had coiled itself somewhere in her middle, and Millicent found herself arching her back ever so slightly, pressing into his hand. The heat awakened by the simple touch, the sensitivity of her body to his caress, thrilled her. She edged closer to him, and Lyon's hand brushed lightly across the sensitive areola of her breast, making her nipple harden in response. Suddenly she knew she didn't want him to stop.

"Lyon." Millicent turned her face to him and brushed her lips against his. He stretched slightly, and his hand came to life on her body. He ran his fingers down over her belly and then up again to explore her breasts, feeling the fullness of one and then traveling to the other. His gentle touch was enough to make her breathe in sharply. Her body was quivering with excitement, and she felt herself growing moist. He seemed to be awakening, but Millicent found herself praying desperately that he wouldn't push her away once he opened his eyes.

She kissed him again, this time using her tongue to tease the seam of his lips. He emitted a groan in his sleep, and her shivers gave way to shudders as she felt him gently pinch an erect nipple.

When Lyon's hand left her breast and moved down her belly to the small triangle of hair at the junction of her thighs, her head rolled back on the pillow. She stared at the gray of the ceiling, and her lips parted slightly. Instinctively, her hips rose against his hand, and her legs opened for him. A soft whimper escaped her as his fingers slipped into the folds of her womanhood, lightly exploring, then finding and stroking the sensitive nub of desire.

Millicent's vision blurred and her breath shortened. Her body began to pulse to a rhythm that she had always associated with fear and pain. But that was before. What she felt now was desire and anticipation so intense she was afraid she might cry out.

Lyon was stroking her harder. She turned her head on the pillow and found his mouth searching hers. She kissed him, but the moment his fingers thrust deep inside her, Millicent's body erupted with volcanic force. She gasped for breath and somehow managed to roll beneath the weight of his leg to face him. Millicent clung tightly to him as waves of passion continued to roll through her quaking body.

Lyon came fully awake at the sound of a woman's quiet cry. Startled, he found himself inches from Millicent's face. Her eyes were shut, but even in the dawn's light he saw the tears squeezing through the corners of her eyelids and falling. He was shocked to find his hand tucked intimately between her legs. He immediately withdrew it.

"Bloody hell," he muttered. "Millicent . . . I don't . . . I was . . . By the devil, did I hurt you? Dear God, I—"

He stopped as she shook her head and wiped the wetness from her face. She looked up at him.

"Do not blame yourself. You didn't hurt me. We were . . . I was caught up in . . . in something."

He saw the glistening tears forming again in her gray eyes. He had been dreaming. He was at Baronsford. No, it was London. A woman had come to his bed. His body was still painfully aroused. It was Millicent.

His body. Lyon's mind started to clear. He was lying on his side. He pushed the covers back with one hand.

"You rolled." She hurriedly pulled the nightgown down. "You rolled in your sleep."

Lyon saw his leg and knee trapping her lower body. It was impossible.

"How?" He tried to move the leg but could not. Frustration quickly replaced his shock. "How did I do this?"

"You were asleep. You weren't thinking about it," she replied gently, pulling herself to a sitting position and trying awkwardly to move his legs off hers. "You just did it."

"That is not possible," he persisted stubbornly, trying again to make it move by pushing his knee. Nothing. "I cannot move the damn leg."

"Don't fight it, Lyon." Millicent managed to free herself. Covering him with the blanket, she finally succeeded in rolling him onto his back. "Your strength is returning. You just need to give it some time. Ohenewaa said that it might happen like this. That one day you would just do it."

"No," Lyon snapped, though he knew that no one else could have moved him into that position. Perhaps . . .

He said nothing about the other times. It was true that he had recently moved his foot and his hand. But each occurrence had come without warning, and the frustration of not being able to do it again seconds later was almost too much to bear.

"It was a freak accident."

"It wasn't," she said patiently, straightening his right arm, pulling the covers over him and tucking them carefully around his chest. "Give it time. Your body is healing."

Millicent's hair hung in a cascade of curls around her face. Lyon's thoughts shifted, and he wondered why he had not told her how different she looked like this, and how much he liked it. She slipped off the bed and went around it, tucking in the blankets.

"Are you warm enough?" she asked.

"Yes." Lyon's attention was no longer on himself. In the dim light of the room, he tried to focus on her face. She had been crying, and the sadness still lingered around her eyes.

"Can I get you something to drink? Some water?"

"No," he said, unhappy with himself at having the audacity to become intimate with her . . . without being awake.

She touched his leg once, smoothing the blanket, and took a step back. "Good night then."

"Where are you going?"

She continued to back away. "To my own bedchamber."

"Why?"

"It is almost morning." She had reached the door and was already pulling at the latch.

"Millicent, wait," he called gruffly.

"What is it?"

"What happened just now?"

"You rolled in your sleep. You moved your leg. That is great progress."

He was not fooled by her hollow attempt at sounding happy. "What else happened? Tell me. What did I do to you?"

She shook her head, but no words came out.

"I acted . . . I behaved . . . dishonorably toward you, didn't I?"

She again gave a quick shake of her head, but her gaze was riveted to the floor. Lyon cursed himself. One thing he was sure of: He had touched her without her consent.

"I must apologize for the way I behaved—for whatever I did—for whatever you are forgiving me for so gracefully. I promise you, Millicent, whatever it was, it shall never happen again."

"Nothing happened. Please go back to sleep." She whispered the words before backing out of the room and softly closing the door.

She was relieved to find the hallway deserted. The household was still sleeping. Millicent's vision was blurred, but she managed to hold her tears in until she was safely inside her own bedchamber. There was no holding back her emotions after that.

He had apologized.

Wentworth had violated and battered her body sexually and physically at every opportunity during their five long years of marriage. He had called it his right as her husband to "educate" her as he saw fit. He had hurt her, killed her unborn baby, almost killed her. He had trampled on her body as if it were dry chaff in the barns.

But Lyon had apologized to her for making that same body feel alive. He had been sorry for touching her without asking her first. Even in his sleep, he had shown her the moon and stars as Millicent never knew they had existed. And Lyon Pennington was her husband, too.

Millicent buried her wet face in the pillow. She had no right to feel bad because in his unawareness he had made her climb to unknown heights of ecstasy. She should be grateful for the experience of learning that there could exist more than just pain and fear between a man and a woman.

He was growing stronger. His limbs were beginning to function. One day soon he would simply walk away. And when that happened, Millicent would need to go on with her own life. The thought terrified her.

The tears came faster. A numbing sadness was wrapping around her soul.

Who was she, Millicent thought, to care so much for him?

A carriage stood at the corner of a dark alley in St. Albans. A groom, with his hat drawn low on his face, waited beside the horses, talking to the driver. The drawn shade hid the identity of the two men meeting inside.

"Mr. Platt's high praise for your efforts convinced me that I should come and meet you in person." Jasper Hyde studied the young workman's cocky expression. "Now, after hearing all about the slave woman and her influence on Lady Aytoun, I am certainly glad that I made the trip."

"As I was saying, Mr. Hyde, her ladyship is relying on her more and more. I doubt any offer of money would convince Lady Aytoun to part with the slave." Ned Cranch lowered his voice and leaned confidentially toward the plantation owner. "But as I have been looking about the place, I've noticed that no one watches her. And she does have a routine."

"And what is that?"

"The woman leaves the house about dawn and roams the deer park in the direction of Solgrave, collecting things in this large basket she hangs from her neck. She gets back to Melbury Hall about the time the kitchen is ready to send up breakfast for the earl."

"How convenient." Hyde felt the twinges of the pain between his ribs but tried to ignore them.

"If ye want, Mr. Hyde, I could just snatch her some morning when she's in the woods." Ned glanced at the drawn shade and lowered his voice to a whisper. "In fact, knowing ye're willing to make it worth my while, I could more easily cut her throat and make it look like she was attacked by some passing gypsy or tinker, maybe. Ye just say the word, sir."

"I will keep that under advisement, Mr. Cranch. Meanwhile, I have other plans in the works that might settle the matter once and for all." Hyde rubbed his chest as the pain started to increase. "But that is good thinking on your part. Right now, you continue to keep watch." He had difficulty lifting his arm enough to toss the man a bag of coins. Cranch had no problem catching it, though.

"Will ye be coming yerself or sending Mr. Platt next time?"

"We'll let you know." Hyde weakly waved toward the carriage door, motioning to the man to get out. He did not like anyone seeing him when he was writhing in pain. He refused for others to see the hold Ohenewaa had on him.

"Thankee, sir."

Ned Cranch stepped out of the carriage into the dark. As soon as the door closed, Hyde tore at his collar and cravat. He couldn't breathe. The pain scorched his chest with the same blazing heat that his bailiffs had used to brand his slaves' flesh.

Hyde had no voice or strength left at that moment or he would have called Ned Cranch back and asked him to go ahead and cut the woman's throat. If he only knew that was a sure way to end the she-devil's curse.

Chapter 19

"You are no more than a bloody bramble weed, Gibbs," Lyon complained as the new steward entered the library.

"Thank you, m'lord."

"Do you not realize that in taking the position of steward, you are supposed to be freeing more of her time? Instead, you're tying her up in knots."

"She's not one to take what she sees as her duty lightly, sir." The Highlander sat down at the writing table with a grace that belied his size. Taking out his pens and ink, he prepared himself to write the correspondence Lyon had wished to dictate this morning. "I've been trying to ease her ladyship's burden."

For three days Millicent had been running in every direction. With the exception of brief glimpses of her when breakfast and dinner were served, or when she was overlooking some devilish new concoction Ohenewaa had devised for Lyon's legs and arm, or when one of the valets was bending him this way and that, she had been difficult to find.

Worse, though, was the matter of her failing to come to his bed again at night. She was extremely tired, or she had to stay up late answering letters, or some such thing. Any excuse she could think of had successfully kept her from being alone with him for any length of time.

It couldn't go on, Lyon thought. He missed her. He missed everything that they shared, from the verbal skirmishes to the kisses that set his blood boiling in his veins. More than once Lyon had cursed himself for whatever it was that had happened that night he'd touched her in his sleep. That was the cause of all of this, he was sure. But staying away from her was not giving him any answers, either, and he needed to change that.

The papers being shuffled on the desk drew Lyon's attention back to Gibbs. The man looked positively dejected.

"Bloody hell, Gibbs. She's not been blaming her busy schedule on you."

"I'm not surprised, m'lord."

"In fact, she's been singing your praises."

" 'Tis like her ladyship to do that, m'lord. She's very generous with her compliments."

"Where is she this morning?" Lyon asked impatiently.

"She is looking over what Cook planned to serve Reverend and Mrs. Trimble tomorrow."

"How long will she be in with him?"

"Not too—" Gibbs stopped himself. "It could take all morning, depending on how involved Lady Aytoun wishes to be with the preparations. I'm thinking that she wants this visit to go well, m'lord."

"Is impressing some country cleric and his wife so bloody important?"

"Mrs. Trimble's lame, sir, and doesn't leave the rectory too often. The woman is making the effort just to meet your lordship."

Lyon snorted. "I don't suppose you would know where your mistress is going after her discussions with Cook."

"Aye, m'lord. The schoolmaster who generally comes out to Melbury Hall on Thursday afternoons is unwell, apparently. Whenever that happens, her ladyship tries to take over the lessons of the older children and some of the workers." Gibbs paused, and then immediately added, "Just so you should know, on occasion she also works with some of the wee ones on Friday mornings."

"There are children here?" Lyon asked in astonishment.

"Aye, m'lord. Black and white and running about everywhere. They're mostly the children of those working on the farms, but a few belong to the Hall."

"Why don't they go to school in the village? What is it . . . Knebworth?"

"From what I hear, they started teaching the wee ones here back in the days of that cur Wentworth. Reverend Trimble and the schoolmaster, a Scot named Cunningham, rode out to hold classes. Her ladyship wanted to continue with reading and writing and the basics of arithmetic. Some of these folks are far past school age, but this is the first opportunity that they've had, m'lord. Most of the younger ones go into Knebworth village for their schooling, but they all still look forward to this gathering at the Hall."

"Take me there." At Gibbs's surprised expression, Lyon gestured impatiently at the steward. "After we are done with these letters, I want you to arrange it so that I am taken to wherever my wife happens to be. Starting today, I wish to keep Millicent company in her daily endeavors."

Millicent was leaning over the shoulder of one of the women and guiding her hand on the slate when she heard the scrape of benches and surprised murmurs. When she looked up, everyone was on their feet and staring at the door. Straightening, she was shocked to see the valets carefully setting Lord Aytoun down just inside the door of the servants' hall.

"M'lord," she greeted him, startled by his appearance. She started around the table toward him.

"Disregard my presence here," he said to the group, motioning with his good hand. "Sit and continue."

Stunned, no one moved. Millicent found both valets were avoiding her eyes and instead staring at the floor.

"What are you doing here, m'lord?" she whispered when she reached his side.

"I've come to see you."

"You might have sent someone for me. If you could give me a moment, I can dismiss these people and—"

"No." He took hold of her wrist before she could step

away. "I should prefer to watch you teach. I have missed your company, but at the same time I understand about your responsibilities. So go about your work, and I'll sit quietly here. I promise to make no more interruptions."

Millicent stared at him, openmouthed. There was no way she could object. "Very well, m'lord. As you wish."

She withdrew her wrist gently and tried to appear composed as she turned back to her students. At her encouraging nod, all but Moses sat down. The giant watchman continued to stare uneasily at Lyon.

"Where were we?" she asked of the group.

Several mumbled hushed comments about being finished with their writing exercises. It was time to move on to reading. Millicent grouped the students in twos and threes and, giving a Bible to each group, assigned a passage for each, telling them to alternate reading every three lines.

Moses was still standing when she reached him, and she found the older man was clearly apprehensive. He also had no partner.

The idea came to Millicent unexpectedly, and she voiced it before she had a chance even to consider how preposterous it was.

"Lord Aytoun, would you consider acting as Moses's reading partner?"

Her question silenced the room. Everyone, Millicent included, was holding their breath. Lyon's gaze moved from Millicent to Moses.

"I should be delighted."

Millicent felt a knot loosen in the back of her throat. She could almost taste the saltiness of the tears that were about to escape. Lyon Pennington continued to surprise her at every turn.

Lyon gave a quiet order to his men, and she hurried to Moses's side to make room for the earl's chair. The black man appeared as surprised as she was.

"All will be well, Moses," she whispered to him.

No sooner had the earl's chair been positioned at the table than Lyon looked up at the older man.

"I understand you have an injured dog. How is it faring?"

"Better, m'lord."

"Did they take off the leg?"

"Nay, m'lord."

"Good. They didn't take off mine, either."

Moses's dark gaze fixed on Lyon's legs.

"Before we start to read, I want you to tell me about it," the earl said, casting a glance at Millicent. "That is, if the mistress does not object."

"Not at all, m'lord," she replied with a smile as Moses sat down.

Chapter 20

"Anything else I can do for ye, m'lord?"
The curtains were drawn. All the candles but the one next to the bed had been snuffed out. The fire on the hearth had been tended. Lyon had changed into his nightshirt, and Ohenewaa—escorted by Millicent—had come and gone. This looked too much like the situation he had been left with for three nights in a row. John would retire and no one would disturb him until morning. *Bloody hell.*

"Where is her ladyship now?" Lyon asked the valet.

"I don't know, m'lord. Sleeping, I should guess."

"Go find her."

"M'lord?"

"Find her and tell her I need to see her."

With eyebrows raised, John started for the door.

"Wait."

The short, round man turned and looked at his master.

"Tell her there is an emergency. Tell her . . . tell her I've fallen from the bed. On my bad arm. Tell her I am back in bed but in severe pain."

John gaped at the earl, clearly uncomfortable about carrying such a message. "Perhaps I should get Mr. Gibbs for this, m'lord. If I—"

"I am telling you to do it. And don't fret so. I shall take full responsibility for the outcome. Wait! Whatever orders she gives—sending for doctors or anything else—it is your duty to make sure nothing is done."

The valet scratched his head and continued to stand

by the door. "Can I say ye cut yer hand or burned yerself again, m'lord? Falling on that arm—"

"Do as I say, you cowardly ape." He gave his man
a reassuring nod. "I shan't make her suffer too long.
I promise."

When the valet left the room, Lyon pushed himself
closer to the edge of the bed. He wanted her within
his reach when she came to check on him. He couldn't
remember the last time he wanted something as much
as he wanted Millicent here right now. Spending the day
with her had been fine. Lyon realized he had been more
content than he had felt in months observing the many
aspects of her involvement at Melbury Hall. This household was indeed like a great family, and Millicent sailed
about like some queen mother, tending to all that
needed to be done.

Lyon adjusted a pillow behind his neck. This had also
been the first day since the accident that he had felt
nearly whole. He'd had no time to regret what was lost
or who had wronged him. Instead, watching his wife, he
had been filled with the simple desire to touch her. And
that was what he intended to do now, even if it meant
tricking her.

Lyon heard Millicent's urgent voice in the corridor,
and he pulled the blanket over his right arm. A moment
later the door of his bedroom banged open and she came
quickly across the floor to him. Her hair was flying wildly
about her.

"Light those candles," she ordered John, who had
paused by the open doorway. "Send Ohenewaa here and
tell Gibbs to send a rider to St. Albans for a surgeon."
She leaned over him and carefully lifted the covers off
him. "Are you in great pain?"

Lyon wrapped his good arm around her waist and held
her against him. "You can leave now, John. Assure
everyone that I need nothing else."

The valet immediately closed the door, and Millicent
turned to him sharply.

"How can you say that when you might have broken
something?" Without waiting for an answer, she gingerly

pushed the sleeve of the nightshirt up to his shoulder and started feeling his bare arm with her fingers. "Where does it hurt?"

"Nowhere," he said, admiring her as she continued to lean over him. She was dressed in her nightdress and a robe that she had obviously not had time to tie at the waist. He stroked her back with his hand.

"I cannot tell what is wrong." She glanced toward the door. "Where is Ohenewaa?"

"She is not coming."

"What do you mean?" Millicent tried to pull away, but Lyon tightened his hold around her.

"I ordered John not to get her, or anyone else, for that matter."

His earlier direction to the valet finally registered, and she turned to him. Waves of auburn hair framed her pale face, and Lyon found himself staring. Her gray eyes looked huge and almost silvery; her lips were full and inviting, and he couldn't wait to taste them.

"Why?" she asked in a small voice.

"Because what is wrong with me now, no one but you can mend."

"Did you fall on your arm?"

"No."

She tried to pull away, but his arm curved around her tighter. She braced herself, planting her hands on the pillow on either side of his head. Her eyes narrowed.

"You tricked me."

"I confess. I wanted to see my wife."

"You have been with me all day."

"I needed you now," he said softly.

"You could have sent for me, and I would have come."

"I'm sure. But that would have been tomorrow morning, with three dozen people around."

"Not three dozen. One person would have been enough."

"Indeed. One too many." Lyon's hand moved up and down her back caressingly. "I must say I don't care for it much when you stay away from my bed."

"Really?" There was a quaver in her voice. She seemed unable to tear her gaze from his lips.

"I miss you," he said under his breath. Her body moved slightly, and her breasts brushed against his chest. "I miss your attentions. And I miss your laughter. I miss this."

As he spoke, he pulled her down to him until her warm breath mingled with his.

"This?"

His gaze lifted, locking with hers. "This."

Lyon drew her mouth to his. She shivered and closed her eyes, and Lyon's lips began to move on hers, possessively exploring each tender curve and trembling contour as if it were an uncharted new world that he had discovered and claimed for his own.

"And there are other things I miss about not having you here, too." Lyon felt the shaking arms give away. Her breasts pressed against his chest.

"What else?"

The wild pounding of her heart matched his.

"Your beautiful body."

His hand glided over her hip to her thigh, urging her onto the bed. She complied, her body stretching out fully on his. Lyon deepened the kiss, plunging his tongue in slowly and withdrawing, realizing it was only an imitation of the act he was beginning to crave. He wanted her. He wanted to make love to her.

With a silent moan of surrender, Millicent cupped his face in her hands, and her lips started moving on his with awakening ardor.

Lyon's mouth became more demanding as he felt his body straining painfully with his arousal. His hand moved restlessly between their bodies. She shifted slightly, giving him room to caress her breast. She breathed in deeply, her flesh swelling beneath his palm, her nipple rising against the nightgown. He groaned in frustration and tore his mouth away.

"Make love to me, Millicent."

Her face was flushed, almost intoxicated, when she looked into his eyes. "I . . . I don't—"

"I'll tell you what to do. Help me make love to you."
He brushed his fingers lightly back and forth over her
nipple through the fabric of her nightdress. "I know the
other night I had started something that I did not finish.
I am sorry if I hurt you. But with both of us awake,
perhaps we can do better."

She started to push herself off him.

"Wait," he said, bitterness creeping into his voice.
"Very well. Whatever you want. I'm certain that when
you married me, you did not bargain for this. What
woman would want to take a cripple and then be forced
to watch him fail as a man? What woman would settle
for a straw man of a husband who might only make the
act of love something weak and foolish?" He shook his
head. "No. It is wrong of me to ask you to accept this
useless body that cannot move even to love you. I only
ask you to stay. I shall be content if you do just that.
And there will be no more demands for—"

"But I like your demands."

Millicent pressed him back into the pillow, kissing him
deeply. Her tongue slipped tentatively into his mouth,
then grew bolder. When she finally pulled back, breaking
off the kiss, they were both breathless.

"What should I do first?"

Her innocent question had Lyon draw a few steadying
breaths. "Take off your robe and nightdress."

With her knees on either side of his legs, Millicent
knelt up slowly. Lyon saw her hands were trembling
when they pushed the robe down off her shoulders. He
held his breath as she began to untie the front of the
nightgown.

"I am nervous."

"So am I," he replied softly. Lyon could feel her gaze
upon him as he pulled the linen material down. She did
not stop him until it clung tenuously to her smooth hips.

She was so beautiful.

Lyon's gaze drifted downward from her face, admiring
her cream-colored skin glowing in the candlelight. His
eyes lingered at the sight of her round, full breasts. He

reached out and touched the curve beneath one nipple, his finger brushing each tight bud.

"You are a treasure. An exquisite and beautiful treasure." He looked into her eyes. "I want to feel your body against me."

Lyon's hand glided to her waist. He slipped the nightdress over her hips and her knees.

"What else should I do?"

"Take this shirt off me," he said, sitting up, his voice husky with desire. Millicent reached over him and pulled the nightshirt up from beneath him, but got no farther.

Lyon stretched out his hand and caressed the smooth skin along her thigh, sliding his hand between her legs. Immediately, she froze and clamped her legs together.

"Don't be afraid," he whispered roughly, sitting forward and taking her breast between his lips. She moaned and arched her back, and this time Lyon's fingers began to probe the dark triangle at the juncture of her thighs, seeking entrance. "Give yourself to me, Millicent."

With a soft moan she relaxed, and Lyon's fingers slipped deep into her wet warmth.

After a moment he felt her begin to pulse against his hand. He stroked her and relished the feel of her growing passion. Her breaths quickened, and then suddenly, with a sob of startled pleasure, she was calling his name. She clutched him to her, burying her face in his hair and curling her entire body around his hand.

As the waves began to subside in her, Lyon smiled. He had never really thought so much about the enjoyment of giving pleasure to a woman. True, he had always prided himself on the ability to please a woman, but this was different. Better.

Even as the thought flickered through his mind, though, she moved one knee over him, and he positioned himself between her legs.

"Take me inside of you."

Millicent's hand moved ever so slowly between their bodies, and Lyon's breath caught in his throat when her fingers wrapped around him. He closed his eyes and

groaned out loud as her fingers tentatively moved down
his length and she positioned herself at his peak. He
heard the gasp as the head of his shaft entered her.

"Now, Millicent."

Their gazes locked as their bodies joined together in
a perfect fit.

Though he could not move his legs, he did not want
to move at all for fear of losing control. The sensations
running through him were those that he had thought he
would never experience again. The pleasure of her tight
sheath closing around him was incomparable. He was
alive again, and Millicent had made it happen.

"You are so beautiful, inside and out."

Her answer was a single tear that escaped one gray
eye and slid down her flawless cheek before dropping
onto his lips. Lyon tasted it and then kissed her as the
urge to move became maddening. His fingers threaded
into her hair, and he drove his tongue into her mouth
again and again with the same sensual thrusts that he
was incapable of doing with his body.

When Millicent tore her mouth away, he almost
groaned with frustration. The thought ran through his
mind that she was already disgusted with his inability to
pleasure either of them. But when he looked into her
face, what he saw was wonder and passion. The lump of
tenderness swelling in his chest was overwhelming. Lying
there, he watched Millicent as she took his face between
her hands and brushed her lips over his lips, his bearded
cheeks, his nose, his ear.

Then she started to move, ever so slightly, on top of
him.

Lyon's fingers tightened on her hip, and he tried to
guide her body. It was obvious that she was not very
experienced in the art of love. She was following the
instinct that nature provided, her body pulsing to the
rhythms within her.

Their mouths met again, and Lyon lay back, letting
Millicent set the pace. He felt the pressure building
within him. The roaring in his head nearly blocked out
all other sound, and his body strained, desperate for re-

lease. But he did not want to let go. There would be no joy in the race if she were not there beside him. Her body was sliding against his, her hips grinding into him. She was panting, and he could see the color rising in her face.

"Lyon," she whispered against his lips. "I have never . . . never . . . felt this."

He moved his hand between their bodies. The moment he touched her, she tipped over passion's edge and cried out, convulsing around him, and Lyon, too, reached that point of no return. As his body shuddered, he erupted within her as a blaze of fiery colors exploded before his eyes.

The sounds coming from the room were unmistakable. A woman's whimpering cries. The man's groans of exertion. Violet put an unsteady hand on the wall and approached the closed door with hesitant steps.

She was no longer aware of the numbness in her hands and feet, or the weight of the basket of food she had carried all the way from Melbury Hall. Against her principles, against her better judgment, she had come. Now Violet felt ill as she stood frozen by the door.

Silently, she prayed that Ned was not in there. Perhaps someone else was using his room for the night. When he had not stopped for dinner at the hall tonight, Violet had thought he might appreciate it if she brought him some supper at the inn. Now she prayed that he had not come because he was away. Perhaps he had been called to St. Albans.

The noises inside increased in volume as well as cadence.

"Neddy!" The voice of the young woman spilled clearly into the hallway. "Oh, my God!"

Violet's insides churned. The handle of the basket slipped out of her hands and fell to the floor. She stared down at the food that had spilled out around her frozen feet.

Suddenly, her blood coursed hotly through her veins. Vi pounded on the door. A muffled curse came from the room, and in a moment the door jerked open. Ned filled the doorway, a candle inside the room shadowing his face.

"By the de'il! What do ye want here?"

Violet stared at his bare chest. His breeches had been pulled up to his hips, but hid nothing. She looked up into his fierce glower and saw the temper brewing there. She didn't care that he was angry.

"I brought you dinner."

He looked down and then viciously kicked the basket with his bare foot. "I've already eaten. Get out."

He started closing the door in her face, but Violet put a hand out to stop him.

"Who is inside there?"

" 'Tis none of yer bloody business."

"Who do you have there?" she said more forcefully, shoving the door open.

With a malicious smirk, Ned let the door swing open. Vi saw one of the young girls from the village peering wide-eyed at her from behind a blanket on the bed. The woman's clothes were heaped in a pile on the floor. Ned's shirt and boots had been thrown carelessly beside them.

Even as she stared, Violet couldn't push away the memory of her and Ned making love on this same bed. Her head was still filled with his whispered words of love. Her only dream for weeks had been that of Ned asking her to marry him. Their future together had dominated her every conscious thought. Another look at the bed and the woman and Violet felt her temper rise, the hot blade of jealousy cutting deep.

"Get out!" she screamed, shoving past Ned and marching toward the woman. "Get out of here now!"

The girl only cringed behind the blanket, and Violet gave a sharp kick to the woman's feet. "You despicable wench. You harlot!"

"Who the de'il d'ye think ye are?" Ned grabbed Violet by the shoulder and spun her around.

Vi didn't see his fist coming. Suddenly she was against

the wall, stunned by the blow, half of her face numb. Her knees buckled and she sagged against rough plaster. She put her hand to her mouth. She could taste the blood.

"You . . . you hit me," she whispered in disbelief, trying to straighten up. Tears started blurring her vision. "How dare you?"

Ned loomed over her. "Ye asked for it, slut. What right do ye think ye have to come in here and spout off?"

"The right of a lover. The right of a woman whose honor you have defiled. Of one deflowered with lies." With the back of her hand she wiped her bloody lip. "I was a virgin, and you took me. You made me believe that you had honorable intentions."

"Honorable intentions? Deflowered?" He gave an insolent laugh and poked a blunt finger into her shoulder. "This is what books does for ye. Well, I'm telling ye, those are big words coming from a brazen wench. Ye spread yer legs willingly for me, an' ye wanted it the first time ye laid eyes on me. Ye followed me around, even into St. Albans, so as to get it from me. An' now, like a bloody bitch in heat, ye can't wait for a man while he goes elsewheres. Well, slut, ye can just wait yer turn."

Tears burned Violet eyes. She pushed away from the wall and faced him.

"You'll be whistling a different tune when I tell Lady Aytoun how you seduced me and then mistreated me. I'll tell her you forced me. You'll be thrown out of that job and run out of this village when I tell people how you raised your hand against me. You are a low, insolent dog, and they'll see you for what you are. You'll never get work anywhere around here ever again when—"

Ned drew back his fist to strike her again, and Violet cringed, covering her face with her arms. Smirking, he lowered his hand.

"And d'ye think all these folk, including yer precious Lady Aytoun, are going to listen to yer bloody whinin' and not ask why ye came here tonight? Why ye keep spreading your legs for a married man?" He laughed in her face. "I didn't force ye to come here, ye stupid chit. You came willingly. Like a bitch in heat."

He continued to berate her, but Violet's mind had snagged on the words "married man." A knot the size of a fist rose into her throat.

"You're lying," she said brokenly. "You couldn't be married and come courting me the way you did."

"Courtin'?" Ned snorted derisively and yanked her roughly toward the door. "This is all the courtin' ye'll be gettin' from now on. Just ye get out of here, for I've a lass waitin' who knows what's what with a man. An' ye best not be spoutin' off back at the Hall, neither, if ye know what's good for ye."

He shoved her so hard through the door that Violet went sprawling onto the filthy floor.

"An' don't ye come back to my door again, slut, or ye'll have more than a bloodied lip to show for yer trouble."

Before Violet could reply, he slammed the door in her face.

Millicent nestled her face into the crook of Lyon's neck and nuzzled and tasted the saltiness on the stretch of taut skin below his beard. Her body still hummed with the sweet after-effects of their lovemaking, and although they were still connected in the most intimate way, she had no desire to move or go anywhere, but simply to stay right here.

Lyon's hand roamed over her back, and she heard a soft laugh rumble deep in his throat. She immediately raised her head and looked into his face.

"What?"

His blue eyes were filled with tenderness when they met hers. "I was thinking that in all my adult life nothing has ever approached what I just experienced. It was like the first time."

Millicent couldn't tell him how much his words meant to her. "I know what you mean. What you gave me just now . . . well, never in my life . . ." Her words trailed off.

"Will you tell me someday about it? About your life?"

Millicent didn't want to think about any of that. "Those years have ceased to exist," she replied softly. She moved carefully, disengaging their bodies, but Lyon's hand wrapped around her waist, keeping her from moving away.

"I am not demanding any answers, Millicent. I am only trying to get better acquainted with my wife."

"I know," she said, laying her hand flat on his chest, feeling his strong heartbeat. "We never removed this."

"I'm a very modest fellow."

Millicent laughed, her fingers trailing down to the hem of the nightshirt, which was still bunched up around his waist. "I see how modest you are."

"But I am quite warm. Perhaps we could remove it."

"It will be a challenge."

"I've seen you at work before," he said, grinning mischievously.

"Very well." She undid the two ties at the neck and then pushed up the linen fabric as far as it would go—which wasn't far. Stretching her body on top of him, she shifted his weight from one shoulder to the other, managing to pull up the shirt to around his broad chest.

"Almost there."

"Hardly," he responded.

Glaring at him with mock fierceness, she sat up, straddling his stomach and pulling his right arm out of the wide sleeve. That worked. Before she could reach for the other arm, though, she found it straying.

"You are a miracle."

He ran his fingers gently across her nipples and down over the curves of her belly, and Millicent felt the rush of liquid heat coursing through her middle again.

"Why do you say that?"

"A month ago, the only plan I had for the future was to find a way to put an end to my miserable life. But now I find myself deliberating on tactful ways of getting you to make love to me again."

"Is that so?" Millicent said, inching backward. The feel of his fully aroused manhood nestling against her body spread another wave of heat through her. Lyon's fingers trailed lower, and Millicent took hold of his hand. "First, I have to remove your shirt."

"Save that for later," he said, gently pulling his hand free and continuing to caress her belly. As he reached the soft mound, Millicent rose up slightly to meet his touch. "It may take any number of tries to get this shirt off."

Chapter 21

"These accusations are quite serious," the dowager said sharply to her physician.

"I am not making accusations, m'lady. I am simply passing on information that has been brought to my attention, information that I felt you should hear. Before conveying it to you, I considered the seriousness of the matter as well as the source—in this case, Dr. Parker—and I decided that Lord Aytoun's health necessitated my speaking to you. I did not believe 'twas in anyone's best interest to allow his lordship to fall victim to any evildoers."

"Evildoers, is it?"

As Dr. Tate waved his assistant out with his medical bag, the dowager motioned to one of her maidservants and whispered instructions to her. The woman hurried out of the room.

"When was the last time you spoke with this Parker?"

"Two days ago."

"And what exactly did he have to say about my son's condition?"

The thin shoulders of the physician straightened. "He was quite concerned. In fact, if I might be perfectly candid, m'lady, he feared that you could be receiving disheartening news any day about his lordship. Without proper medication and regular examinations by qualified physicians, Dr. Parker believes Lord Aytoun is at great risk and may be endangering his life."

"And he was able to tell you this with certainty after only one visit to Hertfordshire?"

"A qualified doctor sees beyond the condition of his patient on a specific day."

There was a knock at the door, and Sir Richard appeared.

"Come in, Maitland." She motioned to another servant to put some pillows behind her back. Propped up in the bed, the old woman turned to the physician. "Can you, sir, in just a few words, summarize all this for Sir Richard?"

Dr. Tate bowed stiffly. "The information I have concerns a slave woman who resides at present in Lord Aytoun's new residence, Melbury Hall."

"The information you have is outdated," the dowager interrupted. "The woman you refer to is no longer a slave but a free woman."

"I beg your pardon, m'lady." The doctor turned his attention again to the lawyer. "I have come upon some distressing information regarding this same woman. She is suspected of having murdered the physician whom she served as a servant for many years. What originally was assumed to be a death by natural causes is now suspected of possibly being caused by poison."

"Suspected by whom?" the dowager cut in.

"Well, I assume by the man's family." The thin man ran a hand nervously down the front of his jacket. "By the proper authorities."

"So you do not know," Lady Aytoun snapped. "Is that it?"

"M'lady, as I am certain Sir Richard will tell you, even with Sir John Fielding's Bow Street Runners looking into it—"

"Which they are not," she retorted scoffingly.

"Even if they were looking into it, these matters take time." The doctor turned to Maitland for help. "Sir, consider the severity of the charges. If Dr. Dombey did not die of natural causes, but rather because of the actions of this slave expediting his end with diabolical brews and potions, what difference does it make if she is officially charged with the crime?"

"The difference is a matter of making false accusations," the lawyer replied calmly. "At her age, having nothing as a former slave, she has enough trouble without respectable people slandering her. Terms such as 'diabolical brews and potions' imply witchcraft in addition to murder, sir. Is that what you mean?"

"I only mean that if one considers the strong likelihood of this African woman murdering her master—and we all know that this is common in the islands—then the dowager's first priority should be to remove her son from this woman's clutches before she murders again."

"My son is *not* in this woman's clutches."

"But he is, m'lady. 'Tis clear that your daughter-in-law put an end to Dr. Parker's visits to Melbury Hall as a means of giving free rein to this woman."

"Are you now accusing the younger Lady Aytoun of wrongdoing?" Maitland asked.

"I am relating what I have heard," Tate responded defensively. "There are witnesses from a nearby village called Knebworth, I was told, who claim the black woman is referred to, unbelievably, as a great 'healer.' Apparently, upon arriving at Melbury Hall, this slave woman was given the best room in the manor house. There are reports of agents of this same woman visiting an apothecary in St. Albans. If your ladyship's daughter-in-law has fallen under this woman's spell and has become blind to—"

"Enough," the dowager ordered angrily. "You are obviously operating under some deluded notion of loyalty to your brethren, Dr. Tate, rather than any loyalty to my family—"

"M'lady, I have been your physician for quite some time now."

"Indeed, sir. Too long, perhaps. But to make you understand where I stand on this matter, I do not believe the gossip of scoundrels. Nor do I suspect every old woman with a wrinkled face, a hairy lip, a squinty eye, or a scolding tongue to be a witch."

"M'lady—"

"Perhaps because I fit that description myself. Now, I

suggest that you take your leave, sir, before I lose my temper. See him out, Maitland."

Beatrice Pennington, Dowager Countess Aytoun, glared imperiously until the physician, mumbling apologies, backed out the door under the stern eye of Sir Richard. Dismissing her maidservants with an impatient wave, the old woman stared darkly at the window.

She didn't want to believe any of this nonsense. All the reports coming from Melbury Hall indicated Lyon was improving. For the first time in months, Beatrice had begun to hope that things might turn out well for her son, after all. She had allowed herself to let go of the past. It appeared that Millicent was good for him.

With a soft knock, Sir Richard reentered the room. From the droop of his old shoulders, the dowager guessed something was wrong.

"Don't tell me you believe this foolishness."

He shook his head.

"Then don't stand there tongue-tied like a block of wood, man. Tell me what is on your mind."

The man sat down in his customary seat by the window. "I received a letter from your son this morning."

"From Lyon?"

"Indeed, m'lady."

"This is good news." She shot an angry look in the direction of the door. "And more proof that this one and the rest of them, too, know little of what they dwell upon. This is the first time Lyon has corresponded with you since his marriage, is it not?"

"Indeed, m'lady."

"A great sign of improvement in itself." She leaned back against the pillows. "So what the devil is bothering you, Maitland?"

"Before I heard Dr. Tate's accusations, nothing. But now, the more I think of it . . ." His voice trailed off.

"Speak up."

"In his letter, his lordship has requested that I send up a few of the Aytoun heirlooms to Melbury Hall."

"What does he want?"

"He mentions specific pieces of jewelry that are here in London."

"And what of it? They are his. He can do as he wishes with them."

"He also directs me to hire and send a secretary up there to him, as his man, Gibbs, has been given the position of steward at the Hall."

"All well and good. Time enough that Highland beast started using a bit of his brain."

"Perhaps we should not take this matter too lightly, m'lady," Maitland commented. "The change—dare I say the improvement—in Lyon has been remarkable. I do not discount the fact that these doctors appear to be overly keen about bringing us damaging reports. But perhaps our wisest course is for me to go personally to Melbury Hall to check on your son's condition. I can go up under the pretext of delivering what the earl has requested in person. And while I am there, I can assess his lordship's improvement and snuff out another potential scandal before it spreads through this idle London *ton*."

The old woman's response was immediate. "There is no need for you to go, Sir Richard. I shall be making the journey myself."

"M'lady, I do not believe the urgency of the matter will allow us to wait until you are well enough—"

"I shall go this week."

"But m'lady!"

"No arguments." She waved a dismissive hand. "The only person who can put an end to all this foolishness is I."

"But you are not well enough."

"Who says I am not?" she challenged. "Millicent has already invited me, and I have told her I would go there to visit sometime. The only difference is that now we shall be arriving without prior warning."

"Then allow me to come with you, at least."

"As you wish, Sir Richard. Besides, getting out of this dreary city might be good for both of us. Make the arrangements."

                         *   *   *

"I ran into the doorjamb in the dark last night," Violet explained to her fellow serving maid. The younger
woman was hanging over her shoulder, looking at the
ugly bruise at the edge of Vi's mouth. "Really, Bess.
'Tis nothing."

"If that's so, then why did ye ask me to go and help
Lady Aytoun dress this morning?"

"I feel silly enough, and you know how she is." Violet
finished applying more of the white powder over the
bruise. "She gets worried for nothing. I thought if I wait
a day or two, then she won't be pestering me about
being more careful and all that."

The truth was that Violet had seen many bruises much
worse than this on her mistress's face when the squire
was alive. The young woman had a sneaking suspicion
that her ladyship would not be fooled by the story of
running into a door.

She had already asked around this morning. What
Ned had said about being married seemed to be true,
or at least some of the servants she talked to had heard
that rumor, too. Violet wondered where her mind had
been this whole time. How was it possible that she had
made such a mess out of her life in so short a time?

The two women descended the back steps together.
Violet paused by the door to the servants' hall, looking
for an excuse not to go in. She could hear the voices of
people gathered there for their noon meal. "I have to
take a walk over to the stables. I'll see you later on."

"Come on, Vi. Ye had no breakfast," Bess chided.
"Why don't ye go in, and I'll run and fetch whatever ye
want from the stables."

Violet shook her head and started backing out. "I
want to check on Moses's dog, and I promised to do
some mending for him. I'll be back."

"But Moses is probably here, too."

Violet was already moving to the door as the young
black woman finished her words. With a wave, she went
outside and pulled the wool shawl over her head.

The true horror of how Ned had treated her had not reached her until now. As she made her way toward the stables, she realized that although she had been abused, she felt like she was carrying a mark of shame. It wasn't so much who did this to her that mattered, but that she somehow deserved it. Well, perhaps she did, she thought.

No, Vi argued silently. Ned had no right to strike her, even if he was a man. She felt sick to her stomach at how unfair everything was.

With the exception of a couple of grooms working in the stalls, the stables were quiet. Moses's dog—her back leg bound tightly with splints and strips of linen—hopped toward Violet, nuzzling her hand before flopping back down on the straw by one of the stalls. Violet moved past the tack room to another small room that Moses had been given.

The small area was clean and tidy, and his clothes were hung neatly on pegs along one wall. Vi found his pile of mending folded in a corner on a barrel by his mattress. Picking up the worn clothing, she sat down on the barrel, took her thimble and a needle and thread from her apron pocket, and went to work.

Her heart ached, and she found herself batting away occasional tears. Violet knew she wanted to stay inside the gates of Melbury Hall, but she was afraid that the time was coming when she would be cast out. That was what happened to girls like her. Girls who foolishly gave themselves over to what they thought they wanted.

She had to take what time here she was given and then face up to whatever the future might bring. She held up Moses's shirt. This was what she needed now. Time to be alone. Time to work and be useful.

The voices of people entering the stables made Vi pull the shawl tighter around her face. She looked up as Amina and Jonah came into the room with Moses behind them. She should have known Bess would not hold her tongue.

Amina was carrying a plate of food. Jonah held a

wooden cup. Both were looking at her with concern, but Moses's dark eyes were angry enough to set the building ablaze.

"Violet is hurt." He moved around the other two and came to crouch down beside her. He pushed the shawl away from her face. "Who, Vi?"

Her chin sank to her chest, but he gently lifted it.

"No one hurts Vi. I'll kill him."

The young woman took one of Moses's large fists between her hands and shook her head. The tears trickled down and she realized that she couldn't be alone and separate. These people loved her like family.

"I don't want you to kill anyone for me, Moses. You are here, and that makes me feel better. I'm safe here. I know that now."

His life had changed. Everything had changed. Before, he had been at the center of a world that was vibrant and filled with action. Now it was as if he were on the outside, looking at the world through a tiny window.

No, Lyon Pennington had never before had to look through this . . . this keyhole at his own life. And the view was so different. Oddly, he found himself focusing on and fathoming the subtle things, the small changes, concentrating on moods and responses, recognizing that so long as an individual had the ability to take a breath, he or she had a life to live. Embracing life despite the hardships was a concept Lyon was coming to appreciate.

This morning, before their guests had arrived, he had joined Millicent downstairs when she had been tutoring some of the younger children in the servants' hall. The group had been lively and noisy. She had been patient and encouraging.

The joys at Melbury Hall were simple. Life was uncomplicated. To Millicent's credit, no one seemed to dwell on how they had suffered before or what was different about them. She had created a haven where people worked hard and lived happily.

So different from Emma's vision for Baronsford. If, indeed, she'd even had a vision.

He shook off the thought. He had no wish, either, to think about his own past.

Lyon focused his gaze on the profile of his wife near the window. She was seated beside Mrs. Trimble. The rector's wife was continuing to speak, but Lyon could tell Millicent's mind was elsewhere. He wondered if she was thinking of the same things that had been occupying his mind for most of the morning—their hours of love-making last night. As he watched her, she absently touched two fingers to the full lips he had so enjoyed kissing.

Lyon admired the soft glow in her cheeks. She had been changing before his eyes since their marriage. Lyon could not believe that he had considered her plain once. Every time he looked at her now, a different aspect of her beauty presented itself. It was as though a different woman had been living within each of the veils that protected her. As her confidence seemed to grow, another veil was peeled away and another woman revealed.

Millicent's gaze flicked away from their guest and locked with his. He saw the memory of their intimacy and the promise of passion reflected in those sparkling eyes. The excitement of what was to come made every limb in Lyon's body feel alive. He wanted her alone again. She had awakened an insatiable beast inside of him, and he couldn't wait to have her again to himself. Apparently reading his mind, Millicent looked away, a blush darkening her cheeks.

". . . will take care of the additions and the renovations of the schoolhouse."

Lyon gave a nod to Reverend Trimble in response to whatever it was the rector had just said.

"The Earl and Countess of Stanmore feel 'tis the right time, considering the continuing growth in Knebworth Village. And though naming the school after Mr. Cunningham is unprecedented, they feel strongly that—considering how devoted that young man was to teaching our children—this is a fine way to keep his memory alive."

"Of course. A fine idea." Lyon recalled hearing the

former schoolmaster's name from Gibbs. "How long ago did this Mr. Cunningham die?"

"A year and a half ago," Mr. Trimble answered.

"He was a young man, I believe you said?"

"I suppose he would have been about your age, m'lord. He was a Scotsman as well."

"And how did he die?"

There was a slight pause. "He was shot."

"Really? A hunting accident?"

"I don't believe so, m'lord."

An uncomfortable silence fell over the room. Reverend Trimble cleared his voice and—sending a quick look in Millicent's direction—began to explain.

"Due to an unfortunate misunderstanding, Mr. Cunningham met his end at Melbury Hall . . . down in the Grove."

A haunted expression marked Millicent's face, and she dropped her gaze to her lap. Lyon remembered seeing the same sadness taking over his wife when Trimble had visited them here earlier. He couldn't help but wonder if the cause might be the same.

Millicent rose abruptly to her feet and walked to the window.

"Then the death of this Cunningham was intentional?" he pressed.

"I was not present, m'lord, when everything happened," Reverend Trimble replied.

"Tell me what you know."

"Those who were there," the rector explained quietly, "say that Squire Wentworth shot Mr. Cunningham."

Lyon told himself it was not jealousy, but curiosity was beginning to stab at him. "Was it a duel?"

"Nay, m'lord. The unfortunate incident had to do with some long-standing disagreements between the squire and Mr. Cunningham over the treatment of the black workers at Melbury Hall. Mr. Cunningham and Lord Stanmore and I—being fiercely opposed to holding slaves—were considered by the squire to be his enemies." Mr. Trimble cleared his voice again and darted a nervous glance at Millicent's back. "The story behind all

of this is too long and tragic for such a pleasant afternoon as this. Sometime when your lordship is willing to
spend an afternoon at Knebworth Village, I should be
delighted to give you the entire history of it."

Before, Lyon had been willing to let the ghosts of
their pasts alone. But after last night he needed to understand all of it. Millicent did not care for her first
husband. That was obvious. But Lyon needed to understand the role of Cunningham in her life.

"Early next week," Lyon announced, "I shall try to
convince my wife to bring me along to the village. There
is much that I would like to learn about my new home
and neighbors."

"There was no reason to assault Reverend Trimble
with all those questions," Millicent said somewhat tetch-
ily as soon as she was back from escorting their guests
to their carriage. She leaned her back against the door.
"Lyon, if there is anything that you need to know about
Knebworth Village's past, I will be happy to provide the
answers. If there are some deep-rooted secrets that you
believe people are keeping from you, I am the one you
should ask."

"And you will answer?"

"I will."

"And I can ask anything?" he challenged, his blue
eyes piercing across the room.

She refused to be baited or to fight with him. At the
same time, she was not going to allow the past to thrust
a wedge of mistrust between them. Mistrust had marred
her marriage to Wentworth, and Millicent was not about
to let it poison this one. Especially now that she recognized how much she cared for Lyon.

"You may ask anything," she answered, pushing away
from the closed door.

"Even if it involves your own past?"

"Even so," she said, determined to follow this through
to the end. "Of course, I expect the same courtesy
from you."

"I doubt that there is much that you do not already

know about me. Gibbs told me you spent a great deal of time in the dowager's company on the day of our marriage, getting answers to all your questions."

"That 'great deal of time' consisted of less than two hours. And how could I have possibly received answers to all my questions when at the time I didn't even know what our . . . our involvement would be?"

"Are you having regrets about last night?"

Millicent turned to face him. The sudden look of vulnerability˜she saw etched in Lyon's face opened her eyes. This man was not Wentworth. There had been no accusations, no distrust. This man wanted to know more about her.

"How could I regret the most fulfilling night of my life?"

Lyon stared at her for the span of an eternity and then raised his hand. His voice quavered a little when he spoke. "Come here."

She went to him without a second's hesitation. He pulled her onto his lap, and Millicent wrapped her arms around his neck and held him.

"I am sorry if I sounded like a man adrift," he said softly. "But the truth is that nothing between us has followed any logical path. We were thrown into this marriage, knowing practically nothing beyond the other's name. Having taken matrimonial vows, I was moved into your care, while neither of us had any idea what demands or expectations such a marriage would bring. And yet so much has changed from that first day." Lyon's hand caressed her and drew her tighter against his chest. "We have both been down this road before. We have been married. And I believe I am speaking for both of us when I say that we want to do better than the first time."

Millicent's head moved beneath his chin as she nodded. She couldn't live through these days dwelling on the fact that their future together could be so brief.

"What the dowager would not have told you about my past was that my first marriage was not as peaceful as she wished it to be. And as I spend more time thinking back over what was wrong, I realize now that the root of my problems lay with my lack of trust. I was a master of *asking* nothing but *acting* on anything that raised my suspicions. I assumed wrongly. I fretted over shadows. I acted rashly on things that I think now might easily have been explained. I didn't ask; I just expected to be told." He let out a frustrated breath. "You didn't even ask, and here I am explaining. Rambling."

"You are not rambling." Millicent pushed her head off his shoulder and looked into her husband's face. "I have been hesitant about discussing my past because those years were nothing but a succession of difficult memories and tragic events. I am almost thirty years old with nothing to be proud of in my life. When I look back, all I see is nothing but total failure."

"You are wrong about that," he said, holding her gaze. "Each step that we take leads us down the road that we were intended to travel. And even the little I know of you is filled with great things. All anyone has to do today is look at Melbury Hall. What you have succeeded in doing here is reflected in everyone who surrounds you, Millicent. You are a wonder—a prize."

His fingers delved into her hair, and Lyon kissed her with enough passion to make her believe.

"Do you know how lucky I consider myself to be your husband?"

Millicent couldn't hold back her tears. She was overwhelmed with everything about this man. He kissed the tears off her face, and his mouth settled on hers again.

"You have a way of making me feel special," she whispered when they broke off the kiss. "Desired."

"And you have a way of making me feel whole." Lyon's fingers moved to the conservative neckline of her dress and started tugging at the small buttons. "From our first moment together you have managed to cast aside all my notions of what I could no longer do."

"Are you referring to taking my head off with that sharp tongue of yours?" she teased, brushing her lips against his bearded cheeks, his lips.

"Well, that too." He smiled. "But do you remember the first day that I arrived at Melbury Hall?"

"You had fallen off the seat in the carriage where Gibbs had propped you up."

"And you tried to help me back onto the seat."

She looked down as his fingers undid one button and moved to the next.

"I learned you had a ferocious temper that day."

"If Gibbs hadn't shown up when he did, you might have learned other things about me, too."

"What other things?"

His blue eyes were mischievous. He took her hand and brought it to his lap, where the evidence of his arousal was pronounced.

"That day, wrestling with me in that confined space as you were, pressing and fitting all your beautiful curves against me, you made me realize that perhaps my manhood was not too far beyond redemption after all."

Millicent tentatively stroked his shape through the breeches. She looked down as Lyon's hand parted the neckline of her dress, revealing the lace of the low-cut chemise she was wearing beneath.

"I always considered myself plain, tedious, lacking passion," she said. "I am struggling with this new me who wants to come out."

"Do not fight it." He placed soft kisses on her face. His hand gently touched her breast. "Do not fight the passion that I know is within you."

"You make me think of doing wicked things."

His breath was more a sigh of delight. "By any chance, do your thoughts run along the lines of latching the door and taking off your clothes and coming back to me?"

Millicent looked up shyly. "Taking off my clothes?"

"Every stitch. I want to see your beautiful body. I want to touch and taste every bit of you before burying myself deep inside."

"You want to make love here in this room?" she whispered, shocked.

"Is that wicked enough?" he asked.

Touching him through his clothing had been the extent of Millicent's thoughts, but she held back her comment when Lyon's mouth captured hers in another kiss.

Blatantly carnal, he thrust deep, sampling and tasting and playing out what another part of his body was eager to do.

Millicent was quivering with need when he broke the kiss. She rose and went to latch the door, but as soon as she turned to him, all her insecurities rushed back in. It was still daylight. Someone could pass by the window. Any minute there could be a knock at the door. And most important, it had been so much safer to make love to him in the half-darkness of the bedchamber, where her flaws were not so obvious. Her back pressed hard against the door.

"Will you be my hands?"

Uncontrollably drawn to the magic of his blue eyes, she swallowed her protests and nodded slowly.

"Undo the rest of the buttons on your dress for me."

She looked down at the partially parted neckline. Her fingers shook when she started unfastening the rest. The weight of Lyon's gaze was on her. The last button ended at the waistline of the dress.

"Now part the dress in the front."

The dark tips of her nipples showed through the thin chemise when she parted the front of her dress. Her skin tingled and burned, and she wasn't even being touched. Not yet.

"Now push it down your arms and step out of the dress and petticoats."

Millicent started doing what he'd asked of her. "I do not think I can go beyond this. I am too embarrassed to reveal—"

"Come here, love."

The softly whispered endearment made her heart soar. She stepped out of the dress and made her way to him slowly.

"You are so beautiful." His voice was husky. Lyon leaned forward, his hand molding the thin fabric to her sensitive skin at her waist, his mouth taking hers in another kiss.

Millicent's fingers delved into Lyon's hair as his fingers gently caressed the curves of her belly, and she shivered when his thumb crossed her ribs and came to rest at the base of her breast.

"You have the most glorious hair. Take the pins out of it."

She reached up with both hands, taking each pin out slowly. All the while she felt his gentle fingers caressing the curves of her breasts. Her skin heated to his touch, and his gaze scorched her.

Her hair came down like a heavy blanket around her shoulders. She leaned her head back when Lyon's fingers combed through the waves.

"I have been daydreaming about this all morning," he said.

Millicent held her breath when Lyon pushed the chemise off one shoulder, revealing only the top of one breast. The sound of a couple of servants passing outside the door broke through the haze that was enveloping her, and Millicent darted a nervous glance in that direction.

"Maybe we should wait until—"

"There will be no waiting." Lyon reached up and pulled the chemise off her other shoulder and drew her back onto his lap.

"But Mrs. Page could be looking for me. Or Gibbs might come to check on you. What happens if they come to the door?"

He placed a kiss on her exposed shoulders, tasting her soft flesh. "I'll tell them I am making love to my wife, and that they can all go to the devil."

"Now I do feel absolutely wicked," she whispered. She undid a couple of the buttons on his shirt and slipped her hand inside, caressing the sinewy contours of his chest. "I think everyone already knows what we did last night."

"And everyone probably knows what we are doing here this afternoon. You might as well stop worrying about what others will think, for there is a great deal that I plan to do to you in the gardens and in the carriage and in every other room of this house." He traced the edge of her chemise, where the tops of her breasts

rose and fell with each breath she took. "Now let me
see you."

Millicent was too aroused to remember any of her
earlier inhibitions. She stood up again and found herself
standing between Lyon's legs. His mouth tasted her
parted lips. His tongue thrust deeply into her warmth.
As he pulled back, Lyon's hand cradled Millicent's face,
then moved down one slender shoulder. He gently
pushed the chemise down her body, until it pooled at
her feet.

"You are stunning."

Tears once again sprang to her eyes as Millicent
basked in the way Lyon's gaze paid homage to her body.
She, too, felt whole and beautiful, and it was because
of him.

He touched her deeply, stroking her moist folds until
she cried his name out breathlessly, and then he kissed
her again.

"Now love me, Millicent," he whispered against her
ear as she continued to float on the waves of her release.

She undid the front of his breeches and straddled him,
drawing him deep inside her body.

It was then—at that very moment as they rose together into those ethereal realms—that she knew she
loved him in more ways than just this.

Chapter 22

When the carriage rolled to a stop by the Fleet Bridge, the stench of the canal rose around them, infusing the air with the foul smell of sewage and other things that Harry did not even want to consider. London was not Jamaica; that was for sure. The clerk looked through the darkness at his employer, sitting across from him, his cane by his knee and a loaded pistol in his hand. Whether they were in London or Port Royal, Harry thought, Mr. Hyde was the same. And Lord save the fool who crossed him.

"Do you understand me?" Hyde was saying, growing angrier by the minute. "You're to blame for this. If you hadn't mucked up the auction, we wouldn't be here now."

"Aye, sir. I'll make good tonight. Ye'll see."

"That I shall. And if you mess this, you blasted cur, the dogs will find your carcass in this fetid ditch. Do you hear me?"

"Aye, Mr. Hyde." Harry grew queasy at the thought of the canal and the unnameable things floating on the dead water. "I'll not fail ye, sir."

"Remember what I told you. Go up this alley a ways until you see the sign of the sheep's head. Around the corner from it you'll find the tavern kept by a man called the Turk. That's the place you'll find the men we want."

"Aye, sir. Half a dozen men."

"At least a half-dozen. You are to pay them a guinea each, with the promise of more if they'll sign on with us. But they'll get nothing if they say a word to anyone.

Tell them your master requires tight lips, or he'll see they swing for it. They're to just wait until we say 'tis time. We shall come for them within a fortnight, and they must be ready to travel. Do you understand me?"

"Do I tell them they keep the money even if ye didn't need them at all?"

"You're a blasted fool, Harry. You think these blackguards would give it back? You'll be lucky to get out of there without having your throat cut. You tell them they keep what you give them tonight. But there will be a much bigger prize if we need to take them with us to get the slave."

Harry looked up the dark alley. He was not particularly happy about going alone into the rat's nest of ramshackle buildings huddled along the edge of the canal.

"Beg pardon for asking, sir, but Mr. Platt seems confident that he can get the woman by lining up witnesses to say she's a witch. Now, to my thinking shouldn't we be waiting to . . . to pay good money to some low-life scoundrels till we're sure that the lawyer's way don't work out?"

In an instant, the silver head of Hyde's cane was pressed up against Harry's chest, pinning him against the carriage seat.

"You listen to me. I am not paying you to think. And I am certainly not leaving the outcome of this to fools like you or Platt or that roaring braggart Cranch. He's a blasted laborer and he thinks he can conquer the world himself. No, I'll not trust any one of you. I'll have plans and alternate plans, and I'll keep my own counsel until I have my fingers around that witch's throat."

Harry nodded meekly. It was true about Ned Cranch. The stonemason might have a way with the skirts, but the man was a bloody blower, to be sure.

"Now get out there," Hyde barked. "Remember, the sign of the sheep's head. And look to your back."

"If I might be so bold as to ask," Will started hesitantly as he scraped the razor over Lyon's throat. "Have ye told her ladyship about this?"

Lyon studied the lanky valet. "You're frightened."

"Ye do look a wee bit different, m'lord, with yer hair cut and yer beard all shaved clean. I'm only thinkin' Lady Aytoun deserves some warnin' afore ye scare her to death wi' yer new face."

"Scare her to death?" Lyon's laughter rang through the room. "Damn you, Will, she has been after me to shave from the moment she set eyes on me. If anything, the woman will be pleased."

Pleased. Absolutely. And not only about his appearance, Lyon thought hopefully. He had a great deal more that he was ready to tell her.

Testing his latest discovery, Lyon slowly pushed his feet along the floor away from the chair as far as they would reach. He then pulled them back. Long Will, intent on not cutting him, was oblivious to the movement.

The past four or five days had been miraculous. Lyon couldn't explain it, but somehow his body had made great improvements in the slow journey of healing. Actually, the improvements were quite small, but unlike the dozen times before, these changes appeared to be permanent. The movement of his fingers in his right hand. The ability to flex his knees and bend his ankles. He had not dared to put any weight on them yet, but the prospect was exciting.

At times during these past few days, especially when he and Millicent were making love, it had been almost impossible to hold back this new discovery from his wife. But Lyon had decided to wait until he was certain, and until he could surprise her with the magnitude of it.

There was so much that he owed Millicent. And there was so much more that he intended to repay.

The valet wiped Lyon's face with the towel and stepped back. Beyond Will, he saw Ohenewaa enter the room. No doors stopped the old woman from going where she wanted to go. Like an apparition, she came and went at any time of the day, and Lyon was accustomed to her ways.

Of course, he owed a great deal of credit for his

healing to Ohenewaa, too. She continued to see to him and prepare ointments for Millicent to administer. Unlike the other physicians who had found their way to his bedside since the accident, this one had believed in his recovery and given him hope. She was another one whom Lyon had yet to tell about the progress he was making.

Lyon saw the old woman's gaze travel down his legs to his feet.

"Is this any improvement?" he asked, touching his smoothly shaven face.

"Some," she responded. "Have you told her?"

"That's what *I* was asking 'slordship," the valet chirped in as he gathered up the shaving equipment. "No disrespect, m'lord, but ye look like a different man than the one her ladyship hitched herself to. An' we dunna want her to boot ye out of Melbury Hall, thinkin' ye're somebody else now."

"Get out, you prattling scarecrow."

With a broad grin on his face, Will left the room. Ohenewaa did not repeat her earlier question, and Lyon made no pretense of misunderstanding her.

"No, I haven't told her yet. But I intend to, this afternoon." He flexed the fingers of his right hand. "I have been waiting, hoping for the moment when I could make some grand gesture like taking a step, or sweeping Millicent off her feet, but I guess that isn't to be."

"Those things will come. You have to exercise your patience as well as your muscles." Ohenewaa put the bottles she was carrying on the table beside the bed. "Your wife takes her pleasure out of the little things in life. Small joys are rewarding, but the monumental ones can be overwhelming. She is much different than what you are accustomed to."

"Has someone been talking to you about my first marriage?"

Ohenewaa snorted.

"Are you so attuned to Millicent's moods and feelings?"

Ohenewaa simply stared at him with her slitted eyes, but said nothing more. Then she turned to the table.

Lyon studied the old woman for a long moment in silence. He watched her capable hands moving purposefully among the bottles and jars.

"Are you able to look into people and heal their souls as well as their bodies, Ohenewaa?"

The dark gaze turned and met his.

"I have met many men with vast experience in science and medicine in my life," he continued. "I have even run across a few spiritual men over the years. But none of them have had your confidence. Or your knowledge of healing."

"There is no magic involved in what I do, or in what I see. But I have seen too much real suffering. And what I have learned from those experiences is that wounds heal or people die. But I have also learned something else. Sometimes the suffering that plagues the body when there is no physical reason is caused by some memory that holds that person captive."

"Do you think guilt stopped me from improving before?"

"You say guilt. I did not say it. Guilt, regret, sorrow. If you look deep enough into your heart, you shall have your answer. But all of these"—she waved her hand at the bottles before her—"have been little more than trifles to distract you. You were on a path to destroy yourself. For your wife, I could not allow that. You are healing now because you have started to push open the door and let the pain that is past seep out. You are allowing the present to move in."

Lyon didn't think he would ever totally recover from the blow of his past. But Ohenewaa was right: He had stopped letting it rule his existence. He was no longer consumed by it.

He looked up to see the old woman gliding across the floor to the door with amazing self-possession.

"Do not forget," she said, stopping at the door. "Little steps."

*   *   *

"I need to get out to greet them. We're not ready. They weren't expected. We need to think of where to put them."

Overwhelmed by the sight of the visitors' carriages driving into the courtyard, Millicent glanced out the upstairs window.

"The dinner—"

"Cook shall see to it," Mrs. Page said hastily. "There will be plenty."

"Mr. Gibbs, please tell his lordship that the dowager and Sir Richard have arrived. Arrange for him to be brought down to the drawing room at once."

"Aye, m'lady."

She turned desperately to the housekeeper. "As far as rooms for everyone to stay in, is there any way we could avoid displacing Ohenewaa?"

"Surely. We'll move Mr. Gibbs into the steward's apartment," Mrs. Page responded. "His bedchamber should suit the gentleman. And if you don't mind giving up your bedchamber and moving in with your husband, m'lady, then we can quickly fix that up for her ladyship."

"Yes. Yes. That will work just fine," Millicent whispered, hurrying away through the house to greet their guests. Although she had invited the dowager to Hertfordshire, she was flustered with the abruptness of the visit. Naturally, she had hoped for a little warning prior to their arrival so that she could plan a perfect stay for the older woman.

It wasn't so much the need to impress, Millicent told herself, but her desire to raise the dowager's confidence in her. She wanted Lyon's mother to be reassured about her initial choice of Millicent as her daughter-in-law.

She paused at the top of the wide, curved stairs and ran a hand down the front of her green velvet dress. Taking a deep breath, she tucked a stray curl behind an ear. *Why tonight?* Millicent thought. On impulse, she had sought Violet's expertise to help her dress differently. She'd wanted to look special for dinner with Lyon tonight. As a result, the gown was too revealing and the style of her hair completely impractical. Of course, this would be the night that they would have guests.

Lady Aytoun and her lawyer had already removed their cloaks in the entrance hall by the time Millicent reached the foot of the stairs.

With a pair of maidservants on either side of her and a silver-headed staff to support her frail frame, the dowager received Millicent's greetings with a wave of one hand. "I shall not be making any apologies for the unexpectedness of my visit here."

"Nor should you, m'lady. We have been expecting . . . hoping for a visit from you for some time now." Millicent offered her greeting to Sir Richard in turn. "And how was your journey from London?"

"Horrible and long."

"We don't need to serve dinner until you have had some rest. But would you care to have a glass of wine or a cup of tea in the drawing room while your luggage is brought up to your rooms?" she asked pleasantly, trying to ignore the way the dowager's keen stare was taking in everything—from Millicent's hair to her gown to the very tips of her slippers. "There should be a nice fire going in there to help you warm up."

"I should like to see my son first."

"Then we can accomplish two things at once. His lordship is to join us in the drawing room as well."

Millicent was not oblivious to the look that passed between the dowager and the lawyer, but she said nothing and took her time escorting the older woman past the bowing Gibbs toward the drawing room.

"And how . . ." Sir Richard asked casually as he surveyed the marble stairwell and painted ceilings high above, "how is Lord Aytoun faring with the lack of visits from any physicians from London?"

"Quite well. In fact, as I have been mentioning in my letters to her ladyship, I believe he has made a vast improvement . . . in his disposition particularly."

"Have you engaged some country doctor, then, to see to him?" the man asked.

"No, Sir Richard. There has been no need for that."
Millicent slowed down to allow Lady Aytoun to catch
her breath. "But he has not been without medicinal
care, either."

"And how is that?" the dowager asked sharply.

Millicent saw no reason to hide the truth. "If you recall the day of our first meeting, I had come upon an
assistant to a deceased physician in London."

"The old African woman."

"Yes. As it turned out, m'lady, Ohenewaa's experience and knowledge in traditional and herbal methods
of healing have proved invaluable in treating your son."
Millicent was aware of a second look that passed between her guests. "As you shall see for yourself in a few
moments, his lordship is now in full control of his
thoughts and actions. He no longer depends on any sedating medications to calm his moods. He is independent
and willful, and Ohenewaa believes that it is only a matter of time before he overcomes the inability to move
his arm and legs."

Neither of her guests appeared convinced by her
speech. Millicent nodded to one of the servants to open
the doors of the drawing room. She peered in, hoping
that her husband was already there.

Someone was indeed there. But the handsome, clean-
shaven, and impeccably dressed gentleman sitting beside
the fireplace could not be her husband. The man's confident gaze took in their visitors before coming to rest
on Millicent.

Her pulse raced. Millicent took an involuntary step
backward and looked away as her heart sank like a stone
into her stomach.

The future she feared had arrived.

Lyon had eyes only for his wife. She was stunning.

The gown fitted her beautiful body like a second skin.
The auburn hair piled on her head was perfect, and
the curled tendrils that framed her pale face accentu-
ated her high cheekbones and sensual mouth. But he
could also see the look of uncertainty in the depths of

her gray eyes. More than anything else, Lyon would have liked to be left alone with Millicent. He wanted to tell her how lovely she looked. Reluctantly, he turned to the visitors.

"I'm sorry I cannot get up, Mother." She was staring at him in open disbelief. "Come in. Please."

Both guests appeared to be rooted to the ground they stood upon, and now that he thought about it, so was Millicent.

"Maitland, you do not look any worse since I saw you last. And you must be well, too, Mother, gallivanting about the countryside in the middle of winter. Come sit by the fire, all of you." He brought a hand up to touch his face and addressed Millicent. "What do you think?"

"I . . . I . . ." Instead of answering him, she turned to the guests. "If you would be kind enough to join his lordship, I need to oversee some arrangements. I shall join you all shortly."

Lyon sensed her discomfort. But he didn't know if it was the suddenness of the unexpected company or if it was something that he had done. Long Will's teasing words came back to him; so did Ohenewaa's questions. He decided not to press her, and as Millicent disappeared from the doorway, he turned instead to his mother and the lawyer, who finally decided to approach the fire.

"You look a little tired, Mother, but much the same as I left you."

"I cannot say the same thing about you." She sat down heavily in one of the cushioned chairs and dismissed her maidservants. The door of the drawing room closed and the three of them were left alone. "You look rested and fit. I can see the Hertfordshire weather agrees with you."

"My improved health is due to far more than the weather," Lyon corrected, drawing surprised looks from the other two. He turned to Maitland. "I assume you received my letter."

"I did, m'lord. And I have in my possession the pieces you requested. We have also brought with us Peter Howitt, a young man who was trained by Walter Truscott and was a clerk at Baronsford for—"

"I remember him," Lyon said. "Any news of Pierce?"

Maitland shook his head, and Lyon was sorry that he had asked. Signing responsibility for the family estate over to his younger brother some six months ago had been Lyon's attempt at salvaging their family. He planned to withdraw and let all the hard feelings gradually fade, while Pierce could take charge and bring David back and the people of Baronsford could continue with their lives peacefully, as they once had. Giving away Baronsford had been Lyon's way of settling the future for everyone, but Pierce had thrown it all back in his face by not returning from Boston in the American colonies.

"And how are things at Baronsford?" Lyon asked, trying not to allow old wounds to begin festering again.

"Perhaps we could discuss this later, m'lord, when we have more time." The lawyer cast a cautionary glance at the dowager, and Lyon respected his wish to wait. It had been so long since Lyon had cared enough to ask about the place that Maitland was obviously concerned that once the discussion began, the dowager would become overtired well before the two men covered all there was to talk over.

He was right. Lyon had so many questions. And he was well aware that his brothers did not share his passion for it the way he did. It was not the place that he missed so much as it was the people. And seeing the care that Millicent bestowed on everyone at Melbury Hall, he now realized how neglected the people there must feel.

"Before you two do that, I have some things I should like to know." The dowager studied him keenly. "These changes that I see in you—these improvements—what is the extent of them?"

"I cannot walk as yet, if that is what you mean." Lyon took satisfaction in watching their stunned expressions as he stretched his feet slowly before him. "But I think it will only be a matter of time."

"This is wonderful, m'lord," Maitland exclaimed.

"Witch or no witch, the woman is a maker of miracles," the dowager whispered in awe, staring at his feet.

"So you have heard about Ohenewaa," Lyon said.

"We have, m'lord. But no report was favorable until your wife spoke of her upon our arrival. And now this!"

Lyon turned to his mother. "Who else has been talking about her?"

"Dr. Parker is still braying like a stung mule over your wife's treatment of him. The man has been filling the ears of everyone in London who will listen to him about the danger Millicent has subjected you to." The dowager smiled. "And from Dr. Tate's description of the situation, this black woman's care should put you six feet underground in a fortnight at the latest."

"So that is the reason for this unexpected visit?"

Maitland started. "You had requested—"

"Indeed," the dowager cut in with her usual abruptness. "I hated to think I had been wrong about Millicent."

"You were not wrong about her," Lyon replied tenderly. "And as much as I thought the idea of an arranged marriage preposterous when you first suggested it, this is as good a chance as any to commend you and to thank you for choosing her."

Their last meeting had been the day Lyon was leaving for Hertfordshire. He had been heavily sedated and, from what little he remembered of their last words to each other, Lyon didn't think he had been very appreciative.

"It is because of Millicent and her stubbornness that I have come this far and improved this much. She is a fighter, Mother. The woman would not let me be."

The sense of relief that passed between the visitors was palpable. Lyon saw his mother lean back heavily against the cushioned chair. A weight had obviously been lifted from her.

"So she is done with all that nonsense about a divorce or an annulment."

Lyon felt a dark cloud form over his own head. He leaned forward.

"What are you talking about?"

"The countess demanded a provision to be included in the marriage agreement, m'lord," Maitland stated quietly. "In the event of your recovery, a divorce would be uncontested."

"Why?"

"Because of her first marriage," the dowager put in, lowering her voice. "Because of the scandalous abuse she received under the brutal hands of her first husband. Because of the shame she still carries at the thought of facing society. Because of not being loved enough even by her own family. Despite the rumors that circulated at the time, they would do nothing to rescue her from that horrible situation."

"I knew nothing of this."

"Reason enough, I should think, for any woman not to want to be exposed to the bonds of marriage ever again."

The fingers of his hand fisted in anger. The fact that Wentworth was a worthless human being had been obvious all along. But Lyon had not guessed at his physical abuse of Millicent. Bits and pieces started to fit into place. He realized his mother was again speaking.

"I am certain you already realize that your wife has great pride. It took a great deal of hard work and courage to take charge of this estate. She has made it a home for herself and for the people she cares about. Though financially strapped, she was happy here. Absolutely content. It took a great deal of persuasion on my part to convince her to marry again at all. But you should consider that what she asked for over two months ago might not be what she wants now."

A seed of doubt had already taken hold in Lyon's mind.

"I almost did not recognize Millicent when I laid eyes on her a few moments ago," the dowager continued in a reassuring tone. "She has changed as much as you have. She looks happy. She glows with an inner beauty. In fact, she is much different than the woman I met in London."

Millicent was happy when people needed her. She had risen to the challenge of dealing with him because of the needs that had crippled him. Recently, they had shared tremendous passion. But they had not spoken one word of the future.

To become whole but to pay the price of losing her was an option that Lyon was not ready to accept. He cared for her too much.

There was a knock on the door, and two servants bringing trays of tea entered.

"I shall forgo the tea. I should like to go up to rest before dinner."

"We keep country hours here, Mother. We dine at seven."

"Very well." The dowager pushed herself to her feet. "This is your chance, Sir Richard, to bring Aytoun up to snuff on all the news of Baronsford. I believe he is ready for it."

Lyon watched his mother go and wondered what else he could be told today that could top the distressing news they had shared about Millicent's bargain.

Pushing herself off her knees, Violet wiped her mouth with the back of one sleeve and leaned against the stone wall of the house. The wind carried spatterings of cold rain, and the young woman raised her face, relishing the feel of it against her fevered skin.

Tonight the taste of cheese had not sat well in her stomach. Yesterday morning it had been the smell of turnips that had sent her running. The day before, she couldn't hold down even a cup of weak tea.

Violet's heart drummed hard in her chest. For the past fortnight she had been sick to her stomach every day. She had stopped denying it: She was pregnant.

The consequences of what this meant, though, had continued to pound at her. Bearing a child out of wedlock. She would lose her position. She would bring shame onto her family's name.

"Are you coming tonight?"

Amina's call as the woman stepped out the back door

forced Violet away from the wall. "I am. I was waiting for you," she lied.

They walked together toward one of the recently repaired cottages just beyond the stables. Amina and Jonah lived there, and nearly every night Amina and a number of the other former slave women gathered there. Violet had been welcome among these women ever since the days just before the squire died. A bond had been formed when, out of fear of Squire Wentworth, she had taken shelter with four of the black women in their hut in the Grove.

Since that time one of them, having being freed, had gone to London. The rest of them, though, despite new positions or living arrangements or marriage, continued to get together in the room of one or the cottage of another nearly every night. For a couple of hours they would gather to talk or sew, enjoying one another's company. Violet had an open invitation to join them whenever she wished, and she often did.

Tonight's gathering was a great relief to the young woman. She felt safe here. And after so many hours of anguishing over her pregnancy, she had been desperate to step outside herself—even for an hour or two. She had no one in whom she could confide this, and that included Ned. She already knew what his reaction would be.

". . . never had a husband, but she left a child behind when they sold her to that Dr. Dombey."

Violet focused on the conversation that was going on around her.

"I had never heard anything about that." Amina lowered the sewing onto her lap.

"That was before your time, child," the oldest of the women commented. She had spent most of her life in the islands, but her talent as a brewer had caused Wentworth to bring her to Melbury Hall. "I have heard our people say Ohenewaa was an Ashanti princess, stolen away from the land to the west of a sacred river in Africa. She had real beauty as a child, and so she was taken up as a domestic servant. She never worked in the field,

like I did before I went to the kitchens. By the grace of
the Almighty, she never took no beatings the way the
rest of us did. 'Twasn't till she came of age that the
troubles started."

"Troubles?" Violet asked quietly.

"Aye. When she started showing signs of being a
woman. I don't know how old she was. Maybe twelve
or thirteen. But the master was quick enough to notice
it. I remember she still had some growing left in her,
the first time that she started swelling up with child."
The old woman shook her head sadly. "But she lost it
at birth. The master's wife wouldn't allow any of us to
go to her the night of her birthing. The mistress would
have been happy to see her die, too. I still remember
her crying out in pain and fear that night."

"You said she left a child behind," Amina said.

"Aye, that I did. This was all before she learned how
to end a pregnancy before it showed. I think it was the
year after or maybe the year after that that she swelled
up again. And this time a boy was born."

"Could she keep him?"

"No chance of that. By then the master was tired of
her. He kept the child in the house, though, and passed
Ohenewaa on to his bailiff and the men. But that woman
was too strong for them. She ran away. They brought
her back and branded her. But she ran away again. They
brought her back and whipped her good that time. But
she kept running."

"She was lucky to survive it," Amina said sadly.

"That is what the rest of us were thinking, too. But
you know, what was so impressive about her was that
every time they brought her back, she became stronger.
With every beating she became more a part of the rest
of us. She was still a young thing, but her name started
getting out. And we stopped thinking of her as the master's girl."

"I am surprised Dombey bought her."

The old woman stabbed the needle into the sewing on
her lap. "He was brought from Port Royal to see to the

master's wife. She was sick in bed with a fever, and that was when he accidentally ran across Ohenewaa. She was sick too then, but she was ailing from the latest lashing she got."

"I remember Dombey when he was much older," Amina said. "He wasn't too bad."

"I don't know," the old woman continued. "Maybe he did have more conscience than most of them. Whatever 'twas, by the time the doctor left, the master's wife died and Dombey managed to buy Ohenewaa."

"But that was only the start of her making a name for herself," another woman, who had been keeping silent, put in. "Quite a few of us got sold off to other plantations right after that." She looked at the oldest woman in the group. "That's when you and me went to the kitchens in that other place. We only saw Ohenewaa from time to time after that. Everywhere Dombey went, he took her, so we only saw her when the doctor would be called up to the plantation."

"She went everywhere, she did," the older woman said. "And being as smart as she was, she learned whatever she could from old Dombey. But she didn't only learn from him. When they was traveling aboard a ship to or back from Africa, she'd spend the passage with our people. As Dombey did as little as he needed to do with slaves, Ohenewaa needed to be down there, below decks, seeing to the sick, comforting them that felt their hearts being ripped out of them, and all the while learning what she could of the land our people was stolen from."

" 'Twas amazing to be working at a plantation and having new men or women come in who already knew Ohenewaa," the second woman said, going back to her sewing. "She became a common thread that linked us all."

The oldest woman smiled. "Especially the women."

"Aye, she knew how to deal with our kinds of problems."

"What happened to her son?" Amina asked.

The older women shrugged. "I don't think she ever went back to find out. Maybe he lived to be a servant or groom or something. Who can say?"

"And what plantation was that?" Amina asked. "Who was Ohenewaa's first master?"

"That was out at the Hyde plantation, child. That was where everything started."

Chapter 23

She must have been crazy to think this arrangement would work.

Millicent laid the book down and rubbed her eyes. She had delayed going up the stairs to their bedroom as long as she could. The dowager and Sir Richard, tired from their trip, had retired soon after dinner. And as it had become part of their habit these past nights, the valets had taken Lyon up to ready him for bed as well.

Millicent walked out of the library and passed through the house. Slowly she started up the wide curved stairs. If this had been any other day—if she had not been so affected by the change in Lyon—she would have been thrilled to rush up there. But for the first time since her marriage to him, she felt out of her element. She did not belong. He was moving too fast, and she was not sure she had the strength to follow.

The reason for these pangs of insecurity was not just his looks. True, he was far more handsome than she had even imagined. He looked like a god. But there was the matter of his confidence, too. And power.

She could feel his masculinity growing. Tonight he had exuded the raw animal potency of a man taking charge of his life.

And that frightened her.

The arrival of the dowager and her lawyer had awakened the man who must have been sleeping inside her husband. When Millicent looked at him during dinner, as he debated the growing unrest in the American colonies with Sir Richard, she had seen a gentleman of intelligence and wit, a member of the fashionable elite, a nobleman beyond her reach. Lyon Pennington, fourth Earl of Aytoun, was a man she barely had the right to dream about.

Violet had moved some of Millicent's clothes over to this room earlier, but she hoped that he would be asleep by the time she reached the bedchamber. Pushing open the door and peering in, Millicent found her hope had been in vain. At least a dozen candles were burning, and Lyon appeared as awake as he had been at noon. He was propped up with pillows on the bed. A book lay open on his lap.

"I was wondering if you would come up, or if I needed to come down and bring you up myself."

"I would like to have seen you try." She closed the bedroom door and leaned her back against it.

"Is that a challenge?"

The touch of a smile on his lips played havoc with Millicent's insides. She cast about for safe ground to step on. "You and Sir Richard were locked in the library for some time this afternoon. It must have felt good to be brought up-to-date with your business affairs."

"Good and distressing. Are you getting ready for bed?"

Millicent pushed away from the door. She glanced at the screen divider and the nightdress that had been laid out on a settee beside it. Tonight the room felt much smaller; the bed looked far too narrow. Lyon closed the book and fixed his gaze on her.

"I never had the opportunity to tell you how beautiful you looked tonight."

"I . . . thank you," she whispered, becoming more flustered. She needed a place to escape to. The screen served the purpose. She had just slipped behind it as a soft knock sounded on the door.

Hurrying to the door, she opened it slightly. Violet stood in the corridor.

"Are you ready to undress, m'lady?"

"Yes, come in."

"No!" Lyon ordered from the bed. "I shall help your mistress. Out with you."

Millicent felt her face burn as Violet stood looking from one person to the other.

"I shall manage, Vi," Millicent said, dismissing her. "Off to bed with you."

Closing the door, she crossed the room as casually as she could and ducked behind the screen.

"I said I'd help you."

"Yes, I know." Her voice sounded odd, even to her own ears. "I can manage."

"The buttons to that dress are in the back."

She cursed silently. He was right. Violet had helped her get into the dress. She needed someone to help her out of it.

"Can I help you?"

Millicent closed her eyes.

"I shan't shave my face again, even if you beg me."

He sounded like a sulking child, and an uncontrollable giggle rose in her chest. He sounded like her. The ridiculousness of how she was acting dawned on her. This was, after all, the same man with whom she had made love repeatedly this week. He was her husband. Clutching the nightgown to her chest, she came around the screen.

"The damage is done," she said. "Now I know how frighteningly handsome you are, so you might as well keep this look."

"Very well, m'lady. Your wish is my command." He tossed the book on the bedside table. "Come here."

Millicent sat on the edge of the bed within the reach of his left hand with her back to him. "If you would do the first dozen buttons, I can handle the rest."

"You cannot be serious," he said with feigned shock. "The 'rest' is what I have been looking forward to all day. So I do it all or nothing."

She looked over her shoulder at the smile on his handsome face. He knew exactly how to melt her heart. "You drive a hard bargain."

Millicent felt the first button open and then the second.

"Now that you mention it, there is something that I need from you."

She heard the change in his tone. "What is it?"

"I need to go to Scotland. I want you to come with me."

Her body tensed immediately. Lyon's fingers moved down her back, undoing a few more buttons.

"During these past few months I had been so far removed physically and mentally from Baronsford that I was not aware of the situation there. I had no idea that the problems going on in the Highlands were spreading south to us in the Borders."

"You mean the land clearings?" she asked quietly.

She knew a little about it. For nearly thirty years, since the defeat of Bonny Prince Charlie at Culloden, the government had been leaning heavily on the Scottish Jacobites and the Highland clans that had sided with the Pretender.

In the newspapers the dowager had been sending up from London, Millicent had read some of the speeches being given in Parliament. From what she could gather, the present problems had really begun in earnest some ten years ago in the Highlands. The value of money was not what it used to be, and the lairds had all begun to raise the rents. Because there were just too many people in the Highlands, wages remained low. Tacksmen—the increasingly affluent men who for decades had leased large tracts of land from the lairds and then sublet the land in smaller plots to crofters—were no longer able to make a living, and had started moving out. The lairds had looked for ways to make the land more profitable, and that was when the trouble really started.

"Sir Richard told me hundreds of vagrants are passing through Baronsford every month. Most of them are hungry, desperate for work. They need ways to feed their families. Others just want to earn enough to pay for passage to the colonies."

She turned to him. "I read someone's speech in the House of Lords. He said that with the tacksmen gone, the tenants' lives would only improve. They would have only one master to satisfy. But these vagrants—"

"Are those same poor tenants." He finished her sentence. "In truth, what has happened is that the farms vacated by the old tacksmen have been let to any stranger who would make the highest offer. These newcomers care nothing for the lowly crofters who have been working the soil for years. The new tacksmen have paid their rent and now are determined to squeeze from those beneath them as large a return as possible for their outlay."

"People can only take that for so long."

"And raising the rents is not all of their troubles, either," he added coolly. "Some of the landowners are combining the smaller farms, doing away with the tillage, and introducing sheep on a large scale. Now, each of those farms would have been occupied by any number of tenant families who worked the soil. The landowners have simply pushed those people out and pulled down their homes."

"How terrible!" She touched his hand. "You said the troubles have reached Baronsford."

"Some of my neighbors have begun the same practice." He held her hand. "Because I have been away for so long, rumors have begun to spread amongst the tenants. After the accident, I transferred control of the land to my brother Pierce."

Millicent already knew this, but she decided to keep silent.

"I assume he has been too busy to come back from the colonies or do anything about it. Still, I feel the problems were really mine, and I have to address them now." He absently caressed her hand. "I have no tacksmen, nor did my father before me, but many of the tenants apparently fear that Baronsford's farms will be next to go."

Millicent had sensed the same kind of fear among the Africans at Melbury Hall after Wentworth's death. Although relieved that their brutal owner was gone, they had been very apprehensive about who was to take over. Many had expected Millicent to sell what she could—including them—and then walk away from it all. But she could not turn her back on her people.

"You must go back. You must make them understand that you are not deserting them."

"I agree. I want you to come with me."

"I cannot," she protested. "I cannot be away from Melbury Hall for so long."

"We could go for a fortnight—maybe a month at most. Then we shall come back."

"But I am needed here. Things cannot function—"

"You know they can." When she tried to stand up, Lyon's hand grasped her arm, forcing her to stay. "You have competent people here who are doing their jobs. There is no reason why you cannot take a few weeks away."

"There are others who can go with you. The dowager—"

"She told me tonight that this is as far from London as she plans to travel. In fact, she is so taken with my recovery that she told me she plans to stay awhile at Melbury Hall. She thinks the place might do her some good as well."

"You see?" She nodded matter-of-factly. "All the more reason for me to stay here. Someone needs to keep her company."

"She has Maitland. And Gibbs and Mrs. Page will look after her perfectly well." He lowered his voice. "I'll tell you the truth. It is not her affection for you and me that will keep my mother here. I think she wants to stay and see if Ohenewaa can do her any good."

Lyon was right, and Millicent knew it. As much as she didn't want to believe it, Melbury Hall was beginning to run smoothly on a day-to-day basis. But still, a mild panic had taken hold of Millicent. It really came down to one thing—she knew she lacked too much to successfully function as an earl's wife at a place like Baronsford. All her ancestors didn't amount to a hill of tea. She was just plain, simple Millicent Gregory. She might be able to fill the role of a squire's widow in a small country estate like Melbury Hall, but beyond that she had no illusions.

"Tell me what is bothering you."

She looked up and saw Lyon's hurt expression. "I am frightened."

He tugged on her arm and pulled her into a fierce embrace. His lips brushed against her hair. His hand moved possessively over her back.

"When we barricade the door," he whispered raggedly into her ear, "the world outside seems to be a frightening place. I have fears, too. I fear the past. I think of facing my own people and I fear they will find me lacking. I am not the man they knew."

Millicent held him tight. She pressed her head against his chest and listened to the stout heart drumming within. Lyon's problems were much more significant, and yet hers threatened to freeze her like a sculpture of snow. She looked down at her legs, frozen with fear and unable to carry her into the future.

"When are you planning to leave?"

"I was hoping to go early next week."

She looked up into his handsome face. "Will you let me think about it?"

He leaned down and brushed his lips against hers. "Yes. But don't ask me to refrain from pressuring you. Or from trying to convince you. Or bribe you. Or whatever else I must do. I need you with me, Millicent."

And she needed him.

Chapter 24

"You there. What's your name?"

"James Wakefield, ma'am."

The dowager glanced at a second boy who stood by the garden wall, keeping a safe distance. The two of them had burst out of the woods and come racing up to the garden gate, laughing and shouting and chasing after each other like a pair of colts. But upon seeing her coming out of the garden, the two had come to an abrupt halt.

"And who is your friend?"

"Israel. He used to live here at Melbury Hall. But now he lives at Solgrave with us."

"I see." The old woman studied James Wakefield. The lad was tall and wiry, though he couldn't have been more than twelve or thirteen. She noticed his misshapen hand, but didn't linger on it. She turned her gaze on the other one. Israel had the most striking green eyes in his handsome dark face. She looked back at James. "And what mischief are you two about today?"

"Mischief?" James answered, shooting a devilish look at his friend. "None at all. But if you forgive us, ma'am, we have some very important business that we need to attend to."

With a deep bow, the young boy backed away from the garden gate and joined his friend. A minute later the two were again laughing and racing each other to the house.

"He is Lord Stanmore's oldest son," the dowager's attendant told her.

Although she had never met them in person, the dowager knew a great deal about the family. Lord Stanmore was from good Scottish stock. His mother was a Buchanan, hailing from the hills around Loch Lomond.

Lady Stanmore was even more interesting. In finding out what she could about Millicent, the dowager had learned about the solid friendship between her and Rebecca Stanmore that had started back in the years when the two were students at an academy for girls in Oxford. Despite the ten years that Rebecca had spent in the American colonies, the two young women had easily rekindled their friendship during the summer that Stanmore had married Rebecca. It was the same summer Millicent had become a widow.

"His young lordship attends Eton, and the black lad, Israel, goes to the school in Knebworth Village," the attendant continued. "The two boys are best of friends, I gather, and visit here often. Cook already had some sweets ready this morning, expecting a visit from them."

Such fascinating lives, the dowager thought, welcoming the feel of the sun on her face. Standing just inside the garden gate, she filled her lungs with the cool morning air and thought, as crowded as Melbury Hall was with all types of people, she couldn't remember the last time she had felt so well.

At the edge of the trees from which the boys had come, she spied a tall black woman bending down to pick up something from the ground. The woman straightened and put her find carefully in a basket that she carried. As she did, the dowager had her first opportunity to look into the wrinkled face. This was Ohenewaa, she was certain. The dowager had been keen on meeting her since their arrival two days ago, but the woman had proved elusive thus far.

She turned to her attendant. "Go ask her to come and join me here for few moments."

The young woman hurried to do as she was told. From within the walls of the garden, Beatrice watched her attendant approach and say a few words to the black woman. Ohenewaa answered without looking toward the garden. The young woman hesitated, then hurried back.

"She asks why you'd like her to come here, m'lady."

"Tell her I should like to thank her."

The servant ran off again. The dowager moved out of the gate and, using her silver-headed staff, poked the cold soil of a flower bed. From here she had a better view of the other woman. The attendant hurried back again and was breathless by the time she arrived at the gate.

"She'd like to know what reason you have for thanking her, m'lady."

"Good Lord! Tell her I need to thank her for what she has done for my son."

The attendant hurried down the hill again. Beatrice noticed that Ohenewaa had taken a few steps up toward the garden. A moment later, the young woman was coming back again. The dowager walked along the path a few feet.

"What now?"

Instead of coming all the way, the attendant called from halfway up the hill, "She says, m'lady, 'twas all his own doing. That she hasn't done a thing."

"Modest, too," the dowager called out, moving down a few more steps.

"Modest, too," the attendant called out in Ohenewaa's direction.

"I did not tell you to say that," Beatrice scolded. She stopped her complaining when she realized Ohenewaa had started approaching her. She continued down the hill.

"What else should I tell her?" the servant asked, looking a little frayed.

"You should go up to the house and rest your voice."

The young woman turned around. "You should go up to the house and rest your—"

"Not her," the dowager snapped, having reached the young woman. "You!"

"I?" The attendant turned around, confused.

"Yes, you," Ohenewaa answered, having reached the halfway point as well.

With a curtsy to each woman, the attendant hurried off toward the house.

Ohenewaa turned her gaze on the dowager. "You should know straightaway that I do not respond well to being summoned."

"That was no summons. 'Twas a request. But no matter," Beatrice said impatiently, waving her hand. "I just wanted to spend some time with you, to get to know you a little, but I am afraid I am not very good at expressing myself patiently when I want something."

"Abruptness is part of your nature," Ohenewaa commented.

"I know."

"And rudeness, I think."

"Sometimes that is true."

"And stubbornness."

"When 'tis called for." The dowager frowned suspiciously. "And how is it that you know me so well?"

She shrugged. "I know your son. Now, what was it that you wanted?"

"If you could put up with a cranky old woman, may I keep your company while you walk and gather your plants and herbs?"

"Since you ask this way, why not? I think the eyes of two cranky old women may be far better than one."

Millicent burst through the library doors, and Lyon smiled as the energy she exuded displaced all trace of quiet in the room. It was a welcome change, and he studied every aspect of her appreciatively. The dark blue dress had a fitted bodice and low neckline. She was wearing a thin ribbon of a matching color around her neck.

"Sir Richard just went upstairs to change for dinner," she said. "The dowager is on her way downstairs. I thought we should take two carriages to Solgrave, as—"

"For days now I have been desperate for a moment alone with you."

Millicent came to an abrupt halt in the middle of the room and stood motionless.

Since the dowager and Maitland's arrival, either she or Lyon had been constantly on the go. Even in their bedchamber, time had been fleeting, for Millicent seemed determined to come up late and escape early in the morning.

Lyon knew what she was doing: She was avoiding giving him the answer he was after.

"You look beautiful tonight."

A soft blush crept into her cheeks. She smiled. "You look rather handsome yourself."

"I have a small gift here for you."

She glanced curiously at the box sitting beside him on the table. "You have given me enough, Lyon. I don't expect any—"

"I know. I want you to have it anyway. Please."

She approached hesitantly. "But what is the occasion?"

"I need no occasion to give my wife a gift."

Millicent reached his side. "But I don't have anything for you."

"You have given me more than I deserve." He took her hand in his, and she sat down shyly on his lap. He handed her the box, and she opened it slowly.

She gasped in shock and closed the top quickly. "These are so beautiful. I cannot accept them."

Shaking his head, Lyon opened the box for her again.

"Yes, you can." He took out one of the diamond necklaces and laid it across the palm of her hand. "Will you wear this for me tonight?"

"But Lyon, this is too beautiful. I could never do it justice."

"Love, this is only a string of cold stones. By themselves they are nothing. You will give them life by wearing them near your heart." He turned her face and brushed away a single tear that had escaped her silvery gray eyes. "You are so beautiful. Please let me do this."

She leaned into him and kissed his lips, and Lyon realized that he was like those stones in some ways. She was giving *him* life by holding him near her heart.

*   *   *

The round face of the baby sleeping so peacefully against Rebecca's chest fascinated Millicent. This past year had gone by so quickly.

"He is truly an angel," she said quietly.

"In his sleep," Rebecca quipped, caressing the soft mat of dark hair on her son's head. "You should have heard him half an hour ago. That was why Mrs. Trent came to fetch me."

They were still an hour from dinner, and Millicent had left Lyon and the dowager and Sir Richard chatting comfortably with Lord Stanmore while she came up to the nursery to visit with Rebecca. She didn't know how to broach the subject, but she really needed her friend's advice. She had been putting off answering Lyon's question for three days. She absently touched the elegant necklace at her throat. Although he was not pressuring her, she knew Lyon wanted to know if she was going to Baronsford with him. And despite everything between them, she was still terrified.

"I cannot believe how much he has grown since I saw him last." She looked up from the child's face to the proud mother's. "But there is something about you that has changed, too. I don't know. But you seem to have this look about you. Are you . . . ?"

Biting her lip, Millicent let the question hang in between them. The immediate reddening of Rebecca's face was impossible to miss.

"You *are* with child again!" Millicent blurted out excitedly. "Is it true?"

The young mother smiled, rising to her feet. "I must be so transparent."

"When? When are you having this baby?" Millicent whispered her question for fear of waking up the sleeping child.

"Sometime toward the end of autumn. We just found out." She laid the baby in his crib and nodded to the nursemaid, who sat sewing by the fire. "Stanmore is thrilled, of course. We brought James home from Eton on a short holiday to celebrate. He is quite

excited, but wants some kind of guarantee for another brother."

Tiptoeing out, the two of them left the nursery. In
the outer room, though, rather than going straight out,
Rebecca turned around and took Millicent's hands in
hers. "I want to hear about you and your marriage. You
look wonderful. You look happy."

"I am, surprisingly. Very happy."

Rebecca gave her a fierce hug. "I am so glad to hear
it. My Lord, to think that I was so wrong about Aytoun!" She pulled back and smiled. "When we were in
Scotland, I received a letter from Reverend and Mrs.
Trimble, praising your husband to the skies. Just spending the few short minutes with him downstairs, I can see
he is nothing like the man rumor had portrayed."

"If there was any truth to those rumors, or if they
were simply vicious gossip, I cannot say, Rebecca. I cannot defend the man my husband may have been before."

"Do not be discouraged, though, if you hear more
talk," Rebecca warned. "The idleness of the *ton* provides a breeding ground for malicious slander."

"I will not allow them to hurt him. I will fight anyone
with my bare hands if I hear them besmirch his name
now." She let out an unsteady breath. "He has come so
far in his recovery, but he still has a rocky road ahead
of him. But I shall tell you one thing, Lyon Pennington
has already proved to be a wonderful husband and a
great friend to me. I just cannot describe in words how
much I have come to value him."

Rebecca looped an arm through Millicent's. "Just
watching him downstairs, watching the way his gaze follows you around the room, the way he stops the very
word on his tongue to listen when you are speaking
across the way, I know that he values you, too. And I
know how difficult it is sometimes to put these things
into the right words. But from my own experience, I can
say that this is what love is all about."

"Love?" Millicent repeated under her breath.

"I would say that it is clear you love him, Millicent.
And I think he shares your affection."

Millicent couldn't stop the sudden tears from rushing into her eyes. She turned away from her friend.

"What is wrong?" Alarmed, Rebecca came around to face her.

"I am so confused and terrified and . . . and . . . I just don't know what to do." She stabbed at the tears. "I am so desperate to do the right thing for him and for myself, but my heart just doesn't let me carry it through."

"Sit with me." Rebecca tugged her hand, drawing her down on a settee beside her. "I want you to tell me what is wrong."

She let out a couple of shaky breaths, trying desperately to calm her nerves. "He . . . Lyon has to go back to Baronsford. He has asked me to go along with him."

"What is terrifying about that?"

Millicent shook her head. "The problem is that I entered into this marriage knowing that it might not last forever. I made them agree that if Lyon were to improve then I would be released from the marriage. I even had Sir Oliver Birch put those conditions in the marriage contract so there would be no objection afterward."

"You were trying to protect yourself, in case he turned out to be not the man that you expected. But that was then, and this is now."

"You don't understand. I was also trying to protect him, too. You see, he is an earl, and I am just . . ." She shook her head. "He needs beauty, style, charm to grace his arm in public, not someone—"

"Stop!" Rebecca snapped. "Stop and listen to what you are saying, to what you are doing to yourself. You are not lacking in beauty or style or charm."

"If I could only make myself believe that."

"Then you must." Rebecca spoke passionately. "Millicent, you cannot allow Wentworth to continue to ruin your life. It is not you talking this nonsense, but him. During your marriage to that degenerate pig, he tried to strip you of your confidence, of your sense of self-worth. He tried to crush you in person and in spirit. And now, after his death, you are allowing him to continue to hurt you . . . even from the grave."

The truth behind her words made Millicent shiver. She forced herself to push away the murky cloud that was enveloping her. She wanted to be able to look into the future without fear. But it was so difficult.

"Your husband needs you. You say he has asked you to go. He wants you to go." Rebecca took both of Millicent's hands and squeezed them as she looked into her face. "If for no other reason, go with him and think of it as a test. Think of it as a way of proving to yourself that you have done away with Wentworth's ghost for eternity."

The valets backed out of the carriage after seating Lyon comfortably for the ride home. Millicent climbed in immediately, and the door closed behind her.

"I like them very much," Lyon admitted. "Both of them. Rebecca is charming and completely unpretentious . . . like you. And Stanmore's progressive views and the way he presents them makes me happy that he sits in the House of Lords. If we only had more people there like him."

"I believe the feeling was mutual." She sat on the seat beside him. "They really enjoyed your company, too."

"Just the two of us?" Lyon asked when the carriage started off.

"I sent everyone else in the other one. I hope you don't mind, but I wanted you all to myself for the ride back."

Lyon wrapped his left arm around Millicent's shoulder and slid her across the seat closer to him. "This is far too promising for such a short ride. Tell the groom to go back to Melbury Hall by way of London."

Millicent's laughter rippled over him. Something had happened tonight. Somehow, during the time that Millicent and Rebecca had spent upstairs, his wife had shed the anxiety that had weighed her down of late. He took her hand and raised it to his lips.

"Thank you."

"For what?"

"For smiling, and for wanting to be with me, and for these obvious plans of seduction."

Her silvery eyes danced with merriment in the dim light of the carriage. She leaned toward him and brushed her lips against his. "And I thought I was being so devious."

He caught her chin and captured her mouth for a much deeper kiss. "This shall be a challenge."

She laughed softly and pressed her body closer as the carriage rolled down the dark country lane. "I do not think there is much that I can do with what little time it takes to go to Melbury Hall. But the dowager and Sir Richard have already told me how ready they are to retire. So when we get back, there is always the prospect of our bed."

Her hand moved beneath his overcoat, and Lyon felt every muscle in his body flex and come to life.

"I don't know if I can wait that long. There is something about the motion of a moving carriage," he said seductively.

The carriage turned onto the road leading to Melbury Hall.

"You make it sound quite tempting, but our bed will have to do for tonight, I think." She stretched up and kissed his neck. "But of course, we shall have plenty of time to try out your carriage idea on our ride to Baronsford."

He turned to her. "You are coming?"

"If you still want me to come."

"Is this answer enough?" he whispered huskily, crushing his mouth down on hers.

"I am so sorry to do this to you, m'lady, just before you go away. But with my grandmum sick and Baronsford being so far away in Scotland and all, there was no way I could get back if she—"

"You don't have to explain any more," Millicent said gently. "I understand perfectly, Violet. Don't give it another thought."

"But I feel so bad about it, m'lady." She turned her face and began straightening brushes on the dresser and then wiping specks of invisible dust.

"You shouldn't," Millicent assured her. "In fact, I have been meaning to talk to you. I've been worrying about you. You've not been looking yourself lately. Why don't you take a holiday while we're in Scotland and go give your mother a hand with your grandmother in St. Albans?"

"I am so much obliged to you, m'lady. I know she could use a little help. But don't you be worrying about me now. I've laid out all your clothes, and Bess will do well for you. She is young and eager to please and is looking for a chance to show that she's able."

As Violet continued to talk about maidservants and dresses, Millicent's gaze kept focusing on the young woman's pale face. She couldn't count the number of times Violet had been sick in the past fortnight. She also had a hard time forgetting the suspicious-looking bruise that she'd seen on the young girl's mouth lately. Something was not right. But as with everything else, there was not much time to probe and prod. She only hoped that Violet would be wise enough to take Millicent's advice and actually go to her family in St. Albans.

"Violet," Millicent interrupted softly. "You do understand that if you ever are in any kind of trouble, you can come to me."

The young woman's eyes avoided meeting Millicent's. Her gaze was fixed on a ribbon she was nervously twisting around one finger.

"Things happen in life," Millicent continued, hoping to make the young woman feel more at ease. "We all make mistakes, Vi. We sometimes find ourselves in situations that we have no control over. What gets us through these things is our connection with other people. Loneliness is a curse; I know that very well. Please remember that I am here to help if you need me."

"I know, m'lady," Violet whispered, curtsying quickly and escaping the room.

* * *

Despite everyone's assurance that life at Melbury Hall would continue on smoothly, Lyon still saw the worry etched on Millicent's face when she climbed inside the carriage and sat across from him.

"Everything will be just fine. Just fine," she muttered under her breath as she settled herself. She turned to him. "It was very kind of the dowager and Sir Richard to stay for another fortnight or so."

"I hope you still feel that way when we get back. I did notice a certain look in the dowager's face that told me she has become quite content here. We might not be able to move her anywhere in the near future."

Millicent smiled. "She is welcome to stay forever, if it pleases her. I am indebted to her in more ways than she could ever imagine." She reached out and took Lyon's right hand affectionately in hers before turning to look out the window again.

A long line of people had gathered in the courtyard to see them off and wish them a safe journey. Millicent waved through the small window of the carriage.

"I don't see Moses," she whispered worriedly over her shoulder at Lyon. "Do you see him?"

Lyon leaned forward and pointed. "There he is, behind Jonah and Gibbs."

Millicent looked again and let out a sigh of relief. "Gibbs and Jonah are developing a solid respect for each other. Since Moses is devoted to Jonah, that makes him like Gibbs. I don't know if our new steward knows that he has taken a protector for life."

"That is the kind of loyalty that Highland cur understands best."

With a shout from one of the grooms and a final wave from the waiting throng, the riders and carriages started out. Millicent continued to stare out the window until the bend in the road blocked her view of her people.

Lyon's attention, though, kept moving from his wife's anxious face to where her hand was clutching his right hand desperately on one knee.

"I used to leave Melbury Hall for months at the time with no guilt whatsoever when Wentworth was alive, but now, going away for a fortnight, I feel like a deserter."

He tentatively entwined his fingers with hers. She didn't notice the movement.

"Last night," he said, "I was listening to Stanmore and Rebecca talk about how guilty they feel whenever they leave James at Eton. Even though he has made a number of friends and has established himself very well as a student there, their worry does not go away entirely. It has to do with family, I suppose."

"You said that to me before." She smiled. "That Melbury Hall is like a family to me. You don't mind that, do you?"

"Hardly. I consider myself damned lucky to be a part of it." He squeezed her hand.

Suddenly Millicent's gaze dropped to their entwined hands. "Do that again."

" 'Tis like making love, my bonny lass. A man needs some time to recover first."

Without letting go of his hand, she moved across and nestled against him. "First of all, that is a lie if I ever heard one. You *never* need time to recover during our lovemaking, and you certainly should not need any now. Squeeze my hand again, Lyon. Please."

Being able to use his hand was not new for him. But now, seeing her excitement, he was relieved to be able to share this progress with her. Lyon gently squeezed her fingers.

Her joyous laughter filled the carriage. Millicent looked up at him in amazement. "Show me more."

"This is the extent of it, for now."

"No, it is not," she challenged him. "I have become too familiar with you and your scheming. I know there must be more. I can hear the rumbling in your brain from here."

He leaned toward her and growled. "What you hear, m'lady, is the rumblings of a starved man, and the sound is not coming from my head."

"We ate not an hour before we departed."

"Sexually starved." He kissed her lips. "Remember all those promises you have been giving me about rocking carriages and straining bodies?"

"But it is daylight," she replied, trying to look shocked.

"That is what curtains are for." He slowly slid his hand onto her knee. "Weren't you asking me to show you more?"

"You are the devil, Lord Aytoun." She leaned forward hurriedly and pulled the curtains closed. "A tempting, scandalous devil who knows all my weaknesses."

Chapter 25

That afternoon Gibbs found the Dowager Countess Aytoun in the drawing room with a book on her lap, nodding comfortably in the chair by the window. The blue eyes focused as soon as he entered, led in by one of her serving maids.

"Do not tell me, Gibbs, that you are here to moan that you already miss your master?"

"Nay, m'lady."

"That's good. Well, I hope you will promise not to make such a complaint while he is gone."

"That depends on how well ye treat me, m'lady," the Highlander said with a half smile.

"From what I've been observing around Melbury Hall, there is a certain young woman whose manner influences your moods." The shrewd eyes narrowed. "So tell me, is Mrs. Page as sweet on you as you are on her?"

"Well, mum, I believe she tolerates me well enough."

The dowager sat back and smiled. "I knew there was a reason why I liked the housekeeper. She is obviously exercising good judgment."

"Och, and here I was hoping ye might put a good word in for me with her."

"Good word . . . that is something we shall certainly need to negotiate." She closed the book that lay on her lap and put it aside. "But I doubt you are here so soon after your master's departure for that."

"Nay, m'lady." He cleared his throat, his back stiffening again. "A messenger has just come down from London, looking for Lady Aytoun."

"Does he bring news from her family?"

"Nay, mum."

"Well, who is he? Out with it, Gibbs."

"He's sent by a Mr. Platt, who happens to serve Mr. Jasper Hyde in legal matters."

"That ghastly man again!" Impatiently, the dowager took the spectacles off her face, her mood obviously souring. "The last thing Millicent needs right now is to worry about someone like him. You didn't tell him that Lady Aytoun has gone to Scotland, did you?"

"Nay, m'lady."

"Good man." The dowager waved off her servants, and the two women hurriedly left the room. "Did you ask what he wants?"

Gibbs walked over and handed a sealed envelope to the dowager.

"It simply says 'Lady Aytoun.' That could be me, don't you think, Gibbs?"

"Without doubt, m'lady."

"And even if it were intended for Millicent, in this situation it would be perfectly acceptable to read it."

"Ye know best, mum."

"It could be a matter of the gravest urgency."

"I'm thinking it must be, m'lady."

"And didn't my daughter-in-law leave Melbury Hall in my hands?"

"Even so, mum."

She quickly broke the seal and scanned the contents.

"That low, disgusting, horrifying man." She looked up. "He does not know when to give up."

"What does he want?"

"Ohenewaa," the dowager whispered, reading the contents of the letter a second time.

Gibbs felt his temper beginning to burn. "Mrs. Page told me, m'lady, that this same messenger came down from London some time ago with a proposal to take Ohenewaa back to Mr. Hyde. Her ladyship put him out on his arse . . . begging your pardon."

"Well, he has added a great deal more weight to his request this time."

"Wouldn't matter at all to Lady Aytoun," Gibbs stated flatly. "Ohenewaa would go nowhere, to be sure."

"I agree, Gibbs." She placed the correspondence between the pages of her book. "But we shall need to act quickly to take the wind out of the man's sails. You said he does not know Millicent is not here."

"Aye, m'lady."

"Tell the messenger Lady Aytoun will meet with this lawyer. Not to accept the proposal, necessarily, but to talk. But the meeting must take place here at Melbury Hall."

"Very good, mum."

"But I want you to put it off as long as you can. Use whatever excuse, but tell him that the meeting cannot take place any earlier than a fortnight off—and even later if you can manage it."

"How about when pigs sprout wings, m'lady?"

"That would be just fine, Gibbs."

"What do ye plan to do?"

"I need to talk to Ohenewaa first. Then I must send Sir Richard to London to look into the accusations Platt alludes to in the letter." The dowager's eyes shone with the challenge of what lay ahead of her. "When we are done with Mr. Platt and Mr. Hyde, Gibbs, I think neither one shall dare to bother our Millicent ever again."

Gibbs did not know the specifics, but he had no doubt that the dowager would succeed.

"Now fetch Ohenewaa and Sir Richard for me, and then go and get rid of that insect of a messenger."

"As you wish, m'lady."

"And Gibbs," she called as he reached the door. "I will be honored to put a good word in for you with your Mrs. Page."

The rain had beaten against the inn walls and the small diamond-shaped panes of glass all night. And this morning, as they were crossing the river Wear out of Durham at dawn, the biting wind had buffeted the carriages all along the arched stone bridge. Millicent pulled her cloak tightly about her and tried to smile at Lyon, who was watching her intently. He'd told her that they should arrive at Baronsford sometime in the middle of the afternoon.

Unlike their first three days of traveling, Lyon's good nature had deserted him once they climbed into the carriage today. And as they rolled northward in silence, the rain and the wind continued to increase with the same maddening proportions as Millicent's apprehensiveness.

They had followed the east road up through England, stopping at Peterborough, Doncaster, and Durham. For this final leg of their journey, though, they had left the better traveled road leading to Berwick, turning inland at Newcastle-upon-Tyne. Passing villages along the way, the carriage had meandered along valley roads and eventually made the steady climb over the Cheviot Hills. Once into Scotland, the rugged terrain, the ancient abbey towns, and the ruins of countless tower houses and castles had fascinated her.

As the carriage bumped and rolled over a rough section of road, Millicent tore her gaze from the wild countryside and looked at the furrows in the brow of her husband. At some point during the day, she had realized that her worries of going to Baronsford were not solely the result of her own lack of confidence, but also a reaction to Lyon's suffering.

And he was suffering; that she could tell.

"Will you tell me about Baronsford?"

He took a long moment to pull himself free of his deep thoughts. "What would you like to know?"

"Did you and your brothers grow up there?"

He looked away from her. Since that first day, when she had met the dowager with Sir Oliver, she'd had little curiosity about the two other Pennington brothers. But now, going back to Baronsford, she couldn't help but think that part of what was tearing at Lyon had to do with the conflict with his family.

"Aye, all of us grew up there."

"Was it a home?"

He frowned at her. "What do you mean?"

"Gibbs told me his reaction to the place the first time he saw it," she explained. "He described Baronsford as a fairy-tale castle with miles of footpaths weaving in and out along cliffs overlooking the river Tweed. He said there is a great deer park, a lake, beautiful walled gardens and greenswards, icehouses and more. But this was only the description of the outside."

"The inside is attractive as well, I suppose. Robert Adam himself did the renovation."

"Yes, Gibbs told me. But is it a home where a family could live?"

Lyon paused before answering. "At one time, Baronsford *was* a home."

She waited for him to say more, but he chose silence. Millicent glanced out the window again, realizing that she could not press him if he did not want to talk. Not now. Not when he was so close to facing the past that had crippled him.

She had faith in him. Despite the words that were still left unsaid between them, Millicent believed that he cared for her. And she was here to offer her support, not to demand attention.

Their knees brushed. Sitting across from Lyon, Millicent looked in time to see that every muscle in her husband's face had gone taut. She looked out the other window to follow the direction of his gaze.

In the distance, perched dramatically on a rocky rise, a monstrous castle reared up imposingly through the fog and rain. She did not have to ask what place it was.

"They lied to the clerk. They didn't say a word about Lord Aytoun and his wife already having left for Scotland," Platt explained. "If your Harry hadn't happened upon Ned Cranch in the village on his way back, I would be going up to Hertfordshire thinking I am meeting with Lady Aytoun."

Jasper Hyde had been wracked with pain during a bout that had struck him earlier this morning. It was over, but he could not shake off the feeling of doom hanging over him.

"Where is Ohenewaa?"

"Still at Melbury Hall."

"A steward would not take it upon himself to do such a thing. Who is running the estate up there?"

"Ned told Harry that the earl's mother, the Dowager Countess Aytoun, was still there. She is the same meddling old woman who arranged for Millicent's debts to be paid off." Platt sat down on the chair across from the plantation owner's desk. "She was the start of all of our troubles. I am not wasting my time going up there to talk with the likes of her."

"You *shall* go!" Hyde snapped. "If you had gone up yourself sooner, we would not have missed her. But it does not matter. They sent a message back saying Lady Aytoun has agreed to meet you. They didn't lie. You will go and meet with the old woman yourself. She has no loyalty to Ohenewaa. It may be easier to pry her loose from this stranger. I will make every attempt to settle this in a peaceful manner."

"And if it doesn't work?"

"Then I have to proceed with my other plans."

"Do you intend to use force?"

"The less you know the better." Hyde pushed to his feet. "Just know this—I *will* take what is mine. They cannot stop me."

Millicent had chosen to stay inside the carriage and wait until the valets had lowered Lyon into his chair. Lyon understood her apprehensiveness. The grim faces of the servants forming the long receiving line were more appropriate for a funeral than a welcoming.

A hard, cold rain continued to fall steadily; nonetheless, Lyon ordered his valets to leave his chair on the wet ground beside the carriage as Millicent climbed out.

If she had been nervous before, she looked terrified as she surveyed the gathering of liveried servants. He reached for Millicent's hand. She was quick to take it.

"I'm sorry for this bloody formality," he said under his breath. "They are here to greet us; that's all. They are not here to judge you. They really just want to see how injured I am. Remember that. Once we get through this, I shall have Howitt show you to your rooms immediately so that you can change and rest."

Peter Howitt, the young secretary whom Sir Richard had brought with him from London, appeared at his elbow. "If ye are ready, m'lady."

Millicent was reluctant to let go of his hand. From the direction of her gaze, he could see she was worried about walking by all these people without any introduction.

"Where the hell are you, Truscott?" Lyon growled.

"Here, m'lord." His cousin's deep voice answered from behind. He looked up to find the man's rugged face, already dripping with rain, smiling down at him. "It is good to have you back, Aytoun."

"What are you trying to do, you blasted mongrel, terrify my wife?" He motioned at the reception line.

"M'lady." Walter Truscott bowed politely.

"Please call me Millicent," she responded in a quiet voice.

"It would be an honor, Millicent. My deepest apology, but our people have been very keen for Aytoun's return, and if not for the rain, I believe the courtyard would probably have looked more like fair day. The tenants and farmhands and the folk from the village are equally eager to see him."

"You are fortunate they didn't show up, or I would have had to bite your head off. Now take her in out of this weather."

"Good to see you're back to your old self, Aytoun. And my sympathies to you, Millicent, for having to put up with him in a confined carriage for such a long journey."

"Somehow she managed to handle me perfectly well." Lyon squeezed Millicent's hand knowingly. Her cloak was already soaked, and droplets of water were glimmering on her face. There was a spark of mischief, though, in her eyes, and he was glad to see it. "This dog Walter here will make the introductions to Mrs. MacAlister, the housekeeper, and the steward Campbell, and will accompany you and Howitt as you pass along the line inspecting the troops."

She was reluctant to go ahead without him, but at seeing Walter's proffered arm, she finally let go of Lyon's hand and headed toward the house.

He watched Millicent walk in the rain with the gray stone structure looming above her. He saw the introductions being made and the bows and curtsies as she moved along. When she disappeared inside, Lyon raised his face into the rain and breathed in a chestful of air. Everything from the scents in the breeze to the chill rising from the ground told him that he was home.

When the valets lifted his chair, Lyon saw all those lining the courtyard staring at him. The last time he left Baronsford, he had been sedated to such a degree that he didn't know his name, never mind where he was or where they were taking him. Now Lyon focused on every face. He answered the greetings with a nod. With the housekeeper and the steward flanking him, he was carried in through the front door.

He motioned for his chair to be lowered in the entrance hall, and the valets started removing his wet cloak and jacket.

"Mrs. MacAlister, where have you situated my wife?" he asked of the housekeeper.

"On the second floor, m'lord. In the west wing." The tall, wiry woman spoke in her usual clipped manner. "The apartments looking over the loch. Hope that suits ye."

"It does indeed. Be sure she gets into dry clothes." He turned to the steward next. "Campbell, I plan to spend the next two hours with you and Truscott. After that, I shall meet with anyone from the village or the farms who needs to see me immediately."

"Aye, m'lord. I'll arrange it and join ye right off."

Lyon's gaze was drawn to the wide curved stairwell. Truscott was descending from the upper floors. Hundreds of paintings covered every inch of available space on every wall. Going back for generations, the likenesses of his ancestors were portrayed on canvases large and small. Lyon's eye lit on the life-sized Reynolds portrait of a woman on the first landing. The bright red of the roses covering an arbor formed a perfect frame for the beautiful woman dressed in white. He looked up into the proud face of Emma.

"Take it down." Lyon snarled as he motioned to his valets to take him away. "Take it down now."

The bedchamber of her master and mistress had been completely swept and aired days ago. Her ladyship's dresses had all been cleaned and replaced in the wardrobe that had been moved in. Violet had no good reason to be up here now, and she knew it. But she had come anyway in the late hours of the night. She sat hidden in the shadows of the darkened window watching Ned Cranch leaving Melbury Hall.

Tonight, waiting for his supper, he had been flirting with one of the young serving girls. Violet had not missed the whispers passing between them, the light touches, the deep blush on the young victim's face as Ned had directed all of his charm her way. Violet had felt sick witnessing the man's treacherous manner. She had heard all his lies already.

But what had made her feel even more ill was the realization of how much she still hurt just watching him.

Violet saw Moses, with a lantern in one hand, cross the gravel of the courtyard. A dog limped from the direction of the stables, and Violet's heart warmed when she saw the way the giant black man leaned down to greet the animal. Violet remembered days not so long ago, during Squire Wentworth's days, when it was more common to find Moses in the stocks on the muddy banks of the stream in the Grove.

The first time she had ever seen him there he had been lying back on the wet ground, one arm draped across his face. She'd watched him for the longest time.

No movements. She had not even been able to see if his chest was rising and falling with each breath. Despite her fears, Violet had approached. She had called out to him, asking if she could fetch him some water or food, and Moses had moved his arm. She had been shocked at the face, scarred and misshapen from countless beatings, she had heard later. But what was more frightening to her, looking on him for the first time, was that the old man had no ears. They must have been cut off long ago, for the scars were long healed.

He had looked so wretched and old and lost that Violet's impulse to run away had left her. She had given him water and had stayed beside him for a short while that day. She had just talked. She didn't remember what she had said, but whatever it was, Moses had never forgotten, and a friendship had been forged on that muddy ground.

Every nerve in Violet's body went taut when she looked down into the yard and saw Ned Cranch walk casually back into the courtyard to speak to Moses. Though the black man showed no concern, the dog seemed wary of the stonemason, her hackles rising and her back legs stiffening. Violet watched Ned try to touch the animal's head, only to have her scramble back a few steps.

"Don't give him even a moment of your time, Moses," she whispered, fighting a worry that was forming deep in the pit of her stomach. Why Ned would be spending time chatting with him had Violet's mind reeling with suspicion. They were so different. While Moses was kind and naïve, Ned was brutal and devious. The black man spoke only the truth; the other never did, it seemed. Unless it suited his fancy.

Violet let out a breath of relief when Moses finally picked up his lantern to continue on his rounds. She saw Ned light a pipe and slowly start walking down the road, too. She was about to close the curtain when she saw the same serving girl with whom he had been flirting before appear from the servant's wing. Violet found herself choking with sudden tears. As she stared, Ned turned and waited for the woman. Together they disappeared into the dark.

The urge to scream, to tear at everything of hers that he had ever touched, flooded Violet's mind. She wanted to forget. She wanted to go to sleep and wake up to find herself free of him. She didn't want to have memories of their lovemaking. She didn't want to touch her stomach and think of the child that was growing there. A child whose father was Ned Cranch.

Violet's face was covered with tears when she closed the curtain and immersed herself in the darkness of the room. If she could only take back the time, correct the horrible mistakes she had made.

The sound of a door opening and then closing across the corridor startled her. Ohenewaa. She was just going to her room. Ohenewaa, who had borne a child out of wedlock herself. Her friend's words came back to her: *Those were the days before she learned how to end a pregnancy before it showed . . . before it showed.*

Violet slipped through the door and started toward the old woman's room.

"What is it exactly that you want from me?" Ohenewaa asked.

She had not missed the red and puffy eyes, the trembling voice, the shaking hand of the young woman when she had come to her door. She had also understood Violet's whispered words about how she had been sick to her stomach for days. But now inside, with the door closed, she wanted to hear the truth.

"I wanted you to . . ." Violet hesitated. "I was hoping you would help me to rid myself of this illness."

"Do you have a name for this illness?" She drawled out the last word.

The pretty chin of the young woman sank to her chest. No words formed on her lips. Her nervous hands were hidden in the folds of her apron.

Ohenewaa saw and heard much more than others thought. It was no secret to her that Violet was with child. And what disappointed her was Vi's choice of the man who had fathered it. From what little she had seen of Ned Cranch, he was a man without a soul when it came to his dealings with women.

"I know that you can help me." Violet spoke softly. "I have heard you know ways to end what I am suffering with."

"Illness? Suffering? Young woman, these are certainly not the right words to use to describe the gift of life."

"You know?" The blue eyes started tearing when Vi looked up. "But I don't want it, Ohenewaa. So please help me get rid of it. I beg you, free me of this curse."

"I cannot help you."

"Please don't say that," Violet pleaded. "I heard the other women talk. They spoke of the ways you helped women on plantations end their pregnancies. I cannot—"

"Was this child forced on you?"

Ohenewaa's sharp question silenced Violet for a second. She wiped the tears off her face, but they continued to come. "No, but I didn't know—"

"Did you go willingly to the man's bed?"

"I did, but that was before I found out how horrible he was."

"I cannot help you."

"But why?" She sobbed. "You have done it before. You have your ways. What difference does it make if I was willing at the time or not? I was stupid. I was tricked and made to believe that we would have a future together. Why can you not think of me as one of the women you helped in Jamaica? Or on board the slave ships? Please, Ohenewaa, give me a new life to live."

"How could I ever think of you as one of those women?" Ohenewaa said harshly. "I cannot, but do you know why?"

Confusion flickered in Violet's eyes.

"Can you even imagine what 'tis like to be an African woman? To be a young girl stolen from your home and your family and dragged on board a slave ship? Do you know the horrors these women endure?"

Violet's chin sank onto her chin. "I . . . I have heard the stories. I cannot imagine, even in my worst nightmares, such suffering."

Ohenewaa approached Violet.

"Then how could you believe I could ever, in my conscience, think of you in the same way as one of those I did help?"

A choked sob escaped the young woman's throat. She shook her head.

"Do you believe this child growing inside of you has the same fate awaiting him or her as those slave children?"

She shook her head.

"Is she a curse, girl? Is she a sickness?"

"Please—"

"Will you hate her because she is a reminder of a *mistake?*"

"No! I can never hate her . . . him." Violet covered her face. Sobs wracked her body. "I don't want to do this."

"Then what are you here for?"

"I . . . I should never have come here. I'm just so lost. So sorry . . ."

Without another word, Ohenewaa took the weeping young woman into her arms and held her.

Chapter 26

"Overwhelming" was a word that kept pushing into Millicent's brain as she followed Mrs. MacAlister, the housekeeper, on a tour of the house. At some point during the afternoon, Millicent had lost count of the number of bedrooms, and the location of the old Eating Room and the second-floor salon, and which wing contained the old armory, and what floor the new library was on, and which sitting room she was supposed to write her correspondence in.

It was beautiful. It was comfortable. It was a marvelous representation of Robert Adams's ideas of aesthetics. No question about any of that.

But Baronsford was too big.

After having a brief dinner with a rather preoccupied Lyon in the old dining room, Millicent found her way back to her apartments, while her husband continued his discussions with Truscott. Wandering into the sitting room off the bedchamber, Millicent collapsed into a lovely upholstered chair and looked into the fire.

Though she should have been warm, she was cold. Though the tiredness of the days of travel should have begun to seep out of her, she was becoming more tense. The grandeur of Baronsford was certainly impressive, she supposed, but it was not the main thing lying like a weight on her spirit.

It was the memory of Emma.

She was everywhere. With Millicent's first steps into the entrance hall, she had found herself faced with a

life-sized portrait of the woman. She was clearly beautiful. Then, in the course of her tour, she had picked up
bits and pieces of information that told her Emma had
had a greater hand in shaping Baronsford as it was today
than had any previous mistress of it.

This had come through most clearly when Mrs. Mac-
Alister had taken her through the east wing. The six
luxurious bedrooms there, looking out over the gardens
and cliffs and the river, had been renovated and decorated by Emma for a specific purpose. She had forbidden
having family, friends, or guests stay in any of them. No,
the entire second floor of that wing was to be a private
haven reserved for her and Aytoun.

And there was more. The drawing room in the old
tower was also for Emma's private use.

Millicent had also been told about the parties in the
ballroom and the dinners in the formal dining room and
the choice of dishes imported from France. "None of
Mr. Wedgwood's things for her," Mrs. MacAlister had
informed her.

Even the arrangement of the portraits and the specially woven carpets ordered from Persia. All Emma's
doing.

Hours later, Millicent's head still echoed with everything she had seen and heard.

Before long her maid appeared, and Millicent moved
into the dressing room while Bess helped her get ready for
bed. As she stood watching the young woman hang her
dress, Millicent questioned her decision to come. She was
of no use here, no use at all. In fact, with all the work that
faced Lyon, Millicent had no idea when she would even
see him again.

Millicent felt insignificant at Baronsford, and she
hated that feeling.

At a knock at the outer door to the bedchamber, Bess
went to answer it. Millicent was surprised to see both
doors from the hallway swing open as Will and John carried Lyon in.

"I am glad you are not sleeping yet. I would have

hated for these two clumsy brutes to have awakened you while getting me ready for bed."

Millicent gaped, lost for words. And the way his gaze moved down her body, as if she were not wearing a thick dressing gown, but rather the most revealing of nightdresses, did not help her to recover. To share a bedchamber with him at Melbury Hall, when they had been short on available rooms, had been one thing. But here! With so much space!

"Are you done with your work for tonight?" she asked for lack of something better to say.

"Tomorrow is another day."

The valets were wasting no time in getting him ready, moving quickly in and out of another dressing room on the far side of the bedchamber. Millicent dismissed Bess, then went to wait in the sitting room, giving her husband privacy.

She took a book from a shelf and sat on the chair. She tried to focus on the first lines. It was so like him to confuse her. Just when she felt totally useless, here Lyon came. And then, to look at her the way he did. She reread the first paragraph again. And then again. No use. No comprehension. She rose to her feet and went to the small writing desk. Perhaps she should write a letter. Again the words were not there.

"Are *you* not done with your work for tonight?"

Hearing his question, Millicent laid her pen down and moved to the doorway of the bedroom. Lyon was already sitting in bed. The valets were gone.

"Tomorrow is another day," she said softly, leaning against the jamb. In a hundred years, she thought, she would never get her fill of him. He looked so handsome, so confident.

"Then come to bed."

She started slowly toward him. "I am surprised to find you here tonight. I was told today that his lordship's apartments are in the east wing."

"You were misinformed. My rooms are where yours are." He reached for the belt of her robe when Millicent arrived at the side of the bed. "I missed you today."

"We have been apart only since this afternoon." She looked down as his hand undid the belt and let it fall to the floor. "And we did have dinner together."

"Too many people there. Tell me what you did this afternoon."

"I was shown around Baronsford."

"It is too damn big."

"It is impressive."

He pushed the robe off her shoulders and let it drop down around her feet. "Do you approve of the place?"

"Baronsford doesn't need my approval."

"I say it does." His gaze met hers. "You are the mistress of Baronsford now."

"I have never had aspirations so high," she replied softly.

Lyon's fingers looped around a tendril of hair that was dangling by her chin. He tugged it gently, bringing her lips closer to his mouth. "There must be something you aspire to."

Millicent placed her hands on his shoulders. She brushed her lips against his. Lyon's arm wrapped around her waist, encouraging her onto the bed. She pulled herself up and nestled against his side.

"Tell me about it." His lips placed feather kisses on her face.

"I aspire to this."

"This bed?" He smiled, pulling her more tightly against him. "This demesne of the night is yours to rule, m'lady."

"And I should like to rule your heart."

The seriousness that took possession of his features made Millicent sorry to have voiced her thoughts aloud. She searched for something to say to bring the smile back into his eyes.

"This is what being so far away from Melbury Hall does to me. I've become foolish, rambling on and saying things that should not be said. I—"

"You already do rule my heart, Millicent."

She watched in bewilderment as Lyon lifted his right arm tentatively, and his fingers brushed away the tears that had fallen on her cheeks.

"You are the only woman whom I have ever known who would have me—as incomplete as I have become—over this place."

She hugged him fiercely. "There is nothing incomplete about you. I love you as you are."

His arms wrapped tightly around her in return. "And will you stay with me always?"

"I shall stay with you as long as you want me."

"Or need you?"

"Yes." Millicent pulled back to look into his face. "I need to belong, though. I need to feel that I can make a contribution. I want to give."

"And take. Is that not part of marriage as well?"

"With someone like you, in a place like this, I am afraid that the scale may tip too heavily to one side. You have title and wealth and every means to give more than you take."

"And you object to that."

"Of course. I want to carry my weight. I want to feel I am as much needed as I need."

"Then perhaps my injuries add that balance to our lives."

She pushed herself up to a sitting position. "I don't know what you mean."

"You do, Millicent."

Lyon's hand was wrapped around her wrist. She wondered if he could feel her pulse beating wildly in her veins.

"If you and I had not married under the conditions we did . . ." He shook his head. "Let's go back even beyond that. Let's say that I was never injured. If I were to approach you, if I wanted to court you—"

"You wouldn't have."

"Why?"

"Because I am plain. Because there is nothing special

about me, Lyon. Not to mention the fact that I would not even travel in your circles in society. You would have had no opportunity."

"And I am telling you, you are wrong about all of that. But what would you have done if I had made a proposal to you and asked you to become my wife?"

"I would have said no. I wouldn't have known you."

"What if we had a torrid love affair, and you could not keep your hands off me? What would you have said then?"

"Still no. We are just not from the same—"

"Same what, Millicent?" he asked sharply. "At what point in our relationship would you feel comfortable enough to trust me with your love?"

"I would have told you I love you, and that would have been enough."

"But it is not enough. I would have wanted a future for us together. I would have wanted to know that your love for me was stronger than the unfounded fears that you had been living with for years."

Raw emotions welled up in her. "I am here now, Lyon. Is that not enough?"

"Will you be here tomorrow?" he asked.

"I will."

"And the day after, and the month after, and the year after?"

"I will be here as long as you want me."

"And need you?"

"And need me."

Rain spattered steadily on the roof of the carriage waiting to take the lord of Baronsford to the village. In the old days, no carriage had been required. It was a familiar sight, for both tenant and villager, to see their laird sitting atop one of his fine horses and riding through the hills. In fair weather and foul, they would see him stopping to talk as they made their way out of their cottages, ready for a day's work.

Aytoun had always been an early riser, and he knew that many of his people cherished this daily connection with their earl. Grievances and complaints did not need to be made in formal settings. Good news passed from one family to another without any difficulty. Someone's hardship was often alleviated before it became a crisis. They were valuable rides he took those mornings. Though he had also been their landlord, the Earl of Aytoun was first and foremost a friend to all of them. And no one missed these morning travels more than Aytoun himself.

Lyon intended to start again. Instead of riding his horse, though, a carriage would have to suffice. Rather than going alone, he would need to take his two valets and his secretary, Peter Howitt, with him.

It would be different, but life down in the village and on the farms was different too, he was told. The village was crowded with vagrant families huddled together, protected from the weather. In the eyes of everyone, Truscott had said, one could see the worry about what lay ahead.

This morning before he left, he had asked Truscott to bring the housekeeper and the steward to the library. What he needed to talk to them about was as important to him right now as anything happening in the village or on the farms.

"I want the two of you to get every available worker and make a sweep of the house immediately." His words were specifically directed to Mrs. MacAlister and Campbell. "You will search out and remove every item that might in any way be associated with my late wife. This includes paintings, clothing, personal items, whatever might remind the new mistress of her predecessor."

Neither one of them seemed surprised by the request.

The steward spoke first. "I can only guess, m'lord, but I'm thinking the collection could be very extensive. What shall we do with it once we've gathered it all together?"

"Put everything in one of the bedchambers in the east wing, if you like. Just lock the door." He turned to his secretary. "Send a letter to Emma's mother, and tell Lady Douglas she is welcome to anything she wishes of it . . . starting with that bloody portrait."

"As you wish, m'lord."

Lyon turned to Mrs. MacAlister. "I also want you to make a point of asking the countess's opinions on everything. From now on, she is to be consulted on all decisions that pertain to the household here at Baronsford—the menus, the seating arrangements for dinners, the purchase of linens, the choice of wine, everything."

"Aye, m'lord. Not unhappy with me, I pray."

"Hardly, Mrs. MacAlister. There is no better housekeeper in the entire British empire."

"Thank ye, m'lord."

"Conferring with her should be no hardship. You will find dealing with Lady Aytoun quite different than . . . than with your previous mistress. I am leaving everything to your good judgment to make her feel welcome here."

He turned to Campbell next. "You will make sure that there is no idle talk by the servants in front of her. No comparisons with Emma will be made regarding her ladyship's actions or dress or conduct. Millicent is her own woman, and everyone shall treat her as such. I know she is English, but there is no finer woman anywhere, and I want the household to recognize that."

Not a word was voiced by either, and Lyon looked from one face to the next.

"Emma Douglas Aytoun is dead," he said flatly. "It is time we laid her ghost to rest. There is a new mistress of Baronsford."

Millicent stayed up in their apartments as long as she could. Lyon had told her that he was planning to spend most of the morning at the village. She asked for a breakfast tray to be sent up, thinking to stay put for the time he was gone. But after writing a letter to Mrs. Page and Mr. Gibbs, she found her attention was continually wandering to the window and the gardens and the lake and the blue sky slowly breaking through the clouds.

Finally losing her battle against temptation, Millicent had Bess help her into some riding clothes and stepped out of their rooms. A young servant hurrying down the hall careened right into her.

"Och, m'lady, there ye be." The girl curtsied. "Mrs. MacAlister sent me to fetch ye. She was wondering if she could have a few minutes of yer time this afternoon to go over some menus for dinners and such for the next few days."

"Tell Mrs. MacAlister I shall put aside as much time as she likes." She started off down the hall with the servant beside her. "I was planning to go for a ride this morning, but I could go later if you think she prefers to speak to me now."

"Nay, m'lady. At your convenience, I'm sure. With the house all helter-skelter as 'tis this morning, I'm certain Mrs. MacAlister—"

"Is there a problem?"

"I should say there is, mum, though I wouldn't know what for. But they're tearing through the east wing and the drawing rooms and the rooms in the old tower and rearranging the portraits and the closets as if the king himself lost his crown and couldn't find it." The young woman shook her head in disbelief. "Anyway, I'm thinking Mrs. MacAlister shan't be having time to even scratch her head while the place is turned upside down."

"And you have no idea what the reason might be for all the activity?"

The servant hesitated, then looked about her and lowered her voice. "We hear his lordship laid down the law this morning."

"The law?"

"Aye, m'lady. We hear he was not pleased that the last Lady Aytoun's things were still about. He said to have everything of hers plucked out and thrown away. He says he has no wish to see anything around Baronsford that reminds him of his old wife."

They were at the top of the stairs, and Millicent's gaze was drawn to the place where Emma's portrait had been hanging the day before. It was gone now, and other paintings had been shuffled about to fill the space.

Uncertainty mixed with a touch of guilt washed through her. She needed to talk to him—to ask why he had given such directions. Last night Millicent had felt that they had successfully passed through an important threshold in their marriage. It had been so wonderful to speak one's mind, to say what the heart was feeling.

Millicent started down the steps. "Please tell Mrs. MacAlister I'd be delighted to speak to her this afternoon."

At the bottom, the servant disappeared into another section of the house, and Millicent asked one of the doormen if either Mr. Truscott or Howitt were around. She was told that the earl's secretary had gone with his lordship into the village this morning, but that Mr. Truscott was in the courtyard at this very instant, ready to ride out himself.

Millicent hurried out and found him there, giving instructions to one of the grooms.

"Good morning, Walter. May I ride to the village with you?"

The tall Scotsman brought the head of his horse around.

"Of course, Millicent. And good day to you. I shall have a carriage made ready at once."

"No, I should like to ride along, if it is all the same to you."

"As you wish, mum." He nodded to the groom, who ran off to have a horse brought up.

"I was wondering," Millicent started again, determined to speak her mind. "Would it be too much out of our way if we were to ride by the cliffs overlooking the river? I should very much like to see where the accident happened."

Platt was beginning to feel like a criminal being led to the dock. He was led by two footmen from the carriage in the courtyard to the door where three liveried servants took his coat and hat and gloves and escorted him to a giant Highlander who glowered down at him with open hostility. This Mr. Gibbs, as he was addressed, said nothing, but gestured with a jerk of the head for the lawyer to follow. With the three servants flanking him, Platt hurried to keep up with the man.

This was not Platt's first visit to Melbury Hall. Some four years ago, while Squire Wentworth had still been alive, the lawyer had come here on business on behalf of Jasper Hyde. The cordial reception he'd received that day was far different from the one he was getting now.

"Ye'll keep to the point," the Highlander growled over his shoulder as he marched Platt through the house. "Ye will speak only when ye are asked to speak, and ye will hold your tongue and listen otherwise. D'ye understand?"

"My word," Platt huffed. "I cannot say but I take grave exception to such rude—"

Gibbs whirled on the lawyer, bending and glaring into his face. "I care naught for your exception or your grave, but ye *will* hold your tongue. D'ye understand?"

"Indeed! Indeed, sir," Platt spluttered, feeling his face redden with fear.

The lawyer fought to calm his nerves. Perspiration was forming on his brow, and when the Highlander finally turned away, Platt quickly mopped his forehead with his sleeve. He knew he should stop right there and thoroughly upbraid the insolent servant for his rude and barbaric manner, but the man was a Scot, after all, and what could one expect?

"See here, sir. I do need to know one thing."

Gibbs said nothing.

"I know Lady Aytoun is in Scotland. With whom am I speaking today?"

"The Dowager Countess Aytoun. And she will receive ye in the drawing room." He opened the door and Platt hurried by him. "Mr. Platt, mum."

The lawyer's confidence immediately returned as he looked upon the frail old woman who was sitting with a blanket on her lap on one of the cushioned chairs. Two young serving maids fluttered about the room. *This* he could handle.

Lady Aytoun looked over the spectacles perched on the end of her nose and studied him. "Mr. Platt?"

"Your servant, m'lady," he said with a deep bow.

"How kind of you to accept my request that you delay this meeting."

Platt had not thought he had much choice.

"With my daughter-in-law already en route to Scotland," the old woman said in a meek voice, "and me somewhat under the weather, if you will excuse the expression, I was certainly not ready to receive any company before."

"I perfectly understand, m'lady."

"Now, please do not stand by the door, sir." She pointed to a chair facing her. "Come and sit here, where I can see you without getting a pain in my neck."

Platt crossed the floor and took the proffered seat.

"The rest of you may leave." She waved at her maids. "You too, Mr. Gibbs."

"I should prefer to stay, mum."

"Why, there is no reason, Mr. Gibbs. This gentleman appears to be quite trustworthy to me. You may leave us."

"If ye insist, m'lady."

Platt cast a haughty look at the ape as he turned to leave. While everyone departed, he made a quick survey of the room. Sunny and quite comfortable. A lovely room. Not very long ago, he had found himself taken with Melbury Hall. In fact, if not for the old woman's meddling, he might have made Millicent an offer for the place. He could have picked it up for a trifle in return for paying off everything she owed to Jasper Hyde.

Indeed, he thought, eyeing the beautiful woodwork and furnishings. This manor house, with its renowned neighbors and its excellent location in the country, would be the perfect country place for someone like him, who was ready to make his mark among the *ton.* In fact, now that he thought about it, perhaps he wasn't too late, after all. Perhaps the younger Lady Aytoun, so busy with her responsibilities as the new mistress of Baronsford, might be willing to part with this country estate. Of course, there was the little matter of his client, Jasper Hyde, but Platt believed once the plantation owner had the slave, he would not care much about anything else.

"What might I do for you, Mr. Platt?"

The lawyer's attention snapped back to his hostess. "My apologies, m'lady. Every time I come here, I find myself more and more smitten with Melbury Hall."

"So this is not your first time here?"

"No, indeed, m'lady. I was a guest of Squire Wentworth's."

"Of course." The dowager nodded pleasantly. "From what I hear, Mr. Hyde and Squire Wentworth were acquainted."

"They were indeed, m'lady. In fact, they were fast friends. Indeed, fast friends."

"Friendship is a valuable thing, Mr. Platt."

"Indeed it is. If I may say, it is a foundation of our English civilization. The bond of friendship constitutes the very core of our gentility. It forms the foundation of our nation's moral superiority in the world today."

"And it is so much like an Englishman to rip away at the fortune of his friend after his demise, is it not, Mr. Platt? So morally superior to tear into the belly of the corpse like some jackal, leaving nothing for his widow?"

Platt cleared his throat. Hyde and Wentworth were cut from the same cloth, he thought. It would not have been any different if Hyde had been the first to pass away. Wentworth would have gone after anything he could get from the holdings of his friend.

"But we digress, do we not?" she said sweetly, putting a smile back on her face. "You were telling me the reason for your visit."

"Indeed, m'lady." He eyed the old woman, knowing he'd best not mince any more words with her. "My client, Mr. Hyde, has made repeated attempts to settle a small business matter with your daughter-in-law. With no success, I might add."

"What is the nature of this business matter?"

"There was a mention of it in the letter I sent."

"I am an old woman, Mr. Platt, with a failing memory. Please humor me. Do tell me all about it again."

"The matter regards a black slave woman called by the heathen name Ohenewaa. My client wishes to buy this woman from Lady Aytoun."

"Surely there must be some mistake, sir. My daughter-in-law does not believe in owning human beings."

"Please allow me to restate my client's request," Platt said patiently. "Mr. Hyde wishes to pay Lady Aytoun all of the expenses that this Ohenewaa has accrued. He would very much like to make an offer of . . . employment to the woman."

The dowager nodded thoughtfully before answering. "Now, why should an important plantation owner such as Mr. Hyde—someone who has made his fortune trading on the very flesh of innocent human beings, a gentleman who must own hundreds of slaves—why should he be so desperate to get his hands on one old woman?"

"The reasons for my client's philanthropy with regard to this woman are private, m'lady," Platt said uncomfortably.

"Ah, philanthropy. And my daughter-in-law declined Mr. Hyde's request when it was made before, I take it."

"There are new circumstances now that might change her ladyship's answer."

"What new circumstances?"

"They were mentioned in the letter."

"Please, sir. My failing memory."

Platt felt the perspiration forming beneath his periwig and trickling down his neck. Actually, it was too warm here in this sunny room. He edged forward on his chair.

"M'lady, I see I must be completely honest with you. I did not wish to involve you personally, out of respect for your position, but you leave me no choice. My client acts in the name of justice. It grieves me to tell you this, but your daughter-in-law may be harboring a murderess. Since your daughter's purchase of this slave woman, certain evidence has surfaced that points to this Ohenewaa as the person responsible for Dr. Dombey's murder."

"I see. And who has been ferreting out this evidence?"

"Why, the proper authorities."

"Pray, give me names of those authorities, and I shall see to it that—"

"I misspoke, m'lady. The names of the witnesses and the evidence against the woman have been collected by clerks in the employ of Mr. Hyde himself."

"And what does he plan to do with this material?"

"Hand them over to . . . to the authorities if his demand is not met. He would like to see justice done without any further scandal attaching itself to your family's name."

"It is so good to have a 'friend' like Mr. Hyde." The dowager smiled. "Is your client a complete dunce, Mr. Platt?"

"I beg your pardon, m'lady?"

"Do you both suffer from imbecility, sir?"

He stared at her, momentarily speechless.

"Do you truly think that my daughter-in-law would believe Ohenewaa's fate could be worse in the hands of the English penal system than in Mr. Hyde's brutal clutches?"

"We have no intention, m'lady, of—"

"I personally would not trust your 'we' with the fate of a dung beetle, my dear man," she said sharply. "Now, back to your accusations. Maitland, are you taking all of this down?"

Platt turned quickly around in his chair and found a door into the adjoining room had been opened. Sitting down at a table was Sir Richard Maitland, and behind him stood an old black woman.

"Incidentally, I have asked our good neighbor, the Earl of Stanmore, a prominent member of the House of Lords, to join us later as well. The complications of what are legal actions and what might be construed as extortion constitute a gray area in my mind—though I believe Sir Richard here would say you have placed yourself clearly in the area of extortion."

"Aye, m'lady," Sir Richard asserted.

"Nonetheless, I am hoping Lord Stanmore will be able to reaffirm our view."

Platt jumped to his feet.

"But about your supposed evidence," the dowager continued. "Since we do not know what it is exactly that you have collected, or what sums you have paid to certain individuals for their testimony, we will tell you what *we* have collected. Ohenewaa, perhaps you could start."

The black woman gazed disdainfully at Platt. "Dr. Dombey died of old age, hastened by his excessive drinking. From our first day of returning to London, the following doctors attended him. There was Dr. Gisborne—"

"From whom I have a statement here." Sir Richard indicated a piece of paper on his desk. "Dr. Gisborne clearly identifies Dombey's condition and his opinion on the reason of death."

"And Dr. Billings," Ohenewaa added.

The dowager's lawyer held up another paper. "And here we have a statement from this good physician as well. He is quite emphatic on the matter."

"I have spoken with a surgeon named Boarham, who was called from time to time to bleed Dr. Dombey before his death."

"Produce him at your peril, Mr. Platt." The old lawyer looked sternly at him. "We have looked into his character. The courts will see him for the corrupt witness he is. I believe he would sell his own mother if there was good profit in it for him."

As Maitland continued to speak, Platt ran a finger along the inside of his cravat. Accusations and false testimony by the likes of Boarham would not stand against accredited witnesses. He thought of Jasper Hyde's comment about other plans if a peaceful approach was unsuccessful. Happy to be ignorant of them, he decided that it was time to lay the problem back in his client's lap. They had clearly been thwarted here.

"If you would please sit down, Mr. Platt," the dowager directed, "we expect Lord Stanmore momentarily. Perhaps you can give him a summary of your own findings regarding this matter of Ohenewaa."

Platt shook his head and cleared his throat. "That won't be necessary, m'lady. I was only acting on behalf of a client, whom I can see has been misinformed and led astray by some rather corrupt individuals."

He started backing toward the door, praying that the blasted Highlander was not lurking outside.

"I shall not trouble you anymore, m'lady. Good day to you all."

With a stiff bow, he yanked open the door and hurried along the corridor. As he turned beneath an archway into the entrance hall, he bumped into a young serving woman who was passing. The woman's eyes fixed on him in surprise before narrowing with recognition.

The lawyer, however, had no time to dally. Grabbing his things from the doorman, Platt left from the house with a shout to his groom and driver. Hyde could do as he wished, but he himself was done with this business.

Chapter 27

On the drive north to Scotland, Lyon had spoken a great deal about his cousin. Walter Truscott was the second son of the dowager's younger brother, William, who had passed away many years ago, leaving the responsibility of raising the boy to his older sister. Having spent most of his years at Baronsford, Walter was much like a brother to Lyon.

Realizing early on that Walter's passion lay in the management of Baronsford, Lyon—immediately after inheriting the title—had asked his cousin to do exactly that. And based on what her husband told her, Millicent thought the young man was doing an excellent job of it.

His polite behavior and interest in her came as a pleasant surprise, too, and she was pleased to know she might find a friend in Walter Truscott. He was kind and considerate, and she sensed from the moment of her arrival that he was trying to make her feel welcome at Baronsford. At the same time, she understood that Walter's temperament lay somewhere between that of Lyon and the dowager. He was not one of those who dispensed meaningless praise. He was candid in saying what he thought.

"This is as far as we can go on horseback," Truscott warned, coming to a low hedge of wild undergrowth near the cliffs.

"Would you mind if we walked to the edge?"

As the man shrugged, Millicent dismounted. Leaving their horses with the groom who rode with them, Walter led her toward an opening in the undergrowth. "There is a narrow path that runs along the cliff here for a way."

He held a branch back, and Millicent passed through it. Immediately she found herself on the very edge of the cliffs. As she looked straight down, her stomach churned at the sight of the rocks below, some protruding from the water, others forming the base of the cliff. Mist rose from the white water moving swiftly over the rocks.

"Does the river always run this fast?"

He took Millicent's arm and pulled her a step back from the ledge. "Yes and no. The river always runs fairly quickly right here, but we have been having a wet winter. So the water is running unusually fast and high."

Millicent glanced down at the rocks below, imagining Lyon the way they had brought him to Melbury Hall. She envisioned Emma's broken body next to his. "Is this where they found them?"

"No." He pointed downstream. "Less than half a mile that way. There is a rocky descent down to a small stone beach where the river bends. Emma's body was found on the rocks near the beach. Aytoun must have been trying to climb down when he slipped and fell."

Millicent was relieved to notice no accusing edge to the man's tone. A cold wind blew in from the east, and she ran her hands up and down her arms to ward off the chill. "Who found them?"

"Pierce did."

She looked up at Walter's solemn face.

"You have not met the rest of the family. Pierce is the middle brother. Younger than Aytoun by three years, he is. And then there is David, the youngest of the three."

"Of course."

"Aytoun doesn't talk about them, does he?"

"I have heard him mention only Pierce's name, and that was in connection with Baronsford."

"Those papers he signed giving this place away are meaningless, I think. There has been no acknowledgment from Pierce. He doesn't want Baronsford, and I believe he would refuse to accept it in any case."

Millicent did not care who owned what. What mattered most was the family that had been torn apart. "How long has it been since they have seen each other?"

"Since Emma's death," he said. "But I know a wedge had been driven between them long before that."

Millicent wanted to ask why, but she held back. What right did she have to question Walter? Besides, she herself was not very good at keeping in touch with her own two older sisters. And she had yet to explain to Lyon the reason for the aloofness of her family. No, any answers to the questions about his brothers—questions that were burning a hole in her tongue—had to come from her husband.

They started walking slowly along the edge of the cliffs. "What do you think happened to Emma? Did she slip and fall?"

"No. I believe she was pushed."

Millicent turned sharply to Truscott. "By whom?"

He shrugged and shook his head.

"You don't believe that Lyon did it, do you?"

"No. He had already put up with her for two years. He was resolved to endure the curse his marriage had become."

Millicent said nothing, trying to absorb Truscott's stunning revelation.

"Emma grew up climbing these hills and cliffs. We all swam in that river in the summer. Her family—she was a Douglas—are neighbors to the east of Baronsford. From the time she was just a wee lass, she spent all her time here. I think even then she was planning her siege of the place. In any case, she knew every slippery edge and every loose rock as well as she knew the Pennington lads." He shrugged again in a matter-of-fact manner. "Despite the foul weather that morning, I do not believe she could have missed a step."

"But Lyon fell. Why not her?"

"He was going down to rescue her, or so he thought," Truscott argued. "You stare down there and see someone's eyes looking up at you from the bottom, and it

can throw you. I saw her down there, too. I believe
Lyon's fall was an accident, but not Emma's."

"But they were both on these cliffs together. If someone had pushed Emma, wouldn't he have seen it
happen?"

Walter gave her a sympathetic look. "He hasn't told
you anything, has he?"

"He has had such a difficult time recovering from his
injuries. It hasn't been very long since he has gotten
back to being himself. But no matter how curious I
might be, I would never bring up anything that might
slow his recovery."

"You are a good woman. Selfless . . . I can see that.
After everything he has been through, it is about time."
He raised his face into the air, as if scenting the wind.
"I will tell you this because I know you will not ask and
because I also know how impossible it might seem right
now filling Emma's shoes at Baronsford."

It *was* impossible, Millicent thought.

"I mentioned it before." Truscott's brooding face
turned to her. "Emma had been planning to be the
Countess Aytoun, to rule Baronsford, from the time she
was a wee lass. She married Lyon not for love of him,
but for love of his title. He was the one who would
inherit everything. And it was this that brought on the
quarreling between the brothers."

He waited a heartbeat before turning his gaze on the
hills across the way.

"Wild, beautiful, untamed she was. In their own way,
each of the Pennington lads was enthralled by her. Each
of them wanted to change her or protect her. Of course,
we always knew that Lyon would be the winner. Or
loser."

Millicent put aside her questions. She focused hard on
every word that Truscott spoke.

"After me, David was the closest in age to Emma. As
children, they were inseparable. As they grew older, she
became the very embodiment of what a woman should
be in his mind. Of the three of them, I think he was the

one who was always in love with her. But of course, he knew he couldn't have her."

He started walking again, ushering Millicent to the side, away from the edge.

"Then there was Pierce. He was always the protective kind. A born hero, that Pierce. He worried about her from the time she could walk. Watched over her through all the wildness. In a way, I think he regarded Emma as a sister. It was his responsibility to teach her and guide her. He had high hopes, but Emma was willful to say the least. She could never be tamed."

Walter kicked a pebble with the tip of his boot, and Millicent watched it roll down the rugged cliffs and bounce high off the rocks before disappearing into the waters of the rushing river.

"Of course, Aytoun was the one with the greatest expectations and the most to lose. He tried, though. He did his best to make her happy in her role as countess. And she did conform to what was expected, I suppose, but only on the surface." He cast a sidelong look at Millicent. "Do you know why Aytoun was called 'Lord of Scandal' among the members of the *ton?*"

"Because of his temper? His duels?"

Walter Truscott nodded. "Duels to protect his wife's reputation. To salvage what he could of his honor. All of those men with whom he fought, every one of them, had supposedly had a relationship with Emma."

"But was it true?" she challenged. "Rumors have a way of starting with no justification."

"Who can say?" he said vaguely. "Emma liked to toy with men. One never knew if she was speaking the truth or lying just to get a reaction. Whatever it was, she thrived on the attention." He paused, frowning. "But she was also as ambitious as she was wild. And becoming mistress of Baronsford—as grand as that might have seemed to her before her marriage—it was not enough once she had it."

Millicent looked back in the direction of Baronsford. Even at this distance, it was immense.

"Most of all, though, she wanted to control Aytoun. She didn't know how to go about it, though, so she started this dangerous game of playing on his jealousy. She soon found that she could not easily manipulate him. The more she flirted, the more reserved he became. In a very short time, Emma became a burden that he was responsible for, but that was the extent of it. No affection."

The conversation she and Lyon had in bed last night came back to Millicent. In a perverse way, that was what she wanted out of her marriage, as well. Not to control her husband—and never by using the methods that Emma had used—but Millicent, too, wanted to know for certain that she mattered to him. That she was the only woman he wanted.

"One of Emma's unforgivable flaws, though," he continued, "was her insistence on pitting the members of this family against each other. She knew how much David and Pierce cared for her, so from the start of her marriage, she used them as a means of riling Aytoun. Complaints she had were not brought to her husband but to his brothers. If anything at all displeased her, she would run to one of them. Of course, the fault for every problem lay with Aytoun."

"Were they so blind?" Millicent asked passionately. "Couldn't they see what she was doing?"

"She had been a part of this family for too many years for them to doubt her."

"What about the dowager? She must have seen through her?"

"By the time she realized what was happening, there were not many choices left to her. Emma was already Aytoun's wife. The dowager's answer to the problem was simply to stay away and let her son work out his own difficulties."

"What happened the day of the accident?"

"Everyone had been invited to Baronsford for the dowager's birthday. Now, Emma had planned it, which made it very suspicious to start with, for she didn't have the best of relationships with her mother-in-law. But still, they all came. Even Emma's side of the family had been invited."

Truscott stopped again and turned to look down at the rocks. Not far ahead Millicent could see the stretch of stony beach at the bend in the river.

"The morning of the party, while most had gone out hunting, Aytoun and Emma had a row. I don't know why or who started it. And, to be honest, at the time I didn't even think it strange, for they often fought when they were together. But then, before we knew it, Emma had run off on foot, and Pierce and Aytoun were growling at one another in the gardens." He turned to her. "I don't know what was said or why Aytoun left Pierce behind, but suddenly he was running after his wife, coming in this direction. Pierce lingered here for only a few moments, and then he, too, went off toward the river. He followed Aytoun and found the two of them down there."

Millicent looked where Walter was pointing and shivered.

"You are sure when you say that someone pushed her down."

"I am."

"But why?" She searched Truscott's dark gaze.

"Because many had come to hate her."

"Jonah told me the stonemason was finishing the first section of the river wall in the Grove," Amina said. "Is something wrong, Vi?"

"Nothing's wrong. Thanks." Wrapping her worn shawl tightly around her shoulders, Violet hurried out the back door of the kitchen and moved down the path toward the line of trees.

Vi had immediately recognized the face of the man who had visited the elder Lady Aytoun. He was the same one she had run into on the stairs that night at the inn in St. Albans. The same one who was going up to meet Ned in his room. Just to make sure she had the name right, Violet had asked Mrs. Page about the dowager's guest. The housekeeper had said he was Jasper Hyde's lawyer, a Mr. Platt from London. Vi knew that Jasper Hyde was the scoundrel who had been trying to ruin their mistress before she had married his lordship, but now the connection with Ned made her furious.

Mrs. Page had also told her that Platt had met his match in the meeting with the dowager, and there was nothing to worry about anymore.

Violet had been too ashamed to admit to the housekeeper that she had seen the lawyer meeting secretly with Ned in St. Albans. She couldn't think of any way of letting them know without having to explain what she herself was doing in that tavern.

The double-dealing, lying, cheating devil.

Jasper Hyde's threat was not completely eliminated. With Ned here, poking his nose and anything else he could manage into the business of Melbury Hall, there was no saying he wasn't sitting and waiting for a chance to cause real trouble.

When she reached the trees, Violet gathered up the hem of her skirt and started to run. Now that she had her head on right, she recalled with a clarity that made her queasy all the questions Ned used to ask her about Melbury Hall. Her only consolation was that she didn't remember ever saying anything that could have caused any difficulties for her mistress.

At a bend in the path, she ran square into the devil himself. Ned Cranch reached right out to steady her.

"What's the rush, lassie? Eager to see me?"

She shook off his hand and stood her ground, refusing to let him intimidate her. " 'Tis finished, Ned. Your true colors having been shown."

"That's a good one, coming from a whore." His smirk turned to a frown. "But what do ye mean by that, I'd like to know?"

"Everybody has figured it out," she lied. "Everyone knows you're being paid by Jasper Hyde. The reason for your being here is to spy on Lady Aytoun and Melbury Hall."

"I don't know no Jasper whatever-his-name-is."

"Is that so? Then why did I see his lawyer, Platt, going into your room in St. Albans? You remember the night."

Ned's gaze narrowed and he grabbed her arm. "So are you going to let them know about us then? About how you played the slut for a married man to—"

"I already told them," she replied, twisting her arm out of his grasp. "And as we speak, Mr. Gibbs has some of the grooms coming down here looking for you. I probably just need to call out for them to come running."

"Ye're a lying wench."

"Believe what you want." Putting on a look of satisfaction, Violet started backing away. "Stand around and wait until they come for you, Ned. I'd love to see them give you the beating you deserve."

That night, when Jonah came up to the house complaining about the stonemason disappearing and leaving a job half done, Violet breathed more easily. Ned Cranch had gone away in a hurry.

Now her only hope was for him to stay away.

Chapter 28

The travels they had made to the neighboring estates had added hours onto their day. It was far later than Lyon had ever intended to stay away, but it couldn't be helped.

As soon as his chair was placed in the entrance hall, Lyon asked about Millicent.

"Nay, m'lord," Mrs. MacAlister said. "She's not yet retired. In the library, she is. Waiting for ye."

"She is not unwell?" he asked, trying not to sound anxious as the servants helped him remove his hat and gloves and cloak.

"She'd not admit it, I'm thinking. But she looks tired." Mrs. MacAlister shot him a look that bordered on reproach. "Her ladyship pushed herself today. Far more than necessary. This morning, a wee morsel of breakfast. Then she leaves with Mr. Truscott. Hoping to find you in the village, she was. By the time she arrives, ye had already gone off to hither and yon."

"Yes, Walter told me that she'd decided to remain in the village when he rode on to join me at Lord Dumfries's." He looked carefully at the housekeeper, surprised by her unexpected concern for Millicent.

"Well, he would have done better to bring her home, if ye ask me." The housekeeper sounded downright disturbed. "The condition of the folk passing through upset her. Her ladyship stayed down there far longer than she should have. And then she rode down along the river. There are more vagrants gathered in the camps down there, where ye allow the gypsies to camp in the summer. She spent time there as well."

As the servants readied themselves to lift his chair, Mrs. MacAlister continued. "I tried to tell her, m'lord. As mistress of Baronsford, I told her, she is far above getting herself personally involved with the needs of vagrants passing through."

"I can just imagine her answer to that."

"I do not see how ye could, m'lord," Mrs. MacAlister said with a note of pride. "But my new mistress said even if she were the queen herself, she'd never turn her back on those in need."

Mr. Campbell cleared his throat nervously, drawing Lyon's attention. "Her ladyship asked me about the number of bedrooms at Baronsford."

"Is that so?"

"Aye, m'lord. And how your lordship might feel about filling them up with *guests*."

"Guests?" Lyon asked, pausing for a moment before beginning to laugh.

She put the closed book on the shelf. She took it down again. She clutched it under one arm and then held it against her chest. She put it back on the shelf again.

Millicent fought to keep herself composed while the servants tried to settle Lyon onto the settee. The hours that they had been apart felt like months, and from the first moment Lyon came into the room, she sensed that his pleasure at seeing her matched how she felt about him.

"This is far better. I have never been so tired of that deuced chair as I was today."

The serving men had not even left the room yet, but Millicent could hold herself back no longer. Sliding onto the settee beside him, she threw her arms around him. He held her tight against his chest before pulling slightly back and smiling into her face.

"I missed you, too." He kissed her lips with such tenderness that Millicent melted against him. The door to the library softly closed behind the servants. It was some time before he pulled away, and even longer before Millicent felt herself floating back to earth.

"I'm sorry I left before you arrived in the village this morning."

She shook her head. "I needed some time to establish myself and get my bearings."

"I understand you did that and more."

His right hand cupped her face. Millicent nestled her cheek into his touch, still amazed at how quickly he was recovering the movement in his hand and arm. "I might have disappointed Mrs. MacAlister with my lack of sophistication."

"Disappointed? You have won her over completely. Out there in the entry hall just now, the woman spoke more words to me than she would have normally used in a year."

"I'm glad. I believe we shall get along very well. She is very capable and quite efficient, and despite her sharp manner, she is a very warm woman."

"Well, I must tell you that you are the first mistress of Baronsford who has noticed that quality in her. She did not have much patience with Emma, who would have dismissed her a dozen times if I hadn't refused to allow it. And as far as my mother goes, their temperaments were too much alike for anyone to guess they could even stand each other."

"She stayed, though, so I suppose your mother must have appreciated her efforts."

"I suppose that is true." Lyon stroked her cheek. "Since you do get along so well with Mrs. MacAlister, then probably you will not mind what I am about to ask of you."

"Is it painful?"

"Very." He settled back with a tired sigh. "We need to throw a party, very soon. I want to invite every landlord and member of the gentility within an hour's ride of Baronsford."

"How large a group would that be?"

"About a hundred. Perhaps a few more."

Millicent settled back heavily, too. "That is very painful."

"And did I mention that we need to do it soon?"

She nodded tentatively, trying to blot out of her mind the image of herself in a roomful of distinguished people where no one noticed her presence.

"Campbell told me you were asking about the number of guestrooms at Baronsford."

Millicent looked up at Lyon and smiled. "Yes, I was."

"This is the reason for the party."

"To compare the size of castles and manor houses?" she quipped.

"Even better. We will stuff their bellies at the same time that we try to shame them into not pushing out their tenants. We shall also try to get a few of them to offer positions to a few of the vagrant families. I tried to do that today by visiting some of the neighboring estates. But it is too difficult to press them one by one. Sir Such-and-such is in London. Baron This-and-that was interested only in hearing about you." He waved a hand impatiently. "We need to bring them all here and try to convince them at once."

"With this kind of agenda, do you think anyone will show up at the party?"

"I think they will *all* come."

"Why?"

"They are all beside themselves with curiosity about the new Countess of Baronsford. And . . ." He pointed to a chair. "More than few of these curs will jump at the opportunity of looking down on me."

"They'll burn in hell first. I shall arrange for you to be carried about on a pedestal ten feet high."

"Such language!" he said, laughing and pulling her more tightly against his side. "Does this mean you will arrange the party?"

"Absolutely. We must do something for those unfortunate wretches."

Lyon kissed her again, and Millicent felt the desire and even the love in his embrace. She felt cherished.

"I know this has only been your second day at Baronsford, but I thought you should know that you have made a great impression." His fingers gently pushed a loose tendril off her face. "And though you have said you have no aspirations with regard to this place, the people here already respect you. They already see your endearing concern for all."

Millicent remembered what Truscott had told her today about Emma loving Baronsford more than Lyon. She imagined the pain that Lyon must have endured.

"I asked Walter to take me to the cliffs overlooking the river today. I needed to see the place where you fell. The place where you lost Emma."

"You mean where she died."

Millicent didn't miss the hard edge in his tone. "A wise man once told me about this road that both of us had once walked before. He told me that we need to do better the second time."

"A wise man, you say?"

"Yes. My husband. The terribly wise Lord Aytoun. Have you heard of him?"

"Oh, yes. The Lord of Scandal."

She leaned against him and traced the hard lines around his mouth with the tip of one finger. "I don't want any secrets between us, Lyon. I don't want anything left unsaid. No assumptions or misunderstandings. Only the truth."

"Truscott told you about Emma."

"And your brothers' relationship with her," she said quietly. "There was so much that I didn't know, and there is still so much about me and my past that you don't know, either. And today, after I left the village and rode down along the riverbank, I ran into so many people who have been pushed out of their homes. Families that have nearly lost hope. And I thought of the two of us and how we have been given a second chance at happiness, and how much I wanted to succeed in that."

Millicent let her hopes rise when Lyon's arm tightened around her. She tucked her head under his chin.

"Being down there also made me realize that now

Emma was no longer the supernatural creature that I
had imagined her to be. Now, knowing more about her,
I realized that she was simply a woman made of flesh
and blood—a human being with all the strengths and
failings that all of us have. Knowing that, I realized I
could survive this road and perhaps even make a difference as I travel along on it. But at the same time, I
recognized how important it was for me to tell you
everything I could about myself, too."

The feel of his arm around her gave Millicent the
strength she needed to continue.

"I was practically given to Wentworth at the age of
twenty-three for the lack of a better marriage offer. My
uncle, who had been my guardian, was too terrified of
the embarrassment and the expense of having a spinster
on his hands forever. So I had to go. It mattered naught
by then who it was to be, no matter how bad the man's
reputation or character." She let out a shaky breath,
resolved to keep nothing back. "I remained married to
him for five years, though I still find it a miracle that I
survived that long. To my husband, I was just a bit of
property, like his land, his sugar holdings, his African
workers, his horses and dogs and sheep and cattle. And
he saw it as his right to abuse us and to cut us down as
he wished."

Millicent felt the tension in Lyon's body as his anger
grew, but she continued to talk. "During those years—
when I was at Melbury Hall and not trying to hide from
him in London—I formed a bond, of sorts, with many
of the black workers that Wentworth held as slaves. During this time I also had the good fortune of becoming
friends with Reverend and Mrs. Trimble and with Mr.
Cunningham, the schoolteacher at Knebworth Village.
These good people, with the support of our neighbor
Lord Stanmore, were trying to improve the conditions
at Melbury Hall that the slaves there were forced to
endure."

She pushed away from Lyon's chest and tried to force
down the lump that was growing in her throat. "Although Wentworth had nothing to fear, my friendship

with Mr. Cunningham became a very sore subject with him. He refused to see that the man's compassion was his reason for visiting Melbury Hall. He preferred to believe that we were lovers. We were *not*, though I think Mr. Cunningham at the end confused his compassion for me with love."

"Millicent—"

"There is more I need to tell you about Cunningham, but let me first tell you something else. Wentworth believed that it was his right as master to use me as he saw fit. In short, I found myself with child. He used to say that it was his right 'to touch as I like and to punish as I see fit.' He preferred to punish, and he beat me once so severely during that time that I was confined to bed for weeks. I also lost the child."

She shook her head when he tried to pull her back into his arms.

"Let me finish. I need to tell you all of it." She blinked back her tears. "After losing that baby, I was lost in my own grief for months. At the same time I knew that I was wearing out my value to Wentworth. It was only a matter of time before he would kill me. He had done it before."

She looked up into Lyon's face. His fury was barely restrained.

"Wentworth's first wife's family owned a number of plantations in Jamaica. That is where he made a small fortune, but just before he decided to move back to England, she died . . . mysteriously. Wentworth told me, during a moment of drunken boasting, that *she* had worn out her value."

Millicent moved her hand over Lyon's fisted fingers. "Then came the summer before last. I accidentally met an old school friend at Knebworth Village. It was Rebecca. She had been in the American colonies for ten years."

Millicent recalled those days of meeting secretly with Rebecca in the Grove or at the church in the village.

"She helped me realize I had to find a way out of that marriage, before I ended up like Wentworth's first wife.

We even went as far as planning an escape to Philadelphia or somewhere in the colonies. But then one day, before we could put our plan into action, Wentworth flew into a rage when Lord Stanmore took away one of the slave children who had been severely abused by the bailiff. After that, everything broke loose at once."

"You are shivering." Lyon's arm wrapped around her shoulders, and he drew her against his side. Millicent forced herself to go on.

"It was June. We had hidden Violet in the Grove to protect her from Wentworth and his lechery. I sent Jonah to the village one night to ask Mr. Cunningham to come at dawn to take Violet away. And he did. But Wentworth and his bailiff, a brute named Mickleby, appeared and claimed that it was I who was running away with the schoolteacher that morning. Wentworth shot and killed Mr. Cunningham that morning."

Lyon's hand gently caressed her. "And Wentworth was killed by Stanmore?"

That was the public explanation, but Millicent wanted him to know the truth. "After killing Cunningham, Wentworth went berserk. He wanted to murder everyone who mattered to me . . . before killing me. He decided to start with Jonah." She held Lyon's hand and looked up into his face. "No one knows this, but Moses killed Wentworth that morning. Stanmore arrived just in time to save Moses's life. To save Moses from having to face the law for killing a white man, and to spare me the scandal that might follow, Stanmore took responsibility for all of it. How much he told the magistrate of what really happened I don't know, but there were never any questions asked later on."

"I knew I liked Stanmore, but what about the bailiff?"

"As he prepared to kill Moses, he died by Stanmore's sword."

"Who else knows this?" Lyon asked, concerned.

"Only the few Africans who were in the Grove that morning. And Rebecca and Stanmore. And I believe Violet learned of it later from one of the women who had been hiding her in the Grove." She held his hand. "You are worried."

"For Moses's life," he said solemnly. "If the truth of that day ever reaches the wrong ears, his life will be worth nothing."

"But no one will know," she said, determined. "Wentworth would have slain many people that morning, including me, if it were not for Moses's bravery. He saved my life. You know him. How gentle he is. And no one who was there would ever betray him."

Shadows flickered on the walls of the servants' hall, and Gibbs sat before the fire, staring into the dying flames. The house was quiet, the doors secured, and Moses was on his watch rounds, but the Highlander could not shake the feeling that was haunting him.

A memory kept nagging at him. A memory of his childhood.

He was only about five, but even then he knew that something momentous was happening. Something that would change his world. He and his mother and sister were sitting before the fire in their cottage on the hillside. His father and older brothers had gone off a few weeks earlier to join Bonny Prince Charlie in his fight against the Hanovers. As they waited that night, they heard the keening cries of the women in the glen, and he knew his father and brothers were not coming back.

This same feeling was haunting him now, and Gibbs did not like it at all.

Mary Page glided into the hall like an angel, guarding her bit of paradise. She was growing fond of him; he could tell. And for the first time in his life, the feeling was mutual.

"Come sit with me, Mrs. Page. Ye have been on your feet this entire day."

She snuffed a guttering candle and adjusted a stack of plates on the table before coming and taking the seat beside him. Her eyes were warm when they swept over his face. "You look as troubled as I feel, Mr. Gibbs."

He reached for her hand and she let him entwine his fingers with hers. "Tell me what is bothering ye, Mary."

"I don't know what is happening, but something is wrong. And I am not imagining this. The entire household is feeling it." She looked about the empty hall. "Violet didn't take a single meal today, and I saw her looking out the windows at the road a dozen times, if I saw her do it once. Ohenewaa has been keeping to her room, and every time I passed by her door, I could hear her chanting her African songs. And then one of the serving maids said she thought she saw Ned Cranch in the shadow of the woods, peering up at the house with an ax in his hand."

"That sounds a wee bit far-fetched, Mary. The stonemason not only left his job here; he has also emptied his room at the inn."

"Now, what do you think happened to him?"

"Maybe he got word that his wife had a bairn. What I don't understand is why he didn't come around to get paid for the work he'd done. Perhaps he's planning on coming back, though I do not know why he went off without telling us."

"You see, Mr. Gibbs?" Mary looked him in the eye. "Everyone is behaving strangely, and there is just no explaining it."

He ran his finger gently over the palm of her hand. "Ye know all this imagining could be the result of having Lord and Lady Aytoun away. From what ye told me yourself, the mistress is not one to spend time away from Melbury Hall. And 'tis ten years since I've been separated from his lordship."

"Do you really think that is all 'tis, Mr. Gibbs? Do you think we are worrying about nothing?"

The way Mary's large eyes were watching the movement of his finger, the innocent way the blush had crept up her cheeks, Gibbs couldn't stop himself from leaning over and pressing a kiss onto her forehead.

"I don't know, Mary. But I can tell ye I feel better having ye beside me."

"The same goes for me, Angus," she said in a small voice, moving closer to his side.

As the two sat and stared into the fire, though, their feeling of foreboding was not easily shaken.

"I did not mean to worry you so with what I told you earlier about Wentworth's death," Millicent whispered against Lyon's ear, curling an arm around his chest. "I am sorry. Now you cannot sleep, can you?"

His head turned toward her on the pillow. "That is not what is keeping me awake. I have been thinking of what Truscott told you about Emma."

"It was wrong of me to ask him to take me there. I should have waited until you were ready to—"

"No. I am glad you went. And I am relieved that you know as much as you do about her." His hand gently caressed her hair and her face. "What has been keeping me awake is the fact that I should tell you the rest of it—of what happened that day."

Until this moment Millicent hadn't realized how mixed her feelings were. The possibility of Lyon's somehow being responsible for Emma's death was a plausible reason for his melancholy after the accident. But she had never wanted to believe it.

Millicent looked beyond her husband and the bed at the half-light of the bedchamber. The flames were burning low in the fireplace. Despite the shadows lurking all around them, she thought, she trusted this man. How fortunate they were to have each other.

"Will you tell me?"

Lyon took hold of her hand and stared up at the ceiling. "We fought. We always fought. Everything about Emma and me was a mistake from the very beginning. We were ten years apart, but it may as well have been a hundred. We did not understand each other. We did not speak the same language. Could not comprehend the other's needs. And this was no one's fault but mine. I always thought I knew what she wanted. I had watched her grow up. I had watched her liveliness and beauty bloom. I thought she wanted only me." He gave a bitter laugh. "Arrogance leads us to make many mistakes. She didn't want me. She wanted Baronsford. And I was completely blind to it."

Millicent wished she could somehow make this easier for him, but she could not think of a way.

"What Truscott told you about our problems was all true. When she became unreasonable, I only became worse. When she withdrew, I became suspicious. As a result, we spent most of our marriage apart. When she was in London or Bath or Bristol, I made sure I was at Baronsford. When she came here with her friends, I would spend the time in the Highlands. And as great a fool as I was, despite all of our difficulties, our mockery of marriage remained tolerable so long as Emma would not disgrace us publicly."

Lyon's gaze turned to Millicent. "Because of Emma, my brothers began to hate me. Pierce and David and I grew further and further apart. But that wasn't enough, so she began to hint at affairs. And then she would question my honor. My manhood. And she would expect me to act on it."

"And you did."

"I was a fool. I think she hoped I would die in one of those duels. Instead, even greater fools than I had to die."

Millicent thought that it was a miracle that Lyon had lived through those times. She pressed her lips against his heart.

"The day she died—the day of the accident—I should have known she was up to something."

"But Walter said everyone was visiting because of the dowager's birthday."

"All of our families were there at Baronsford. Over two hundred guests were arriving for the ball in my mother's honor, but that was just an excuse to have us all there," he said quietly. "She had an announcement that required a worthy audience."

"What was her announcement?"

Lyon's eyes were hard when they turned to her. "She wanted a divorce."

Millicent felt herself go cold.

"The greatest scandal she could create, and a public announcement to disseminate the news. Emma wanted to have the sympathetic ears of everyone who admired and loved her when she announced why she could no longer tolerate being married to me."

Millicent thought of her own divorce request to the dowager and Sir Richard before marrying Lyon. But that had been under very different circumstances.

"What did you do?" she asked.

"I told her no, though not in so calm a fashion. We fought, and she told me she would do as she wished. She was going to make the announcement, and I could live with the scandal of it. And then she ran away."

"And you went after her."

"Not at first. I told myself this was all just another ploy. That she was playing with me like a toy soldier. That she would never do such a thing, and I was not going to rise to her bait. And then I came downstairs and ran into Pierce."

"He talked you into going after her?"

"Not exactly. He was angry because he had seen Emma upset, running away in the direction of the cliffs. He started lecturing me again on how I did not treat her well, and how I was undeserving of her love. He asked me how I could upset her so, considering her condition."

"Her condition?"

"Pierce told me that Emma was pregnant. She told him that she and I were going to make an announcement about it that night."

Anger washed through her.

"I went after her. I ran out there after Emma. But before I could reach her, though, I heard the scream. By the time I got there, she was at the bottom."

His hand rubbed his forehead, back and forth. "When I started climbing down those rocks, I wasn't in search of answers. I remember thinking, She cannot be dead."

His voice caught in his throat, and he closed his eyes. Millicent kissed the tear that squeezed from the corner of his eye.

"Lyon, I am so sorry. So sorry for what you had to go through."

"I think what hurt me most about everything was to wake up so much later and find my brothers had gone. They believed—they still believe—that I pushed Emma off that cliff."

"You cannot know what they believe." She soothed her husband without knowing those other men, without understanding them. "They might have left because of their own guilt with regard to your marriage. They had served as a wedge between you and Emma. Perhaps by going away, they were just trying to cope with their grief."

Lyon's gaze fixed on her face, and then he pressed her head closely to his heart. "Thank you for your trust in me."

She listened to his strong heart beating beneath her ear. "Did you ever find out if Emma was truly pregnant?"

"I was told later that she was," he whispered. "But I know that the child was not mine."

Chapter 29

The kitchens at Baronsford were a combination of modern and ancient. The bakery, with its fine new ovens and solid wooden tables and protected shelves for the dough to rise, offered a sharp contrast to the three huge open hearths with their iron spits and swinging arms. Within those wide stone arches, pork and mutton and beef had been roasted over fires in exactly the same way for centuries. Even now the smell of oat porridge wafted from the cauldrons that were hanging over the fires.

"I am very happy with everything you have chosen, Mrs. MacAlister." Millicent took another loaf of bread from one of the cooks and wrapped it in a cloth before putting it in the basket.

"Cannot be all good. An important party, this is. There must be something that displeases ye."

"Nothing at all." She smiled pleasantly as a servant took away two of the filled baskets and replaced them with empty ones.

"The selection of the late-supper dishes," the housekeeper pressed.

"Love them."

"The dessert menu."

"Outstanding."

"The china."

"Beautiful."

"The cakes with the topping of fresh berries."

Millicent shot Mrs. MacAlister a look. "That was not

on the menu you were speaking of this morning. Where are you going to find fresh berries in March?"

"I was just testing, m'lady. Just to see if ye were listening."

Millicent's laughter made the housekeeper's tight lips twitch—slightly.

"I cannot understand why you find it so difficult to believe how delighted I am with the arrangements you have made for this large party. I trust your judgment. You amaze me with your thoroughness. You are very good. You are amazingly good, Mrs. MacAlister."

The housekeeper shook one of the cloths open and handed it to her, ready for the next loaf of bread. Millicent considered this a peace offering.

"And ye are too good, m'lady," Mrs. MacAlister finally said. "It has been a few years since we've seen our mistress in the kitchens."

Before Millicent could respond to the compliment, Mrs. MacAlister took the bread from the cook and started wrapping it herself.

"But this is one thing we can do, m'lady. Preparing food baskets for the vagrants. And our mistress can spend a wee hour with the dressmaker. The woman was fetched from Edinburgh yesterday, she was."

"I asked for no dressmaker."

"I know," the woman said, a wicked gleam in her eye. "His lordship gave me directions, he did. Said to see to your wardrobe. And so I am."

"But—"

"'I trust your judgment,'" the housekeeper said, mimicking Millicent's English accent. "'You amaze me.' 'You are amazingly good, Mrs. MacAlister.' Now, should I trust your words or not, m'lady?"

"Verrra well, Mrs. MacAlister," Millicent said, mimicking the housekeeper's burr. "Ye have me there, so ye do."

As she was being led away by her own maidservant, Millicent was pleased to hear surprised laughter behind her.

*   *   *

Jasper Hyde paced the length of the rooms he had taken in the coach inn on High Street in St. Albans. The large windows of the front room looked out at the ancient clock tower, and with each passing minute, the plantation owner was becoming more impatient. When Harry led Ned Cranch in an hour and a half later than was expected, he was ready to shoot the blasted stonemason, and leveled his pistol at the man's chest to make his point.

"To get all the answers ye wanted, Mr. Hyde, there was no way I could get back sooner," Ned explained defensively, ignoring the gun. "But ye'll be happy to know I've figured out the whole thing."

"Start talking," Hyde snapped, "before I blast a hole in you."

The stonemason did not look frightened. "We can't go down the road to Melbury Hall, snatch her, and go merrily on our way."

"Why not? You were ready to do that single-handedly. Now you're saying it cannot be done with a half-dozen men?"

"Aye, it can." Ned spoke calmly. "But we have to go about it different now. Things have changed since the earl and his wife left for Scotland. I've been keeping watch over the place, and what I see is that the black woman don't venture into the woods no more. And even when she does move about outside, there's always a handful of other blacks hanging about her. 'Tis like they know somebody's coming after her. I think they've got wind somehow, and they mean to protect her."

"A handful of slaves are no match for the paid cut-throats we've hired, Mr. Cranch."

"Maybe, sir. Or maybe not." Ned shook his head and moved into the room. "I'm thinking these freed slaves are not like the ones you're used to on your plantation, Mr. Hyde. These have tasted freedom, so they're bound to be fierce in protecting their own. There's also another thing to consider here, too. The road out of Melbury Hall passes close to Solgrave and goes through Knebworth Village. Any open attack on Melbury Hall and they'll send someone through the woods to the neighboring estate or the village. We'll find ourselves trapped, unless ye wish to climb the Chiltern Hills."

Hyde's temper flared. "Then what the hell do you propose?"

"We need to be making a distraction." The cocky stonemason had the nerve to sit down on a chair. "I think ye should go and fetch your men and bring them back to St. Albans. We can all of us meet at the tavern where I am staying by the brickyards. In the meantime, I'll talk to my lass over in Knebworth Village and arrange a way to get me inside Melbury Hall on the night when ye're ready."

"You told me you had your women in the house itself."

"I did . . . I do. I've a couple of them on the string, sir." He shook his head. "But the servants in that house are a strange bunch. They're just too loyal to their mistress for me to rely in them in a situation like this."

The man's reasoning was sound. "What do you plan to do once you're inside?"

The stonemason's gaze was confident. "This is the way I see it. We meet at the tavern, and I explain the lay of the land to your men. Then we separate and meet at the Grove. That's a bunch of empty huts in the woods to the back of the Hall. Meanwhile, I have my girl hide me in her cart and take me to Melbury Hall. Once there, I sneak out and start a fire in the stables. Now, with all the commotion of the fire, everyone is sure to empty out of the house. We'll probably have folk rushing up from Solgrave and the village to help. That's when your men come out. We snatch Ohenewaa and go on our way." Ned Cranch grinned proudly. "What do you think?"

Hyde moved to the window as he considered the plan. Another minute ticked by on the clock tower. Time was running out, and he rubbed his chest.

"Forget the stables, Mr. Cranch. Burn the house."

She was huddled beneath a cart to keep out of the falling rain, a small bundle of woolen plaid with the face of an angel.

Millicent noticed her as she handed out the contents of a second basket of food to a family of five gathered around a smoking fire. The young girl's gaze flitted nervously to the groom who was carrying the last basket.

Millicent took the food from the groom and walked toward the cart.

"She'll take it, but the lassie willna eat any of it herself." An old woman stood at the head of an ancient cow still harnessed to the cart. "She's already hoarding half a loaf o' bread from the basket ye gave us yesterday. She thinks her bairn'll be born with a full set o' teeth."

Millicent crouched in the deep mud beside the cartwheel and held the basket out to the girl. "It isn't much, but you might take some of this bread and cheese and dried meat."

A thin arm reached tentatively from the folds of wool. A cold hand brushed Millicent's. As the girl took some cheese, Millicent caught a brief glimpse of the young girl's swollen belly.

"You are close to the time for having your bairn, are you not?"

The girl pulled the food beneath her plaid wrap.

"Why not come to the house with me," Millicent encouraged gently. "This is a rough place to bring a child into this world."

A look of terror appeared in the girl's eyes, and she shrank back farther beneath the cart and turned away.

"She'll not be coming out," the old woman called from her fire.

Millicent reluctantly pushed herself to her feet and turned to the woman who had spoken. "Is she your kin?"

"Nay, she's no kin o' mine nor anyone else's hereabout. But I've been sharing my cart with her since I found her on the Glasgow road."

"Do you know if she has any family she is going to?"

"She's going nowheres, mum. She has no kin, I'm telling ye." The woman glanced back at the cart. "All the poor creature ever says is that her name is Jo. I dunno if she's a faerie child or just cast out on account o' the child swelling in her. I reckon there's no man she's going to, and no husband she left behind. Leastwise, she never mentioned any."

"I should like to take her back with me to Baronsford. She'll at least have her child in a dry room with a fire to warm her. Will you ask her if she'll come with me?"

"She understands everything ye are telling her, mum, but she'll not listen to me any better than she does to ye." The old woman pointed beneath the cart. "Look at her. The daft creature is terrified now, just by ye asking."

Millicent looked for Jo and found the young girl had indeed crawled back away from her. Her plaid was pulled over her like a shroud.

"If you would come along, perhaps she would feel safe."

The old woman shook her head. "I ain't moving from here, mum. When the river goes down and these folk move, I need to be right here. Nay, I need no dry room for a day." She pulled her wool shawl tighter around herself and went over to the smoky fire.

Millicent forced herself to be strong, but the knot in her throat would not allow her to breathe. She looked once more at the mother-to-be.

Millicent had been ignoring the signs, but she was certain she herself was with child. As she looked at the frightened woman, the difference between them was crushing. Jo, with little hope of a future for either herself or her bairn, steadfastly clutched at broken scraps of bread beneath a cart in the rain. And Millicent, with a husband and a home, was delaying the moment of telling Lyon only because she wished to find the perfect time.

The groom touched her arm. "His lordship is here, m'lady."

Millicent looked up from the bank of the river and saw Lyon's carriage stopped behind the one that had carried her down here. Lifting the edges of her muddy cloak, she trudged up the mud-slick ground toward her husband.

As she drew nearer, Peter Howitt immediately

stepped out of the carriage and hurried down to assist
Millicent up the muddy slope.

"Is there anything I can do for you here, m'lady?" the
young man asked eagerly.

"I would be grateful if you would arrange for these
empty baskets to be taken back to the kitchens. They
need to be filled and brought back—with more blankets
as well."

"I shall see to it immediately."

Stepping up to the carriage door, Millicent took one
look at Lyon's outstretched hand before her tears began
to fall. He pulled her inside and into his arms. The door
of the carriage closed behind them, and she sobbed
against his cloak, lost to her heartache over the misery
outside.

"Certainly not the beautiful Scotland that you hear
about, is it, my love?"

"It is so sad, Lyon." She wept. "These people have
been stripped of everything. What is waiting at the end
of the road looks to be nothing either. They've been
torn away from their kin, their land, their homes. And
still, they are so proud."

Lyon gathered her tightly against his chest, placing
kisses against her hair. "These are a strong people, my
love. They come from folk who survived the rough wooing of King Henry and his English raiders. They've
fought off reivers and marauding armies and treachery
of all kinds. Now these folk have been pushed out by
the very people who have grown fat on their labors. But
they are strong and proud, as you say. And with a little
help from compassionate ones like you, they'll survive
this, too."

He drew her face up and brushed away the tears. "But
you cannot let yourself fall apart like this anytime you
come down here. These people need you to be strong,
too. They need you as I need you."

Millicent kissed him, knowing at that moment that she
had never loved anyone or anything as she loved this
man.

The carriage rolled gently toward the house. When

he broke off the kiss, she still could not stop the tears from falling.

"There was something else."

She nodded and closed her eyes to block out the image of the young girl beneath the cart. But it wouldn't go away.

"There is a young woman out there with no husband, no kin. She is about to have a baby."

"You could have brought her back to Baronsford."

Millicent shook her head. "I tried. She'll not come. But it is so sad. Why must it be like this? These people—these landowners—pushing their people out. These are their own countrymen. Their own clan folk, they tell me. How can we inflict this kind of injustice on another human being?"

Lyon lifted her chin and touched her face. His eyes glistened.

"That party is only three days away. That is our best chance to reach these landowners. We cannot change the minds of every one of them, the same way that we cannot save every poor vagrant out there. But we shall try. You and I together will do our best to make a difference."

Chapter 30

⌒

"It was bad enough that every member of this household was walking upon eggshells for the past few days, but now you assign a personal protector to watch over me as if I do not know to behave appropriately, or to dress properly, or to be at the right place at the right time." Millicent shifted her glare from Lyon to his secretary, who was standing right outside the closed carriage door, waiting for her to come out.

"I have no such concern. You are misinterpreting this entirely." Lyon took hold of her chin and drew her gaze back to him. "And the only reason why I am sending Howitt along is to get him off my back. He is more nervous about me not behaving properly tonight than Truscott and Campbell and Mrs. MacAlister together."

"Well, if you were an agreeable, good-natured, polite, and soft-spoken gentleman, none of these people would be so concerned, now, would they?"

He smiled at her. "Let the bloody wretches take their chances. You love me as I am, and that is enough."

Millicent looped her arms around her husband's neck, drawing her face near his. "This is a very dangerous relationship we have," she whispered. "You only say a few words, and you can have your way with me."

"You come back sooner from your visit of the vagrants along the river, and you and I might be able to retire to the library, or to our bedroom for an afternoon rest. Then I can work on perfecting other methods of having my way with you."

His mouth followed up immediately with a kiss, and Millicent was lost in the taste and texture and heat of their mating lips and tongue. She pulled back slightly to catch her breath.

"I think you have mastered the technique very well, in any case."

His hand reached under her cloak. "But there are a few other skills I still need to work on."

She leaned into his touch. "I was told the guests might be arriving anytime from the early afternoon on."

"We'll just let that nervous flock of titmice at Baronsford entertain the bloody intruders until we are ready for them."

He drew her more tightly against him, and Millicent relished the feel of his lips grazing her neck. Then she looked over her shoulder and found Howitt standing at a respectful distance from the carriage, moving impatiently from one foot to the other.

"I think your secretary is anxious for us to get started."

"Remind me to dismiss the scoundrel tomorrow."

"I'll do that."

Millicent still had stars dancing in her eyes when she stepped out of the carriage and stood waiting for it to drive away toward the village. She still had not told him anything of her pregnancy, but the news would wait until after the party tonight. A second carriage, which had carried more food and Howitt and couple of the servants, was parked on the road a few steps away.

"I promised Mrs. MacAlister to get you back by noon, m'lady," the young man said, having already lined up the servants with baskets of food to distribute. "So perhaps if we start in different directions and—"

"That would be just fine. But before we begin, you will explain to me why you are so uneasy." She stood before him, refusing to move.

"Why . . . nothing, m'lady." He was avoiding her eyes. "This uneasiness you refer to is just one of my many flaws—"

"Stop right there, Mr. Howitt," she scolded quietly.

"The entire household is a wreck, and you know it. Has the king been invited without telling me?"

The young man's gaze met hers nervously.

"I am much easier to deal with when I am *told* what the problem is."

He let out an agitated breath. "The truth of it is, mum, the last time Baronsford was preparing a gathering of this magnitude was the day . . . well, the day of the accident."

Millicent should have guessed. With Lyon injured, and Emma dead, there was no reason to celebrate after that terrible day. And more than a few members of the household at Baronsford were probably feeling a little superstitious.

"In spite of the tragic events of that day," the secretary continued, "many of the guests who stayed on that night behaved in a fashion that was less than genteel."

"Whispering about what had happened?"

"Speaking openly of scandal," Howitt said flatly. "That is why we are all determined to make this night so perfect. Begging your pardon, we understand and support what you and his lordship are trying to do. At the same time, we would like to show these people that Baronsford has not suffered from the previous countess's death. We'd like to show them that since your arrival, we are faring even better than before. We should like these guests to see how fortunate we are to have you."

"I am honored, Mr. Howitt, by your words." Millicent fought back tears and tried to calm her emotions. "We shall all do our best. So let us, then, be off. We shall see to our mission here and be on our way back to Baronsford with plenty of time to ready ourselves. We shall be back before they expect us."

As she turned toward the muddy river, Millicent never imagined that so soon after speaking those words she would be forgetting the hour, the day, and the guests. Her lapse in memory came just as she came upon the cart belonging to the old woman, and asked about the girl Jo.

*   *   *

The burly, muddleheaded Earl of Dumfries had taken it on himself to show up far earlier than everyone else at Baronsford. After two hours of being closed up with him in the library, listening to the man's whining, Lyon was ready to pick up his favorite pistol and shoot him squarely between his squinty black eyes. He refrained, however, unwilling to ruin the library's handsome Persian carpet.

Though he was in large part responsible for much of the problem in the Borders, he sulkily argued that if Lyon were to speak tonight for the protection of the land and its tenants, then he would be unfairly represented as a villain before their peers.

Just as Lyon was about to tell the earl that he was a fat, jabbering mealworm, Walter Truscott appeared at the door. The rest of the guests were beginning to arrive, and Lord Aytoun still needed to get himself ready. He was surprised, though, when his cousin followed the servants who carried him up to his dressing room.

"What's wrong, Walter?" he asked.

"Millicent has not yet returned."

"Howitt is with her."

"I believe he is. We have seen no sign of the carriage or the servants or the two of them."

"Did you send someone to the riverbank?"

"An hour ago. No news yet," he said with a frown. "I am riding down there myself right now. I don't want you to worry about anything. I shall bring her back. She must have been distracted and lost track of the time."

"Go," Lyon snapped. "I need to know she is safe. I don't care a straw about the strutting popinjays coming here tonight. I care only about *her*, Walter. Bring my wife back."

The doctor that Millicent had sent Howitt to fetch from Melrose had come too late. Jo had died with her tiny, tartan-swaddled daughter in one arm while her other hand had clutched Millicent's.

The crowd of onlookers just stared. No one whispered

a word, and then most of them simply shook their heads and turned away. Millicent didn't attempt to mumble words of solace. It was a hard world, and they knew it well.

From the few whispered words the dying Jo had spoken before the end came, Millicent had pieced together an understanding of what had happened to the young woman. It was a story of suffering. It was a story of betrayal.

She was relieved when Truscott arrived. He knew what to do, and he took charge of the arrangements.

After what felt like a lifetime later, Millicent found herself standing on the muddy bank of the river, holding the sleeping bairn beneath her cloak while her people wrapped Jo's body and carried it up to the village kirk.

The old woman who had shared her cart with Jo stood next to Millicent. "Ye will take the bairn?"

"I believe that would be best."

"Aye. Part o' that lassie lives on through her bairn. I heard her. What she whispered to ye about her life. Mayhap someday the wee one'll find justice for her mither."

Perhaps someday. But not for a long time.

"Will you stay with us? Come back to Baronsford. You can be there and watch her as she grows."

The old woman shook her head. "Nay, but thank ye. I may just come back, though, to see how ye've done by her."

"You are always welcome," Millicent whispered.

She watched Truscott's solemn face as he came down the hill. She knew it was time to go.

In the carriage, Millicent pushed back the cloak and gazed at the baby's pale face. She admired the small tightly fisted hands. She would do right by the child. She and Lyon would both cherish her and raise her with their own.

Millicent nestled the bundle in her arm more snugly against her chest. There were so many things that she needed to tell her husband—about this new addition to their family, and about the other one that was growing inside her now. She could hardly wait until everyone was gone tonight.

"From the number of carriages and horses and grooms in the courtyard and down by the stables," Howitt said, peering out the carriage window through the fading afternoon light, "it looks as if most everyone has arrived."

Truscott frowned. "We can pull the carriage around to the side entrance if you wish. No one needs to know you have returned until you've had a chance to change."

"No," Millicent said. "We will go in the main entrance."

She expected an argument, but he surprised her by immediately relaying her wishes to the grooms.

"And everyone was hoping so desperately to avoid another scandal," she said to Howitt.

Walter Truscott leaned over and touched her hand. "I shouldn't worry too much about that, m'lady. You do as you wish and let them see what their greed is doing to innocent folk."

The carriage stopped before the impressive entrance of Baronsford. Truscott stepped out and assisted Millicent from the carriage. She could hear the whispers even before reaching the open doors. A few late arrivals stood just inside, shedding expensive cloaks and hats. Millicent looked down at her mud-stained cloak, at the boots caked with muck.

"I can find my way from here," she told Truscott before going up the steps.

As Millicent stepped inside to the bows of the surprised footmen, no introduction was made. Instead, an immediate hush fell over those who were gathered in the entrance hall. Then like a giant wave, the whispers rolled and spread into the other rooms, through great hall and the saloons and the ballroom. Then, like the calm before a storm, silence once again fell. Even the musicians in the ballroom ceased their playing.

Millicent stopped at the base of the great curved stairway and glanced at the place where Emma's portrait had hung. Then she turned and moved through the separating throngs of guests, looking for her husband.

She heard his voice, and then, just inside the doors of the great hall, Millicent saw Lyon. He was handsomer than any man she had ever seen in her life. She stopped a dozen paces from where he sat.

"I was by the river at the vagrant camp. At least fifty more families, with all their meager belongings piled on small carts or on their backs, came into the village. There is hunger, sickness, but they somehow retain their pride. They have nothing else."

Millicent's voice quavered but she continued to speak as if there were no one else there. She was talking only to Lyon.

"I was delayed in returning. Today we lost a young woman." She shook her head. "No, she was really little more than a child. Without a home, with none of her kin at her side, without anyone who loved her or knew her to help, she died on a stretch of mud on the bank of the river giving birth to this beautiful girl."

She gently pushed back the cloak to show the tiny infant in her arms.

"That was why I was late. I hope you understand."

Millicent pulled the cloak over the sleeping baby and, without looking back, went out through the hall and up the stairs.

By the time Millicent reached the top of the steps, her entire body was shaking. She could hear the voices of the guests as they all began to speak at once. Hurrying servants pulled the doors to her bedchamber shut behind her as sobs began to wrack her body in waves.

She didn't know what she had been thinking. She had made a fool out of herself before everyone who mattered. Mrs. MacAlister hastened into the room right behind her.

"I shall take care of this angel, m'lady. Ye must change." The housekeeper gently took the baby. Her soft words and gentle manner made Millicent cry even harder.

The servants' hands tugged at her clothes, undressing her and dressing her again, brushing her hair. Millicent endured it all in a daze. She wondered how Lyon was managing with the embarrassment of his new wife's behavior. How was he going to explain her to these people?

I hope you understand. She shuddered.

The dress they had pulled onto her had silver threads woven into the fabric. Millicent sat and watched skilled hands frantically trying to arrange her hair.

"One of the women in the kitchen is nursing her own bairn of two months," Mrs. MacAlister explained. "I think this wee one is just waking up. She'll be looking for some food, too, she will."

Millicent nodded gratefully to the housekeeper and watched the woman disappear out the door. All the tugging and pulling and arranging suddenly come to a halt, and they all stood back. She stared into the looking glass at the strangely familiar woman staring back at her.

Millicent slowly rose to her feet. The idea of walking out of this room and down those steps was terrifying.

There was a knock at the door, and someone opened it.

A hush fell over the room, and Millicent turned to see who was at the door.

It was Lyon, standing in the open doorway.

Her breath caught in her chest. Tears welled up in her eyes, blurring her vision, and she reached a hand toward him just as she felt the room around her begin to whirl.

Two servants caught Millicent just as her knees buckled beneath her. By the time she regained her senses, she had been conveyed to a settee and Lyon was beside her, growling orders at everyone. She sipped the wine that was being held to her lips.

"I'm fine." She took his hand and, despite his objections, pulled herself to her feet. "You're standing. You—"

"I wanted to surprise you, but I never thought I would frighten you like this, my love." His arms wrapped around her, drawing her against him.

"How? When?" The tears would not stop. "This must be a dream."

" 'Tis no dream. I shall explain everything later."

Millicent remembered the guests. She recalled the importance of the gathering. At the same time, she could not stop thinking of his legs supporting him. She held him tight, fearing he might fall, but she was the unsteady one at the moment. She took a deep breath. "We should be downstairs."

"Are you certain you are feeling better?"

"I am. I am indeed." She wiped the tears and took his arm. She was ready.

Chapter 31

As recently as a fortnight ago, Millicent would have considered this night a borrowed dream. A lifetime of doubt had been cast to the wind, though, as she had stood proudly beside her husband in the ballroom of Baronsford, discussing everything from politics to the living conditions of the vagrants to what might be done to improve their situation.

At times, Millicent had surprised herself. Here she was, speaking with such passion. She cared naught if the scrutinizing looks directed at her were critical or approving. She was happy with who she was and how she looked. What meant the most to her, though, was the fact that the most important person in that room, Lyon, was openly proud of her. For the first time in her life, she felt complete.

It was only after the rest of the guests had either retired or gone home that the earl of Dumfries—the first guest to arrive, according to Lyon—decided to leave. As his carriage rolled away from the door, Millicent sank against her husband's chest.

"You were magnificent," he whispered in her ear, his arms wrapped tightly around her.

"And *you* are standing." She looked up with amazement at him. "I still cannot believe it. Standing."

Lyon had not been able to climb the stairs. When he had appeared in the ballroom, standing beside his wife shortly after going up after her, though, word had spread with amazing speed through the assembled guests. Millicent had seen many staring as if they were witnessing a miraculous event. Others stood looking on in silent awe. Many of Baronsford's household staff came up to admire their laird's recovery, as well.

"And do not forget the steps I took, too."

Millicent hugged him fiercely, fighting back her tears. "I shall never forget that. But how long have you been hiding this from me?"

"The feeling in my limbs has been coming back slowly, and I was looking for the right opportunity when I could share with you something significant." He brushed a tear off her cheek. "Seeing you tonight coming in here with that bairn in your arms and facing these wolves so bravely, I could wait no longer. You taught me, showed me, this had to be the moment."

"I love you, Lyon." She kissed him. "I shall never forget this night."

When she pulled away, she saw him lean heavily on the cane he held. She quickly motioned Lyon's valets to bring in his chair.

"You are not putting me back into that."

"We shall only use it to manage the stairs for a while." She lowered her voice. "This is the quickest way to get you upstairs and to our bedroom."

"In that case"—a wicked grin broke onto his face— "there are other things about my recovery that I am looking forward to showing you."

Millicent blushed at his suggestive words.

Will and John positioned the chair behind Lyon. He handed the cane to Millicent and sat down without the aid of the valets. "When will I get a chance to meet the new addition to our family?"

This time Millicent could not hold back her tears. He understood. Without her having to ask, Lyon knew that they would be raising the child as their own. She walked ahead of his chair as they ascended the steps. "I checked on her once tonight. She was fed and sleeping. I shall ask Mrs. MacAlister to bring her to us if she is awake."

He nodded. "Have you named her?"

"I thought perhaps she should be called Josephine. Her mother's name was Jo."

"That is a beautiful name."

When they reached their apartments, Millicent went to her own dressing room, where Bess was waiting to get her ready for bed. Mrs. MacAlister sent word that the infant was asleep and it would be best to wait for the morning for his lordship to see the bairn. Millicent returned to their bedchamber to find the valets gone and Lyon already in bed. He had been told the housekeeper's recommendation.

"I suppose we should enjoy this night of sleep, as I can only imagine we shall have some sleepless nights with a bairn in the house."

"Will you mind it?"

He laughed and stretched a hand toward her in invitation. "I've been waiting a lifetime for this."

"Have you really?" Millicent removed her robe and climbed into the bed. "Do you really mean it? Do you want a child of our own?"

"A houseful of them! And I do not care how we get them, either." He pulled her close to him. "What hurt me most during the years that I was married to Emma was being separated from my family. I felt isolated, alone. After the accident on the cliff, I realized that my brothers had severed the last ties that bound us. They had moved away from me, and that cut me deeply." His hand cupped her face. "I have made a vow to mend that rift, if they will allow it."

"That is a good thing."

"But that is only a small part of what I dream of for the future."

"What else do you dream of?" she asked.

"Of making you happy. I love you, and I promise to do my best to make up for all the sadness of your past."

"You have already done that, love."

His fingers delved into her hair, and he brought her mouth to his. She cherished his tender touch and felt her body come alive. He peeled away her nightgown, and Millicent looked into his face.

"When you mentioned the houseful of children . . ." Her voice trailed off.

"I meant it. It matters naught how we get them," he repeated. "I will not have you worrying about heirs and other such nonsense. There are hungry bairns and orphans amongst the poor. There are those who need a home wandering tonight on the London streets. There are the children of Africans who have been stolen away from their homes who need families. We'll have no trouble filling up our house, I should think."

She pressed a finger against his lips. "And there is the one who is growing inside me now. Do you think we might raise this one amongst all the rest?"

It took a moment for her words to sink in, but then he was the one overwhelmed with emotion. His fingers threaded into her hair.

"Do you mean it? Right now?" His voice shook. "You are carrying our child now?"

Millicent nodded and wiped away the tear that trickled down his cheek. "Yes, my love. A part of the two of us is growing inside me right now."

"Tonight, when you became light-headed, I should have guessed there was something more than excitement. Our child!" He lifted her chin. "But how are you feeling? You are not eating properly. You are certainly not getting enough rest. Doctors. We have to find a good one to look after you. But . . . Ohenewaa! She can—"

"Stop," Millicent scolded with a smile. "You shall not fuss over me like this."

"I shall do as I wish. I intend to provide perfect care for my wife and bairn." Lyon rolled her on the bed until she lay beneath him. "Wait, this might not be a good position for you, bearing all my weight."

Millicent looped her arms around his neck and pulled him back to her.

"I shall tell you what is good for me," she said, silencing him with a kiss.

Chapter 32

Violet asked the groom to wait with the cart by the shops facing Knebworth Village's market square and walked up the hill toward the rectory. Mrs. Page's basket of baked goods for Mrs. Trimble hung from one arm. In the other, she carried a bundle of London newspapers she had been told she should leave with the new schoolmaster.

The morning sky promised to be clear, and the smoke from the breakfast fires and the fragrant smell of bread baking somewhere smelled domestic and good to her. Passing the blacksmith shop and the livery stable, Vi was startled by a woman who jumped at her from behind a cart, grabbing her arm. Violet immediately pulled her arm away and took a step back when she recognized her.

"Don't you dare talk to me."

"Please, I've something important to tell ye."

Violet stepped toward the middle of the street, turning away from her. The last time she had seen the wretch had been in Ned Cranch's bed at the inn.

"Please, Violet," the girl pleaded. "I know yer name's Violet, and ye work up at the Hall."

She reached for her arm again, but Violet shook her off. "Get away from me, I'm telling you."

"He's coming back," she hissed, looking around nervously. "And he means to do something wicked out there at Melbury Hall."

The warning cut through Violet's anger. She took a few more steps toward the rectory before she stopped and glanced over her shoulder. The young woman was standing by a carriage in the yard of the livery stable. She was watching Violet.

Glancing up and down the street at the few people who were moving about, Violet backtracked to the miserable creature.

"If you're lying, I swear . . ." The words withered on Violet's tongue as the young woman pulled away the shawl around her neck, showing Vi the black and purple bruises there.

"He was better to me than he was to ye. At least folks won't see these unless I show them myself." She covered up the marks again. "He almost choked me to death, though. The bastard. He was just using me. Using us."

Vi did not want to feel any sympathy toward the woman, but she could not help herself. Ned was the one at fault. They were just two simpletons who managed to fall victim to his charm. How many others were there? she thought. "Why did he do this to you?"

"Because I wanted to know why he wanted me to take him to Melbury Hall." The young woman's voice quavered. "He said 'twas none of my business, and if I didn't do as he wanted and keep my trap shut, he'd kill me."

"When is he coming back?" Violet asked.

"Tonight." The girl's eyes scanned the street again. "He told me he's coming back before supper, and I should take my pa's cart. Says I'm to hide him under a tarp in the back with the iron bars and casks of tacks I take up from my pa's smithy to the Hall every fortnight or so. He wants to get to yer place around dinner, so's he can slip out when we get there, and no one will see him. He's up to no good, I just know it. But I don't know what to do about it."

"Do you know where he is now?"

"St. Albans. I think he's staying in the tavern where he always goes to—the one out by the brickyards."

Violet looked up the street and saw the wagon from Solgrave that carted milk to St. Albans every morning. She knew the driver. Shoving the basket and piles of newspapers into the woman's hands, she quickly gave her directions what to do with them. "After you're done, tell the groom waiting by the shops that I had to go to St. Albans. Tell him they should watch out for trouble tonight."

"I can't tell them nothing about Ned. He'll kill me."

"You just tell the man what I told you and leave Ned's name out of it. I'll take care of the stonemason. Be sure to tell them to watch out for trouble coming their way."

Without another word, Violet hurried to catch up to the wagon rolling down the village street.

At noon on the final day of traveling, Lyon reached out to help his wife climb into the chaise. After stopping to warm up at a wayside inn, she had reluctantly handed the infant, Josephine, back to the nursemaid riding in the carriage behind.

"I've uprooted everyone," she said again. "And so soon after our arrival at Baronsford."

"You did not. We had planned on being away only a fortnight." He pulled her next to him on the seat. "We have done everything we could possibly do at Baronsford . . . for now."

"Walter Truscott told me before we left that the mood among the tenants is much improved. He says there even appears to be progress on some of the other estates."

Lyon entwined their fingers. "Unfortunately, all of these could come to an abrupt end when some other landlord decides to clear his land. The people's confidence is fragile. With good reason."

Millicent's voice was hesitant. "Truscott also told me that I should encourage you to get in touch with your brother Pierce. Since you signed those documents some months ago, the possibility exists that he might decide to go against your wishes and sell the properties . . . or even clear the land himself."

"Pierce would never do that to Baronsford," Lyon replied confidently. "But I do need to reach him. I just wish that this first attempt to communicate with him did not have to involve the business of land and inheritance."

Lyon needed to think seriously about how to approach his brother. He didn't care a rush about getting back the properties. The last thing he wanted was to have Pierce merely send back a signed document, reversing everything. More important, Lyon wanted his brother back.

Millicent placed a kiss on his clenched jaw, and he smiled at her upturned face.

"You shall do what's right," she said. "I have faith in you."

Violet stood in a dark corner of the tavern and watched him.

The place was packed with men, and a traveling fiddler sat on a stool in the corner, sawing away feverishly at a jig, his battered hat in front of him with a couple of dull copper coins peeking imploringly from it. The men in the room were singing and roaring with laughter as two drunken brickmakers danced in a circle, jostling those nearby in their hilarity and drawing shoves in return.

Ned had one hand around a cup of ale and his other arm around a buxom wench. As Vi watched him, she realized he didn't look quite so handsome to her. His features were thick, his limbs heavy, and his movements jerky. His eyes glittered from the drinking.

He was supposedly going back to Knebworth Village in a couple of hours. The question of what no-good he was up to gnawed at her.

When Ned's attention was drawn to the door of the crowded tavern room, Violet looked at the half-dozen rough-looking men who all entered together. Behind them she saw Jasper Hyde's clerk, the same one who had been sent up to Melbury Hall a number of times. She drew back when she saw a swarthy gentleman enter behind the clerk. He had to be Jasper Hyde, she decided. Leaning on his cane, the man motioned the group to a corner, where Ned joined them.

Violet moved closer, keeping to the shadows along the wall. She could hear snatches of the conversation over the din of the room.

"Ye all stay in the Grove until you see the flames coming from the house," Ned barked. "Harry and the master here both know what we are after. As soon as they point her out to ye, make a grab for her and head out again toward the Grove. We shan't be using any roads getting out of there."

Fear gripped Violet's stomach as Ned continued to talk. They were going to steal Ohenewaa, and they were going to burn Melbury Hall to do it. Violet pushed away from the wall, not knowing how to stop them, and yet knowing somehow that she had to try.

The noise in the room was getting louder. More people were coming in. Violet could not even hear herself think. Ned looked to be through with his talking, and the men were ordering ale and talking amongst themselves. She saw him say something to Jasper Hyde and motion to the ceiling. As Ned got up to leave, however, an eager wench latched onto his arm.

Violet realized he was going up to his room. The stairs. She remembered vividly the dark corridor. Her gaze searched the room and came to rest on a man stretched out on a battered settle near her. In spite of the ruckus, he was snoring away with his mouth wide open. The blade of his knife glinted beside his hand.

She walked toward him with purpose. The man didn't stir at all when she took the knife and hid it under her cloak.

Violet looked over her shoulder and found Ned had succeeded in shedding the woman. He was heading toward the door leading to the stairs, and Hyde was giving orders to his clerk and the other men. Pushing her way through the crowded room, she hurried out ahead of the stonemason.

The narrow hall at the base of the stairs was dark, with the exception of a little light coming in from the tavern. Violet moved into the shadows and waited. Her fingers clutched the handle of the knife. Ned's large frame broke through the light. He walked toward the stairs, and Violet stepped out.

"Ned."

He turned, his surprised expression quickly giving way to anger. "What the devil are ye doing here? Following me again, are ye? Can't get enough, ye silly chit? Well, I'm through with ye."

"This is not about me, Ned." She came closer. "You cannot destroy Melbury Hall. Too many people's lives depend on that place."

"Ha!"

"I have a little money, Ned. If that's why you're doing this, I'll give it all to you."

Understanding made his eyes glint in the dark. "Bugger off, slut. What I'm going to make out of this job, ye shan't be dreaming of making in yer lifetime."

"He wants Ohenewaa. He is daft to think she's a witch. That's all a lie. Don't ruin so many lives because of some nonsense."

"What do I care? She's a filthy slave." He towered over her, and then his face changed as a thought occurred to him. "And ye're a greedy whore. Ye came here because ye want yer cut, don't ye? Ye heard I'm using my other woman to help me, and ye don't like it that I didn't ask ye."

"No. I'm here to stop you from doing the wrong thing. From hurting good people. You cannot—"

Violet winced in pain as Ned grabbed a fistful of her cloak and hair and jerked her about. "I think ye fancy those slaves, especially that stupid one, Moses. That's why ye want to save them. Ye filthy whore. Admit it. Ye fancy the thought of letting them—"

With all her strength, she drove the knife upward into his chest. His hand on her hair tightened. He took a step back, stumbling as he dragged her with him.

"The black bastards."

"You are the bastard," she hissed into his face. "And yes, I choose their lives over yours. And even over my own."

Vi jerked the knife upward, and he stumbled again,

falling backward against a wall but still taking Violet
with him. When he struck the wall, she felt the knife
sink deeper. His eyes went glassy, and his knees buckled
under his weight. As Ned sank slowly to the floor, Violet
went down with him. Small bubbles of blood appeared
at the corner of his mouth, and his breathing stopped
with a single shudder. His grip eased on her hair.

"Ride 'im good, lass." A drunkard laughed and
slapped Vi on the side of the head as he stumbled by in
the narrow hall and started up the stairs.

Violet's fingers uncoiled from the hilt of the knife. As
she stood up from his lap, she saw the dark stain of the
blood on the front of Ned's smock. She took a step back
and stared at the man she had once thought she loved—
at the father of the child growing inside of her. Violet
pulled the cloak tightly around her and stepped into the
merry commotion in the tavern.

There were people all around, but their faces were all
blurred. She had killed a man. The wailing sound in her
head blocked out the music, the shouts. She pushed her
way out of the tavern and onto the street.

The air was fresh and clean, and as she started up the
street, her mind suddenly grew clear. There was no way
she could make it back to Melbury Hall in time. She
had warned them. She had done what she could.

Her only path now led away from here. She had to
go someplace far enough away that she wouldn't bring
shame down on her mother and grandmother. Or on
Melbury Hall. The thought of leaving them, of never
seeing them again, sent a shaft of hot steel through her
heart. But she had no choice. She could not shame them.

At another inn just up the alley on High Street, the
daily mail coach was preparing to leave St. Albans. The
driver was climbing up and the team of horses snorted
and stamped impatiently in the cold air. Vi stopped and
counted her money. Ten shillings and a few pence.

It was enough to take her away from St. Albans, at
least. And when the coach would take her no farther,
she would just walk from there as far as her legs would
carry her.

Chapter 33

"I am always complaining about people arriving unexpectedly at Melbury Hall and here I have done the same thing to you," Millicent said as a way of apology to the housekeeper.

Mrs. Page and Gibbs had been racing around for the past two hours and had succeeded in settling everyone new who had come back from Baronsford. "We started a couple of days earlier than we had planned and never sent a rider ahead to warn you."

Mary looked adoringly at the baby in Millicent's arms. "You bring back this kind of joy to the house, m'lady, and you think we'd mind an army of guests? Not at all. May I hold the little darling?"

She handed the sleeping Jo to the housekeeper. This had been the same kind of reaction she had received from everyone. The dowager, Ohenewaa, Amina, even Gibbs. So far Sir Richard had been excluded from holding the infant, since he had been sequestered in the library, discussing some business affairs with her husband. "By the way, where is Violet?"

"She went to the village this morning on an errand, and then ran off to St. Albans."

"To see her mother and grandmother?"

"I don't believe so, m'lady." An anxious look crossed Mrs. Page's face. "The groom she went to the village with this morning said she'd sent a message about trouble coming our way. He said that Violet went on to St. Albans to see Ned Cranch."

"The stonemason?"

"Aye, the missing stonemason. He left in the middle of his job, right after you and his lordship went to Scotland. Mr. Gibbs can tell you everything else about it. But there have been some strange doings with that man . . . and I am afraid Violet is involved with him."

"How?" Millicent asked worriedly. "He is a married man, is he not?"

"He might be, m'lady, but I don't think our Violet knew ar~ `hing about it when he started courting her."

"W̖. ̖ was this?"

Millicent could hardly believe what she was hearing as Mary went on to tell her that as far back as Christmastide, Ned Cranch had been wooing Violet at every opportunity.

"Violet hasn't been feeling well, either," Mary whispered. "I am only guessing, but I'm starting to think she might have gotten herself into trouble."

Millicent remembered the bruise on the young woman's face and her inability to hold down food. "Will you look after the baby while I go and talk to Mr. Gibbs? I want someone to go to St. Albans after her."

"Of course, m'lady."

Everyone made mistakes in life. But after holding Jo's hand and watching the young mother die after childbirth, Millicent was not going to allow another young woman to be lost to the world. She knew Violet would not go to her mother's house. She wouldn't want to bring disgrace to their doorstep.

No, Millicent had to bring her back to Melbury Hall.

Jasper Hyde could tell the London men were becoming restless. They stood in a circle a distance from him, leaning on their cudgels and shooting quick glances his way as they muttered together. Night had already fallen. Through the break in the trees, they had seen that a number of carriages and riders had recently arrived at the Hall.

As the hours passed, the danger of a watchman or

dogs discovering their hiding place was becoming more likely. And still there was no sign of Ned Cranch.

"Blasted cowardly braggart!" Jasper Hyde cursed under his breath.

"I thought he left the tavern before us," Harry complained in his ear.

The last Hyde had seen of the stonemason, he was going up to his room. Burning sensations and a squeezing pain filled the cavity of his chest, and Jasper Hyde thought of a dozen different ways he would make the stonemason suffer if he did not appear soon.

Hyde had considered staying behind at St. Albans and letting those whom he had paid so handsomely finish the job. But the nagging feeling that something might go wrong—that like so many other recent instances his damnable luck might turn on him—had persuaded him to come along. Now at least he was satisfied with that decision. He would carry this through no matter what the danger. No matter what happened to Cranch.

One of the men he had sent to spy on the house came running back. "No sign of 'im. And no sign of any cart comin' from the village. But I couldn't get inside the stables, in case the rockhead might be hidin' there."

"Any place closer to the house to hide?" Hyde asked.

"There's the stable, but there are a couple of grooms still seeing to the horses. And the carriages are out front. They'll be bringin' them around soon. There's gardens in the back of the house and by the servants' door."

The pain was getting sharper, and Hyde knew time was running short. He called the men together. "You two go to the front and keep watch there. You four come with me to the back of the manor house. Harry, you set fire to these cottages."

The clerk looked around at the circle of decrepit buildings.

"Once you are through here, go to the back of the stables and set fire to them, too."

"Now ye're talkin'," one of the men said with a grin. "We come fer action."

Holding the pistol in one hand, Hyde had to put all his weight on the cane to keep up with the others moving through the woods. He was having trouble breathing. Fatigue was wrapping a tight fist around his chest. A pain in his head was clouding his vision as they got closer to the house. Suddenly he saw a shadow run ahead of them in the woods. But as he looked again, he saw nothing. His mind was playing tricks.

"The little bugger did it," one of his men said over his shoulder. The crackle and spark of flames could be heard rising from the Grove through the winter wood. Hyde tried to hurry to keep up with everyone else. Somewhere ahead the shouts of warning about the fire could be heard.

The pain stabbed him again in the chest. He saw the shadow pass closer to his left. He realized who it was. But it couldn't be.

"Tano," he whispered.

"D'ye say something?" The man closest to him turned around.

"No, go on. Look for an old black woman as they come out of the house." Hyde's mind was giving way to strange thoughts. Uncontrollably, he was crossing the great divide of many years. He remembered a night like this. He was a child, running barefoot with his friend through the meadow above the canefields. With Tano.

The edge of the woods lay ahead of them. More shouts came from the vicinity of the stables. Harry had reached there as well.

The pain in his chest and his head was unbearable, but he pushed on. There was a rustling sound in the trees to his right. He lifted his pistol and turned sharply. He was there, as clear as day. Tano was hanging in irons, left to die. His dark eyes were open and accusing.

Hyde backed away and tried to run, but his feet were too heavy, and he stumbled to his knees. One of the London men stood over him.

"Damn you, Ohenewaa!" he cursed into the night, shaking off the man's hand. He pushed himself to his feet, clutching his chest with one hand.

Through the remaining fringe of trees, he could see people pouring out of the house. Servants were running in every direction and shouting. Horses, freed from their stalls, were running about wildly.

Hyde stopped by the edge of the trees and stared at the chaos. Tano, named after a sacred river in the western lands of the Ashanti, was two years younger than Jasper in age. They gave him the Christian name Thomas, but his name was Tano. From the time they were young boys, he had surpassed Jasper in size and strength and courage. None of this mattered, though, for he was black and Jasper was white. Tano was a slave and Jasper would someday be his master. But for as many things that set them apart, there were others that made them the same. As children they thought the same, dreamed alike, tolerated each other . . . and though no one spoke of it, they shared the same father.

"I don't see no old woman," one of the men said into Hyde's ear.

"Find your way up to the house without being seen. Set it on fire, and she will have to . . ." His words trailed off.

Amidst the smoke and mayhem, Jasper saw Ohenewaa walking toward them. There was no doubting it; she had seen them, but she was still coming.

After their father, Rufus, had passed away, Tano had become more openly rebellious. With every problem in the slave quarters, Jasper had seen evidence of Tano's involvement. He could look away only so long. But even after Jasper began to have him punished for his transgressions, the slave had only become stronger.

The pain in his chest was spreading. His hands were shaking, but Hyde dropped the cane and wrapped his fingers tightly around the pistol.

Last year, during one of the slave uprisings, Hyde had reached the end of his patience. One of his bailiffs had been killed. Three other white men had been injured. Over two dozen slaves had escaped to the western forests of the island. It was all he could take. He had ordered Tano to be hung in irons.

Ohenewaa continued to walk toward him. This close, he could see the woman's eyes flashing angrily in the dark. He stepped out of the woods and raised the pistol until it was pointed directly at her heart. Tano had died, and she had cursed him.

"You must die, witch."

A woman screamed from somewhere to his right, and he turned his head. Out of the corner of his eye, he saw someone standing beside him. Tano. And at that moment he felt the pain explode in his chest even as he heard the crack of a pistol firing.

Millicent saw Jasper Hyde go down on his knees, and she turned to see Lyon lowering the gun. A half-dozen grooms raced past her toward a retreating group of men. To her left, Moses had Hyde's clerk by the scruff of his neck, and Gibbs was running down from the stables. She turned her attention back to Ohenewaa and saw her crouching over the bloody body of Jasper Hyde.

Millicent rushed toward them and knelt beside the old woman. Lyon approached and kicked Hyde's pistol to the side.

Hyde's breathing was labored. His eyes were open, but there was a hole in his chest near his heart. "He's here. He wants to take me with him."

Ohenewaa sat in silence.

"I cannot bear the pain. The heat of the branding iron . . . is scorching my breast. Do you hear them . . . the sound of chains?" A tear escaped the man's eyes. "You cursed me, woman."

"This is Tano's curse."

"Release me," he whispered, the words barely escaping his lips. "Please . . . let me live . . . help me."

She placed a hand above the open wound on his heart. " 'Tis too late."

"Then . . . forgive me." Hyde's eyes looked up into space. "Please, Tano . . . forgive me."

Millicent saw a tear drop from Ohenewaa's face onto his chest. The old woman's hand stretched out over the dying man's head. "He forgives. Go now."

Hyde's breathing stopped and his eyes glazed over. The old woman closed the lids and touched the man's forehead. Millicent sat beside her until Ohenewaa turned to her.

"Who was Tano?" Millicent asked.

"My son," she said, looking back at the dead man. "Tano was my son."

Epilogue

"You should write a letter to your sons."

The dowager peered over the tops of her spectacles. "I thought you said you were not getting involved with my problems."

"I am not." Ohenewaa put the basket of new greenery on the stone bench beside her and glared at her friend. "But you should know that I consider you a stubborn woman."

"And why is that?"

"You have the power to put an end to all the trouble between these three boys."

"They are not boys, but men. They started their disagreement, and they should finish it."

"You are helpless . . . and blind, too . . . and pigheaded. And if you don't do something to help your son with his brothers—"

"You shall cast a spell on me?"

"I do not know any spells."

"Then show me how to do some other magic."

Ohenewaa's dark eyes narrowed. "Not that I know anything about the dark arts, but even if I had that kind of knowledge, I would never entrust it to *you*."

"What if I promised to do some good with it?"

"Such as?"

The dowager shrugged. "Maybe I shall use it to find perfect wives for Pierce and David, as I did for Lyon. Never mind any letters. Marriage is the way to bring them back again to the family."

"You underestimate your shrewdness, old woman. And Sir Richard's hard work. You managed all of this before with no magic."

"But I am getting old, and my days are numbered. And I am weak."

"You might save that idle talk for your family. It does not work with me. I know there is nothing wrong with you."

"I still believe you know about those dark arts. You are just an ornery old witch and holding out on me just to be spiteful."

"And I believe you should take less snuff in the morning. Now, start with small steps. Write Pierce a letter and have it delivered at the same time as Lyon's. Then you need to start working on your youngest son. What is his name?"

"David. Perhaps. I shall think about it."

The dowager took a deep breath of fragrant spring air. She admired the flowers that were springing out of the ground in every corner of the garden. Mrs. Page and Gibbs were pretending that they were looking intently at a rose arbor at the lower end of the garden, but she knew better. Gibbs was still as gruff as ever, but there was a certain boyish spring that had recently begun to appear in his step. It was love; no doubt about it.

The dowager's gaze was drawn to two young servants shaking out linens by the house.

"Has there been any more news of Violet?" Ohenewaa asked.

"No, they didn't find her in St. Albans. Millicent is still upset over it."

"At least she did not run off with the stonemason."

"Indeed, but what an ignoble fate he met with, to be murdered by some drunk in a tavern."

"He deserved it," Ohenewaa stated.

Again both women fell silent, content to watch the activities of the people coming and going around the manor. Lyon and Millicent were walking along the garden path. He was still using the cane, but his legs were getting stronger every day. She was carrying the baby.

"Perhaps they'll bring her here, so we could hold her," Ohenewaa said, a note of hopefulness in her voice.

"That baby is a perfect lady. And I even like the name Josephine."

"Joseph was the prophet sold into slavery, was he not?"

"He was."

Ohenewaa nodded with satisfaction. "It shall be a challenge when their own baby arrives this fall. Two infants in the house."

"That's what they have us for. To help them."

"Do you plan to stay that long?"

"I am, if you are." The dowager laughed, watching Ohenewaa's face crease into a frown.

Millicent heard the laughter, and she glanced over her shoulder at the dowager and Ohenewaa. The two women were involved in one of their daily disputes.

"It might kill them to admit it, but they really like each other," Lyon said, following the direction of her gaze. He laid his cane aside and sat down on a nearby stone bench. "Can I hold her now?"

She smiled and handed the baby to him before sitting down beside them. The swallows had returned, and a number of them were flitting and swooping about the chimneys. She glanced toward the path that led from the Grove, where once the slaves had lived. They had pulled down what remained of the huts after the fire. Construction on new cottages had already begun on higher ground. The damage to the stables had been small, and the repair work had already been accomplished.

Life was changing, Millicent thought. Buds of flowers and leaves were appearing on the trees. The fields were growing greener, and daffodils were poking their heads up along the walls and paths. Laughter, happiness, and contentment surrounded them. Melbury Hall was alive again.

She glanced back at her husband.

Josephine's small head was nestled against his chest.

His large hand was gently caressing the baby's back. His blue eyes were loving when they met hers.

"Next year at this time, I'll have two of them nestled here."

"Who ever would have imagined such a thing?" she whispered, smiling at the vision of her own dream.

Author's Note

As you might have guessed by now, *Borrowed Dreams* is the first in a trilogy of books about the men of Baronsford. While Pierce and David search out their own lives, they are subsequently drawn back to their home, where the mystery of Emma's murder waits to be solved.

Millicent Gregory Wentworth was first introduced to our readers in *The Promise*, where Rebecca Neville and the Earl of Stanmore forged a future together. We hope the change wrought in Millicent since meeting her in *The Promise* has provided a satisfying journey for you all.

As with all of our novels, with this book we have tried to depict a place and a time in a way that mingles the real and the imagined in an entertaining way. The issue of slavery in England and in the sugar islands of the West Indies is one that we have introduced in our earlier work. We hoped to give our readers another glimpse, through the eyes of Ohenewaa, of the trauma that innocents suffered throughout centuries of injustice. Many authors contributed unknowingly to our account of the slave trade through their work. We'd like to thank James Pope-Hennessy for his work *Sins of the Fathers: The Atlantic Slave Traders*, and Marcus Wood for his *Blind Memory: Visual Representations of Slavery in England and America*.

The Highland clearances were only touched upon in this book. In the following stories about the men and women of Baronsford, we will enjoy together more of the history of Scotland as it unfolds.

Finally, we'd like to acknowledge, with gratitude, the hard work of the many people at NAL who contribute to our books—Hilary Ross, John Paine, the production staff, as well as those in marketing and sales. Thank you all.

As always, we love to hear from our readers.

May McGoldrick
P.O. Box 665
Watertown, CT 06795
mcgoldmay@aol.com
www.maymcgoldrick.com

*Japan as
Number One*

Japan as
Number One
Lessons for America

Ezra F. Vogel

HARPER TORCHBOOKS
HARPER & ROW, PUBLISHERS
NEW YORK, CAMBRIDGE, PHILADELPHIA, SAN FRANCISCO
LONDON, MEXICO CITY, SÃO PAULO, SINGAPORE, SYDNEY

A hardcover edition of this book is published by Harvard University Press. It is here reprinted by arrangement.

JAPAN AS NUMBER ONE. Copyright © 1979 by the President and Fellows of Harvard College. All rights reserved. Printed in the United States of America. No part of this book may be used or reproduced in any manner whatsoever without written permission except in the case of brief quotations embodied in critical articles and reviews. For information address Harvard University Press, 79 Garden Street, Cambridge, Mass. 02138. Published simultaneously in Canada by Fitzhenry & Whiteside Limited, Toronto.

First HARPER TORCHBOOKS edition published 1985.

Library of Congress Cataloging-in-Publication Data

Vogel, Ezra F.
    Japan as number one.

    (Harper torchbooks)
    Reprint. Originally published: Cambridge, Mass. : Harvard University Press, 1979.
    Bibliography: p.
    Includes index.
    1. Japan—Social conditions—1945–   . 2. Japan—Economic conditions—1945–   . 3. Japan—Politics and government—1945–   . I. Title.
[HN723.5.V63 1985]   306′.0952   85-27227
ISBN 0-06-132055-2 (pbk.)

86 87 88 MPC 13 12 11 10

To David, Steven, and Eva
May they live in a better America

Preface

IN 1958, fresh with a Ph.D. from Harvard University in Social Relations, I set out as a social scientist seeking generalizations about the family and mental health that would hold true cross-culturally. I chose Japan not because I was a Japan specialist, for my ignorance was vast, but because Japan of all the modern countries seemed most different and hence the most critical for testing hypotheses about modern society. I was convinced that to make meaningful statements about the family and mental health in Japan I first had to become immersed in Japanese life. By the time my wife and I had been engulfed in two years of language study, research, and Japanese-style living apart from foreigners, I found myself far more interested in Japan itself than in social science generalizations. In my field work report, *Japan's New Middle Class*, I tried to delve into the inner life of Japanese families who were first our research subjects and later our friends, leaving generalizations to others.

For the next two decades I could not satiate my curiosity about Japanese society. I went to Japan almost every year, continued to revisit old friends, read the research reports of others, and kept reorganizing my thoughts each time I taught my course on Japanese society at Harvard. New mysteries,

new subtleties, new dimensions of Japan kept appearing, and its constant change was a seemingly inexhaustible gold mine for intellectual curiosity.

In the last several years, however, I have found myself, like other Americans, increasingly preoccupied with what is happening in America, with the decline of our confidence in government, with our difficulty in coping with problems such as crime, urban disorganization, unemployment, inflation, and government deficits. When I first returned to the United States from Japan in 1960, I had not even questioned the general superiority of American society and American institutions. In almost every field we were substantially ahead of Japan, our capacity for research and creativity was unexcelled, and our natural and human resources seemed more than adequate. By 1975 I found myself, like my Japanese friends, wondering what had happened to America.

In the meantime the country I originally chose to study for other reasons had become extraordinarily successful. Japan still does not have the world's largest gross national product, nor is it the leading country in the world politically or culturally. Yet the more I observed Japan's success in a variety of fields, the more I became convinced that given its limited resources, Japan has dealt more successfully with more of the basic problems of postindustrial society than any other country. It is in this sense, I have come to believe, that the Japanese are number one.

Astounded by recent Japanese successes, I found myself wondering why Japan, without natural resources, was making substantial progress in dealing with problems which seemed so intractable in America. Convinced that Japan had lessons for other countries, I was no longer content to look at Japan only as a fascinating intellectual mystery. I wanted to understand the success of the Japanese in dealing with practical questions. My first inclination was to examine how such Japanese virtues

as hard work, patience, self-discipline, and sensitivity to others contributed to their success. But the more I examined the Japanese approach to modern organization, the business community, and the bureaucracy, the more I became convinced that Japanese success had less to do with traditional character traits than with specific organizational structures, policy programs, and conscious planning. For several years I have been wrestling with the problem of understanding Japan's successes, and this book is the result of my intellectual labors.

I have wondered why it is that the full scope of Japanese successes has not been presented more forcefully to the American people, especially since the most knowledgeable American business, government, and academic specialists on Japan are so acutely aware of them. I have concluded that the answer is deceptively simple. Most Japanese understate their successes because they are innately modest, and more purposive Japanese, wanting to rally domestic forces or to reduce foreign pressures, have chosen to dramatize Japan's potential disasters. On the American side, our confidence in the superiority of Western civilization and our desire to see ourselves as number one make it difficult to acknowledge that we have practical things to learn from Orientals. I am convinced that it is a matter of urgent national interest for Americans to confront Japanese successes more directly and consider the issues they raise.

Since my message departs from conventional wisdom about matters of great importance, it is vulnerable to criticism. Some will say I have seen Japan only through rose-colored glasses, that I can see harmony but not conflict, that I think more of the privileged than the underprivileged, that I am concerned with efficiency but not democracy, that I underestimate the difficulty of borrowing from a different culture, and that my faith in America is wanting. I hope the reader will conclude that I make no effort to conceal Japan's difficulties, but the aim of this work is not to present a rounded, balanced

picture of how Japanese society works and how the individual is shaped. Its purpose is to describe selected aspects of the Japanese national system that are so effective that they contain lessons for America. Japan has many institutions America would not want to copy, and these will be mentioned. The successes Japan does have come at a price, and the price needs to be considered. Japan is by no means a utopia and to some extent shares the full range of problems found in every modern society. If at times my description of Japanese practices sounds like a model rather than an empirical description with all its complexities, distortions, and imperfections, it is not because I desire to idealize Japan but rather because I wish to elucidate the essential features of a model we might consider for adoption. The desirable features of the Japanese system are often based on cultural traits different from our own which are not easily adopted, but deep structural changes are possible, as the Japanese proved in borrowing from the West. If anything, this book is written because of faith in America, a faith that we do not shirk difficult problems, that we will not be satisfied to hide behind "the American way" to preserve indefinitely undesirable remnants of the past, and that we can make necessary adaptations, even if they fly in the face of once-conventional wisdom and require learning lessons from people we had not regarded as mentors.

I am indebted to the following people for helpful comments on the manuscript: Walter L. Ames, Hans Baerwald, David Bayley, John C. Campbell, Robert E. Cole, Albert C. Craig, William G. Cummings, Richard Dyck, Glen Fukushima, William L. Givins, Nathan Glazer, Andrew C. Gordon, Carl Green, Thomas Hout, Charlotte Ikels, Robert Immerman, Alan Jehlin, Eugene J. Kaplan, Yoshio Karita, Donald Klein, Thomas Lifson, George C. Lodge, David MacEachron, Gary Marx, Terry C. McDougall, Michael McMullen, James C. Morley, Richard Neustadt, Kazuo Nukazawa, Daniel C. Oki-

moto, T. J. Pempel, David Plath, Lee Rainwater, Martin Rein, Edwin O. Reischauer, David Riesman, Thomas Rohlen, Patricia Steinhof, Katsuhiko Suetsugu, Keizo Takemi, Ray Vernon, David Vogel, Donald Warwick, and John Wheeler. I am especially indebted to George C. Lodge for his stimulating discussions of American business and to Manabu Hara, Yoichi Funahashi, Suzanne H. Vogel, Nicole Seligman, and Anna Laura Rosow for cooperation in research. I am indebted to countless numbers of Japanese friends for offering their help, especially to Tsutomu Ouchi, Seizaburo Sato, and Yoichi Miyazawa. I am indebted to Aida Donald and Susan Wallace for editorial advice and assistance.

Contents

PART ONE

The Japanese Challenge

I

A Mirror for America

IN 1976 WE AMERICANS celebrated our bicentenary with fitting fanfare, but we let the year pass without seriously reflecting on the suitability of our institutions for the next century. Our press and television have dramatized the difficult problems our nation is straining to contain, but they offer little analysis. We know that institutions that once served us well are now less effective, but it is more manageable and certainly more interesting to personalize the cause, to attack someone's corruption or secrecy or his failure to provide proper leadership, than to search for institutional alternatives. Our response is to make a new proposal, enact a new regulation, or bring in a new charismatic figure to clean up some organization, quickly.

We are at a loss to understand why these efforts are not more successful. Public-spirited politicians, although sensitive to the inadequacies of government, must respond to short-range political pressures, having no mandate to consider fundamental changes. Business leaders are acutely aware of the increasingly complex problems created by the political, social, and economic environment surrounding the traditional business arena, but they have neither the leisure nor the organization to respond to them. Academics, falling victim to their own specialization

and having little personal experience in management, are inadequately prepared to confront problems which are in essence systemic and holistic.

One of the best vantage points for looking at our institutions, for reexamining our assumptions and considering alternatives, is from another place that faces similar problems but finds different solutions. As world leadership is shared by more countries, we will have more to learn by studying their successes. Of these other countries, Japan, the world's second largest economy, a modern democratic nation with a free enterprise system similar to our own, offers us the best perspective.

Considering the nature and scope of Japan's successes, it is remarkable how little interest Americans have shown in profiting from the Japanese example. As Japanese institutions begin to function more effectively than foreign ones, many Japanese now return from foreign study tours discouraged that they found so little to learn, but they still scour the world for useful lessons or hints of lessons. Where American institutions lag behind, America is still unprepared to learn from countries outside Europe. Japan is studied by some Americans as a fascinating culture with an interesting history, a subtle literature, intriguing customs, and profound religious thought. But those who seek to learn from Japan are from the world of culture, not from the world of affairs. It is perhaps understandable that the Japanese, in the habit of looking abroad for things to learn, continue studying, while Americans in the world of affairs, in the habit of teaching the rest of the world, find it difficult to assume the posture of the student, even when such indifference to or casual dismissal of foreign success blinds us to useful lessons.

Japanese institutions provide a particularly illuminating mirror for America for several reasons. For one, Japan, unlike Western countries, has consciously examined and restructured

all traditional institutions on the basis of rational considerations. America's political system was designed almost two hundred years ago for a premodern agricultural society, and it has not undergone any consciously designed major reorganizations since then. New institutions have grown up piecemeal, with no overall conceptualization of their desirability. Japanese institutions have undergone two major explicit reexaminations in the past 110 years to determine which institutions were desirable. In 1868 Japan began a two-decade-long study of the best institutions in the world in each sector: government, business, education, military, and the arts. After World War II, under the direction of the Allied Occupation, Japan again undertook a basic revamping of institutions to make them more democratic and more effective. Although the Occupation ended in 1952, the Japanese continued reorganizing for several more years, particularly in commerce and industry, which had not yet modernized when the Occupation ended. In both the late-nineteenth and mid-twentieth centuries Japanese leaders attempted to select institutions appropriate for a country in their circumstances and with their cultural tradition. The resulting institutions more closely resemble foreign models than those of traditional Japan, but Japanese leaders endeavored to select the best models and then to make additional improvements. In preparation for this selection, Japan developed specialists who analyzed the strengths and weaknesses of comparable institutions in each modern country; no country is more experienced in evaluating the effectiveness of existing institutions and in creating or reshaping institutions by rational planning to meet future needs. By looking at Japan we can make use of this detailed evaluation of modern institutions.

A second reason why Japan is a useful mirror is that of all the fully industrialized democratic countries, Japan, as the only non-Western one, is the most distinctive. One should not overstate its uniqueness: many of the practices to be discussed

in this work can be found to some extent in Europe, Canada, or Australia, and Japanese institutions were molded as much by conscious decisions as by tradition. But Japan drew creatively on its own tradition and adapted a variety of European institutions in new and different ways. Because of Japan's efforts to recombine different traditions, no modern fully industrialized country presents a greater contrast to American institutional structure and provides greater opportunities for examining underlying assumptions.

Third, circumstance has forced Japan to pioneer in confronting problems that are just beginning to distress America. America established its patterns of government–business relations in an era when natural resources were, for practical purposes, unlimited and people could dispose of their refuse without devastation to the environment. In the future, it could be disastrous if the government made no effort to control energy resources and environmental pollution. When America was a loosely populated country with ample land and economic opportunities, people could have maximal independence with minimal governmental interference. Now with increased crowding it is desirable for the government to give some direction in the distribution of population. Before modern transportation and communication, many decisions were wisely decentralized to states, but with increasing mobility it is desirable for the national government to bring some order to increasingly complex, overlapping, and inconsistent state regulations in fields such as taxation, welfare, and education. In an earlier era when American trade and commerce were overwhelmingly geared to internal markets, it was not essential to have a foreign trade policy. Foreign trade has by now grown so rapidly that some American industries are in danger of being eliminated and workers unemployed unless America develops a trade policy consistent with the comparative advantages of our economy.

In all these spheres Japan faced the same problems earlier and responded more energetically. With almost no natural resources, Japan decades ago had to adopt energy policies to confront shortages that America is just now acknowledging. With population overcrowding, Japan had to find collective arrangements that represent everyone's interest and reduce the individual's disruption to society as a whole, a problem less serious in America before urban congestion. In 1868, with over two hundred fifty local lords, Japan had more difficulties in responding to the competition of other nations than America did in 1776 and therefore worked harder to provide central authority. For over a hundred years, to avoid foreign conquest and catch up with the modern West, the Japanese government had to assume leadership in dealing with broad issues in planning, restructuring, modernizing, and phasing out declining industries, a leadership America is only now beginning to consider desirable. As a small island dependent on international trade for resources and markets, Japan decades ago began developing a foreign trade policy that America now regards as necessary. In short, Japan pioneered in developing policies appropriate for America's new circumstances.

A fourth reason why Japan is a useful mirror is that Japanese institutions have been extraordinarily successful. These successes are not only economic but political and social as well. While many are worthy of emulation, this is not to say that Japan has an overall higher quality of life than America, a judgment that would be subjective at best. Even though the Japanese are dealing with many problems more effectively, they suffer from excessive crowding and serious shortages of resources, problems from which America is happily spared. Japanese institutions may not ensure even Japanese success decades from now, because the Japanese are highly vulnerable to world energy shortages, protectionism against Japanese exports, and growing competitiveness from developing countries

with lower labor costs, all of which could have serious effects on Japan regardless of the effectiveness of its institutions. It is difficult to argue that the present form of Japanese institutions is best even for Japan in the future, for they must be adapted to an era of slower growth rates and increasing protectionism. One cannot conclude that adopting Japanese institutions will enable America to escape serious difficulties, because even the best Japanese institutions are imperfect and many other factors aside from those considered in this book will affect our success. And not all Japanese institutions are desirable and worthy of emulation. However, using measures America has traditionally used to determine success, it is readily demonstrable that in many areas Japanese institutions are coping with the same problems we confront, more successfully than we are. Could we not profit by showing the same eagerness to learn from the East that Japan has shown in learning from the West?

Many readers who note the Japanese successes in the pages following will find ways to ignore Japanese patterns on the grounds that they are costly, that they have inherent even if not clearly unidentifiable weaknesses, or that they do not easily fit the American tradition. I ask only that the reader who is wont to say, "It won't work here," suspend his final judgment until the last chapter.

2

The Japanese Miracle

I F JAPAN WERE an American state, it
would rank fifth in geographical size, following Alaska, Texas, California, and Montana. A population
of 115,000,000, half the size of America's, lives in this area,
making Japan the most densely populated major country in the
world. About one-sixth of its land is arable, and even with high
productivity per acre, well over thirty percent of its food
supplies must be imported. With virtually no petroleum, iron
ore, coal, or other mineral resources, Japan is dependent on
imports for almost eighty-five percent of its energy resources.
It imports more timber from North America than it produces.
Producing Japanese foodstuffs requires more farmland in
America than is available in Japan. From 1945 to 1947, as six
million soldiers and civilians, some of whom had been overseas
for decades, returned to be supported by the home islands,
food shortages and malnutrition were widespread. One might
properly wonder, as many Japanese did, whether·a country the
size of Montana with virtually no physical resources could
support over one hundred million people.

By 1952 when the Allied Occupation ended, Japan had
almost recovered its prewar levels of production, but its gross
national product was little more than one-third that of France

9

or the United Kingdom. By the late 1970s the Japanese GNP was as large as The United Kingdom's and France's combined and more than half the size of America's. The Japanese were producing approximately as much steel as the United States, but in more modern and efficient plants. In 1978, of the world's twenty-two largest modern blast furnaces, none was in the United States and fourteen were in Japan. With more modern plants and higher productivity, Japanese steel was outcompeting American steel in American as well as foreign markets. Making good use of its comparative advantage first in labor costs, then in economies of scale, modern technology, and organization, Japan built up highly competitive industries in field after field.

In the early 1950s Japanese radios, tape recorders, and hi-fi equipment were less competitive than their American counterparts, but before long they dominated the market. The Japanese watch industry eclipsed the justly famous Swiss watch industry. The British motorcycle industry was virtually eliminated by the Japanese motorcycle industry, and of the several most successful motorcycle companies in America, only one, Harley-Davidson, is non-Japanese. The German dominance in camera and lens production before World War II has given way to the Japanese. In optical equipment the Japanese are similarly dominant. Even in fields remote from Japanese tradition Japanese companies often outperformed their Western counterparts. By the 1970s the sales of Steinway and other American piano manufacturers were no match for Yamaha; Muramatsu's Western flutes were competing favorably with American ones. Japanese dominance extended into such diverse fields as bicycles, ski equipment, snowmobiles, cut pottery, and zippers. In the late 1970s, as the cost of new Japanese ships ran twenty to thirty percent lower than European ones, European countries were forced to resort to nonmarket mechanisms to limit the number of ships purchased from Japan. This forced

Japanese shipbuilding companies, in the wake of the oil crisis, to operate at much less than capacity, but even then Japan outdid Europe and America combined, for it produced about fifty percent of the world's shipping tonnage.

In 1958 Japan produced fewer than one hundred thousand passenger cars, and through the early 1970s Volkswagen was the major foreign car exporter to the United States. Soon thereafter Toyota's and then Nissan's (Datsun) American sales surpassed the German manufacturer. By 1978 Volkswagen was replaced by Honda, which became the third largest automobile exporter to the United States. During 1977 Japan exported over four and one-half million cars, while America exported only a small fraction of that number. Japan sold almost two million cars in America, while about fifteen thousand American-produced cars were sold in Japan. If market forces alone were operating, Japanese car exports would have increased substantially in 1978, but Japan chose to restrain its exports artificially to avoid political repercussions in Europe and America.

The effort to explain these Japanese successes as a result of cheap labor is out-of-date, for by 1978 with devaluation of the dollar, Japanese wages were slightly higher than those in the United States.* If anything, modernization of facilities and productivity increases are more important in explaining Japanese superiority. Economist Dale Jorgenson surveyed various factors in industrial production and concluded that on the average the modernity of technology used in Japanese manufacturing had edged past the United States by 1973. In 1975 one Japanese worker could produce about one thousand English pounds worth of cars every nine days, whereas at Britain's Leyland Motors, to produce the same value a worker took

* Since changes in dollar values do not always reflect changes in yen values, dollar values throughout the book are calculated at 180 yen per dollar, the approximate exchange rate in October 1978.

forty-seven days. In 1976 none of the major European car producers (Fiat, Renault, or Volkswagen) was able to produce as many as twenty cars per man-year of labor, but Nissan employees produced forty-two cars per man-year and Toyota turned out forty-nine. In 1962 the Japanese produced roughly one hundred tons of steel per worker, compared to four hundred in England; but by 1974 Japanese productivity in steel was estimated to be two to three times that of England. By 1976 a typical Japanese worker in a ball-bearing factory produced about three and one-half times as much as a worker in RHP, the leading English manufacturer.

In several major fields such as computers, industrial chemicals, and film, Americans are still more successful than their Japanese counterparts, and in these fields Japan still protects its industries. In computers Japan already constitutes the most serious challenge to IBM and other multinationals of American origin, and Japanese-made computers are already gaining an increasing share of their domestic market while their protectionism declines. In copying machines, Japanese market share is growing rapidly. America is clearly superior in military and nuclear technology, although Japanese technology has improved so rapidly that Japan and the United States are now engaged in large joint research projects. The Japanese have at least temporarily given up their effort to manufacture large airplanes, partly because of pressure from the United States to buy American planes and ease the trade imbalance. Nonetheless, many parts for American planes are produced in Japan.

One measure of Japanese and American competitiveness is in the trade balance. America's trade imbalance with Japan approached ten billion dollars a year by the late 1970s with few signs of abatement despite dollar devaluation and political pressure. But if anything the imbalance understates Japanese industrial competitiveness, for much of America's exports are

in agricultural products and raw materials. Japan's trade policy until the late 1960s was among the most protectionist in the world, and that once greatly impeded American attempts to penetrate Japanese markets. Despite rapid trade liberalization in most areas, Japanese ministries still occasionally create special difficulties for competitive American products, and until the mid-1970s the United States government did not adequately represent the interests of American companies in their efforts to break into Japanese markets. But the primary reason for the trade imbalance, as the Boston Consulting Group's 1978 study for the United States Treasury Department has shown, lies not in Japan's protectionism but in America's inferior competitiveness and lack of interest in cultivating exports to Japan. America's competitiveness has declined compared not only to Japan but to other countries. From the late 1960s to the late 1970s, of goods purchased by Japan from overseas, America lost about forty percent of its market share to Australia, Korea, Taiwan, and other Asian countries.

The extent of Japanese superiority over the United States in industrial competitiveness is underpublicized in America, but the true state of affairs was reflected by a high official of a leading Japanese research center who privately acknowledged that the United States with its highly competitive agricultural sector has by now taken the place of Japan's prewar colonies, supplying agricultural products and raw materials to a superior modern industrial machine.

Unless America's competitiveness is improved, short-range palliatives—including devaluation of the dollar—are likely to have little effect and the imbalance may well increase. Given the decline in America's research capacity compared to Japan's growing interest in research, the lack of encouragement by the United States government to American business compared to Japan's encouragement of its businessmen, and America's

shortage of foreign capital compared to Japan's growing surplus, there is every reason to expect that the competitive gap will continue to widen.

In areas where Japanese competitiveness has increased so rapidly as to threaten large American industries, the United States felt it necessary to impose nonmarket mechanisms to reduce the Japanese threat. In the 1960s when Japanese textiles threatened to overwhelm the American textile industry, political pressures from America eventually led to "voluntary quotas" by Japanese companies to avoid formal tariff barriers. In the 1970s when it appeared as if several major American television companies might be forced out of business by Japanese competitors, Japanese companies similarly held back on sales to the United States. In the case of steel, a complicated formula, a trigger-price mechanism, was used to restrain steel imports, a substantial part of which came from Japan. In the late 1970s, as Japanese automobiles became so competitive that they were already outselling American-produced automobiles in California, Japanese car manufacturers raised prices to restrain exports to the United States and thereby avoid more serious American protectionism. In textiles, steel, television, and automobiles, informal restraints on Japanese exports to the United States relieve immediate trade tensions, but as long as this informal protection continues, it reduces pressures for American industries to rise to Japanese standards of competitiveness.

In international trade the Japanese have had to learn to communicate in English and to adopt patterns of trade developed and originally dominated by Western countries. Despite these obvious disadavantages, the Japanese have begun to dominate international commerce as they dominate industrial production. Mitsubishi Trading Company, Mitsui Bussan, Sumitomo Trading, C. Itoh, Marubeni, and Nissho Iwai are rivaled only by each other, not by any foreign trading com-

pany. For example, these six companies, to say nothing of other large Japanese trading companies, conduct over half the two-way trade between the United States and Japan. Because of their superior information and contacts around the world, a sizable portion of international trade not involving Japan is now channeled through these large trading firms.

Japanese investment in the United States already exceeds American investment in Japan and is growing at a much more rapid rate as more Japanese companies establish plants and purchase stocks and property in the United States.

Stagnation has been a serious problem in most modern countries, and both the American and Japanese governments are reluctant to stimulate their economies substantially for fear of inflation. In the wake of the oil shock of 1973 the Japanese government erred by overstimulating the economy, leading to a very high rate of inflation for over a year. Except for this brief period, however, in recent years Japan has not only maintained a higher growth rate than the United States but has kept its increase in wholesale price index lower.

During the 1950s, economic success was partly at the expense of the Japanese consumer, and the social infrastructure for wage raises lagged behind growth and productivity increases. However, in recent years per capita income and ownership of consumer goods have grown about as fast as the gross national product and therefore far more rapidly than in other countries. So striking has been the growth in consumer purchasing power that foreigners in Japan now have difficulty maintaining the standard of living of their Japanese counterparts without special allowances, and Japanese in America consider luxury goods and restaurants very moderate in price. There are many ways to calculate personal income, but if one includes subsidized housing, by 1978 Japanese wages had already surpassed American levels and are continuing to grow at a faster rate. To be sure, sewage systems are not yet universal

and house size and car ownership still lag behind the United States although the gaps are narrowing. The retail distribution sector is not as efficient as America's and prices are high by international standards. Using conventional price indices, Japanese wages as of 1978 still buy less, but the average Japanese spends less than public rates on housing and uses less beef and other products that are high priced on these indices. Japanese lead the world in household diffusion of television sets (especially color sets) and cameras. In possession of videotape recorders, Japanese consumers are substantially ahead of the United States not only in percentage but in absolute numbers of owners. The quality of ski equipment on an average Japanese ski slope compares favorably with the equipment on the most exclusive ski slopes of Europe or America. Although some may disagree with the subjective judgment that quality of clothing in Japan is superior, on average, to that in the United States, there is widespread agreement that the variety and quantity of sports uniforms, clothing for weddings and other ceremonial parties, company wear, and casual wear exceed that of any other population, probably by a substantial margin. If anything, the Japanese maintain their belongings in a better state of repair than do Americans.

Transportation and communication systems within Japan are rapidly pulling ahead of their Western counterparts. With short distances Japanese use fewer airplanes than Americans, but in rail transport the Shinkansen bullet train route from Tokyo to Kyoto, opened in 1964, is more rapid and comfortable than anything the United States is currently considering even on the most heavily traveled routes, although in 1977 America purchased some of this fifteen-year-old technology. This line has already been extended to Fukuoka in the southern island and, though delayed by objections to the noise, is being extended toward the very northern tip of the main island.

Rapid and convenient rail service throughout the country is superior to European as well as American service.

The speed of the mail service undoubtedly compares favorably with world standards, but it is in the application of new electronic communications systems that Japan excels. Video machines and facsimile reproduction machines attached to telephones are more widely used than in any other country. It took some one hundred computer specialists four years to devise the system, but by the mid-1970s a customer could go into any regular local branch bank and have funds transferred to any other account in any local bank in the country by computer in the same day. The computer systems for controlling steel production are more sophisticated than any Western counterparts. The idea of putting all books and magazines on computer tapes and having this information available through a telephone or television system to every household in a nation is not unique to Japan, but Japan is far ahead of the United States in working out the organizational, technical, and legal problems. It is not impossible that Japan might begin to implement this system in not much more than a decade, far ahead of the United States.

With the extraordinary movement of Japanese from the countryside to the city after World War II and the unparalleled rapidity of change caused by industrialization and Westernization, one might expect social disorganization to be immense, for the strain on many people has been substantial. It is difficult to find meaningful cross-cultural measures of social disruption, but one such indicator is the extent of crime. Observers uniformly note that people walk anywhere in Japan at all hours of the night, fully confident of their personal safety. To an extent that would shock Americans, the Japanese carry a great deal of cash with them because they pay large bills with cash rather than checks. Taxicab drivers give

no indication of worrying about their personal safety. These subjective judgments are supported by the data available. Americans studying Japanese crime records, which are more complete than American records, indicate that around 1960 the rates for major crimes such as homicide, assault, theft, and rape were several times higher in America than in Japan. From 1960 to 1973 American crime rates rose 110 percent and other modern countries' crime rates went up also, except for Japan, where they declined further.

One might suspect that the Japanese neglected culture and education in their efforts to obtain rapid economic growth, but if anything cultural imports have proceeded as rapidly as technological imports and have been diffused among the population with equal speed. Japan leads the world in percentage of young people who complete high school, about ninety percent. Although a higher percentage of Americans enter a university, a higher percentage of Japanese complete universities. Although the average number of years of formal schooling is very similar in the two countries, Japanese children attend school slightly longer hours each day and about sixty more days per year than their American counterparts. They spend far more time in supplementary educational classes, and most do substantial extra studying in preparation for high school or university entrance examinations. Westerners familiar with the Japanese educational system observe that Japanese students, on the average, are more familiar than most Western students with world history and current events. In mathematics and science, the only areas where there is reliable quantitative information on comparative international skills, Japanese youth substantially outperform their counterparts in modern Western nations. The Japanese also rank high in music and artistic capacity and in physical agility. The Japanese young people's knowledge of English far surpasses the American student's knowledge of a foreign language, although their knowledge of spoken English

cannot compare with that of most Europeans. But given that virtually no Japanese knew English in 1945, the progress of Japanese in learning a foreign language within a generation has perhaps been unique among large nations, and the progress continues.

It has often been noted by foreign observers that the Japanese absorb an extraordinary amount of factual information for entrance examinations at the high school and university level. Despite sometimes intense cramming, Japanese adults retain an unusual eagerness for data on topics as diverse as international affairs, politics, history, science, and the arts. Although one or two countries rank ahead of Japan in readership of daily newspapers, if one combines readership of books, magazines, and newspapers, Japan is clearly ahead of any other country. Whether, as some foreigners would argue, the programs of the two national TV channels, NHK and NHK Educational Television, are qualitatively superior to public network programs in other countries is difficult to evaluate, but they are in any case outstanding. Through the major dailies, the ordinary Japanese reading public gets a breadth of information about basic world developments that compares favorably with the best of foreign newspapers.

With an industrial output which has now surpassed that of the Soviet Union concentrated in such a small area, the Japanese have confronted a most severe pollution problem. Since the early 1970s when the problem gained prominent attention, the Japanese have responded with pioneering techniques now being studied by Americans seeking new solutions to their pollution problems. The standards for pollution control for new plants and the amount spent on pollution control by the mid-1970s surpassed that of any other country. By the late 1970s the most serious sources of pollution had been substantially reduced; for example, American and European auto manufacturers had to make special appeals to be allowed to sell new

cars in Japan for they did not meet Japanese standards for emission, which by the late 1970s were the most rigorous in the world.

The Japanese national health insurance program does not offer high benefits by Western European standards. However, an observer in Japan is impressed that people seem lively and wear their age well, that obesity and debilitating illnesses seem uncommon. These impressions are supported by the statistical data that is available. By the mid-1970s Japan had the lowest infant mortality rate of any country in the world. Perhaps the best overall measure of a nation's health system is the longevity of the population. In 1955 Japan's average life expectancy was over four years shorter than America's. By 1967 Japan's average life expectancy surpassed America's, and in 1977 it surpassed Sweden's, to become the longest of any nation in the world.

The question of satisfaction with life requires more subjective judgments. If one looks at international public opinion data on complacency and self-satisfaction, the Japanese rank low. They seem to have aspirations for betterment as high or higher than any country in the world. But foreigners who observe the Japanese in public commonly conclude that in a sense of involvement in purposeful activity, of dignity in performing their work role, and of pride in personal appearance, the Japanese rank very high. It is tempting to dismiss the Japanese as automotons who know nothing but work. According to the 1977 International Labor Organization Yearbook of Labor Statistics, in 1976 the average American work week was 40.0 hours and Japan's average work week was 40.2 hours. If one took full account of unreported overtime, a typical Japanese may work an average of three or four more hours a week, but even then the total work week is in the range of Western European countries. Those who have observed Japanese families and other groups in private have concluded that in zest

for life, delight in carefree relaxation, and enthusiasm for recreation, the Japanese are no laggards. As they say of themselves, they like to work hard and to play hard. Many thoughtful Americans visiting Japan express amazement at the tidiness of urban facilities, the reliability of public transportation, the courtesy of commercial personnel, the affluence of department stores, the quality of restaurants, and the virtual absence of derelicts and alienated slums. They end by wondering, like Japanese vistors to America, why Americans cannot make their cities and their organizations work as well.

In gross national product, standard of living, political power, and cultural influence, Japan is not number one in the world today. In gross national product per person, Japan surpassed the United States in 1977 or 1978, according to varying estimates by economists; but barring significant yen revaluations, even if present trends continue it will take well over a decade before Japan's gross national product surpasses that of the United States. With all fringe benefits added in, the average Japanese family income has surpassed that of its American counterpart, but in purchasing power, as measured by conventional economic estimates, the average Japanese in 1978 had not yet surpassed his American counterpart. Although measures of purchasing power are subject to question, because the package is geared to American tastes and the Japanese are more frugal, pay less interest because of fewer debts, and draw more income from savings, there is no doubt that Americans enjoy more housing and yard space.

Japan has thus far chosen to maintain a low posture in international political affairs, to cooperate with other nations rather than take initiatives, to defend its own interests rather than assume responsibility for preserving peace and order around the world. Its political influence cannot now compare with that of the United States.

In cultural affairs, national influence tends to lag decades

behind economic power. Western European nations that can no longer match Japan in economic power still enjoy greater cultural respect and influence than Japan, and the Japanese still pay respect to the manners and arts of Western Europe. More Japanese take piano lessons than Americans, to say nothing of the number of people studying Japanese arts and music. However, in Western art and music, despite rapid Japanese advances, America still enjoys a preponderance of outstanding artists and musicians. The Japanese lag far behind in the number of Nobel prizes received for science and literature, although there may be grounds for wondering whether they receive the recognition they deserve. The Japanese on the average engage in more physical exercise than their American counterparts, but Americans clearly outperform the Japanese in most international athletic competitions. The gap between the United States and Japan in political power and cultural and athletic performance is narrowing, but not as rapidly as the gap in economic capacity. At present, in political and cultural influence and even in gross national product Japan is not the number one power in the world.

Yet in the effectiveness of its present-day institutions in coping with the current problems of the postindustrial era Japan is indisputably number one. Considering its limited space and natural resources and its crowding, Japan's achievements in economic productivity, educational standards, health, and control of crime are in a class by themselves. This success is more striking when one considers how far behind Japan was in many of these areas not only in 1945 but even in the mid-1950s, after recovery from World War II was essentially complete.

Many Americans seem interested in finding some explanation of how the Japanese have used unfair tactics to outperform other countries; charges that they are imitators, narrow economic animals, and dumpers and that their government and

business have illicit intimacy are not uncommon. Such facile attempts to explain Japanese success may ease American anxiety about our performance, but not only are they unfair to the Japanese but they blind us from learning about Japanese success and condemn us to falling further behind.

Japan has serious problems aside from crowding. Its universities are generally mediocre, discrimination against Koreans and the descendants of Tokugawa-period outcasts (*burakumin*) widespread, defensiveness against foreign contamination relentless, government bumbling in planning projects such as Narita airport sometimes distressing, and big business treatment of public complaints often arrogant. Since the focus of this book is not on a rounded picture of Japan but on practices potentially useful for Americans wanting to improve our country, such problems will be considered in detail only where relevant to the question of whether these problems are essential parts of institutions we might want to borrow. The institutions that follow were chosen because they are crucial for understanding overall Japanese success and because they could be models that America would do well to emulate.

PART TWO

Japanese Successes

3

Knowledge:
Pursuit and Consensus

I F ANY SINGLE FACTOR explains Japanese success, it is the group-directed quest for knowledge. In virtually every important organization and community where people share a common interest, from the national government to individual private firms, from cities to villages, devoted leaders worry about the future of their organizations, and to these leaders, nothing is more important than the information and knowledge that the organizations might one day need. When Daniel Bell, Peter Drucker, and others hailed the coming of the postindustrial society in which knowledge replaced capital as society's most important resource, this new conception became a great rage in Japan's leading circles. But these leading circles were merely articulating the latest formulation of what had already become conventional Japanese wisdom, the supreme importance of the pursuit of knowledge.

It is not always clear why knowledge is needed, but groups store up available information nonetheless on the chance that some day it might be useful. Information gathering is general and specific, long-term and short-term, formal and informal. Organizations send out observation teams and invite in experts. They gather information from classrooms and golf

courses, from conferences and bars, from think tanks and television. They gather it from professionals and amateurs, friends and foes. New friends are cultivated because they might provide access to information, and new groups are formed to select and process the information. Potential sources are carefully nurtured so that further queries can be processed as needed. New areas of knowledge are explored to provide new clues, and people are assigned to spend several years mastering potentially profitable specialties. The process is nothing if not thorough.

Group Learning: Routine and Urgent

Whenever two people are together, the one imparting information is accepted as the teacher, and the listener becomes the student. Everyone is expected to be a student part of the time, and a good student is admired at any age. The good student displays modesty, humility, persistence, and forbearance. In a group setting, if the student thinks the teacher less than fascinating, he may doze discreetly; if he finds the teacher less than outstanding, he conceals it. He may not challenge the teacher's wisdom. He accepts the framework of assumptions of the teacher, and if encouraged to ask a question, finds one that will enable the teacher to demonstrate his abilities. The student is bound by his role as a learner and seeks to learn what he can; he does not try to impress others with his cleverness.

Study is a social activity which continues throughout life. By the time Japanese youth complete formal schooling, not only have they acquired general information, but they have acquired the habit of studying in groups. Even if they read alone, they discuss their reading with peers. University education may be more important for certification than learning, and the social atmosphere may impede probing, but it does not impede groups of students from continuing to learn, nor

does it impart such confidence that students can consider themselves expert before they begin their employment. After he is employed, the school graduate is prepared to receive his specialized training and he remains receptive to broad generalized training. At his work place the new employee first undergoes long periods of specific training as an apprentice with properly humble status and throughout his later career frequently participates in a variety of study groups. An employee is encouraged to engage in work-related study even when there are no study groups, and a housewife, young or old, is encouraged by family and friends to study how to be a better housewife, mother, and, later, a better mother-in-law and grandmother. Adult education courses, offered by local communities, companies, newspapers, and department stores as well as universities, are extraordinarily popular.

.Off the job, an employee is constantly looking for opportunities to learn what might be useful for his work; but he also tries to learn important things with no apparent immediate relationship to his work, for they might prove useful in the long run. When a foreign visitor comes to Japan, most Japanese almost instinctively think, "What can I learn from him?" and the three million Japanese who now travel abroad each year look for little hints of new ideas they might apply at home.

The penchant for study may be rooted in groups, but in no arena is it more clearly manifested than in the mass media. Sports magazines, adult comics, some weekly magazines, and some television shows are almost exclusively for entertainment, but newspapers, magazines, and television are also expected to convey generous amounts of information. Not only do Japanese spend more time reading than their American counterparts—whether it be newspapers, magazines, or books—but a higher proportion of the media they encounter is designed to enhance knowledge and skills. Each of the two largest Japanese

newspapers have a circulation of about six million, much larger than that of the largest American daily. The several largest Japanese newspapers, each with more specialized reporters and more foreign correspondents than any American paper, can provide their readers with highly detailed background information. Because these large newspapers are national rather than local, public awareness of national and international issues is greater than in the United States. Japanese newspapers in 1976 had a circulation of sixty-one million, the same as the United States or almost twice as large a circulation per population.

Numerous serials inform Japanese specialists in an almost infinite variety of areas of interest. Herbert Passin, chairman of Columbia University's sociology department, commented that when he wishes to give new ideas an airing in Japan, he and Japanese intellectuals can find many publications where their ideas will be immediately printed, whereas in America it would at best take many more months to find an outlet. Some thirty thousand new books are now published in Japan each year, about the same as in the United States. Since World War II approximately one hundred fifty thousand books have been translated into Japanese. Not all of these are for conveying information, but the amount of information flowing into English from other languages is miniscule compared to that translated into Japanese.

Educational television is generously funded, and a significant proportion of programming time is devoted to basic educational courses rather than to elite entertainment. Courses on five foreign languages—English (at several levels, from "Sesame Street" to adult programs), German, Chinese, French, and Russian—are available on the regular weekly schedule of the national education network. In recent years special programs for farmers, small businessmen, and mothers of children of various ages have appeared. The audience for educational television expects charts, graphs, and illustrations but is pre-

pared to watch programs that in the United States would not be seen as particularly fascinating. In the late 1960s, for example, when computers first gained widespread attention, over one million copies of the textbook to accompany the educational television program on computers were sold in one year. Even on commercial channels, information programs abound and several programs a day present favorite foreign television shows dubbed into Japanese.

Although basic learning continues everywhere and at all ages, information gathering becomes focused and takes on a special campaign-like intensity when an organization recognizes an issue as preeminently important. During the course of the several years that a given issue such as planning a railroad or promoting venture capital or revising local tax systems is dominant, nearly every member of the organization works with some aspect of it, exploring new angles and seeking and relaying new bits of information.

The process usually begins long before the exact nature of the issue has been precisely defined. At this early stage, government or business leaders may begin to consult knowledgeable individuals or may assign representatives from their organization to an exploration of approaches to the problem, the subissues that are involved, and the resources and people who might best be asked for advice. After a period of consultation, they begin to send out people to do more intensive observation and study. The researchers assemble, summarize, and, when necessary, translate books and articles. Study groups begin to confer on subissues. Later meetings are held to evaluate what has been learned and to define what else needs to be learned. People are sent out again to ask the same questions in order to verify certain points and to focus on new, slightly different problems. Staff members consider all important relevant options and at later stages redefine issues and select especially promising approaches for restudy with more thorough-

ness. They mull over, digest, recognize, and redigest their information as their options gradually narrow and decisions emerge.

BASIC LEARNING ILLUSTRATED: SPORTS

The process of learning skills on a national scale may be illustrated by the Japanese approach to studying sports. When China began to expand its contact with non-Communist nations in the early 1970s, the first sports team it sent abroad was table tennis, the one sport in which the Chinese were world champions. China next sent out men's and women's volleyball and basketball teams, sports in which they are almost as strong.

The standard Japanese approach is different: they choose instead a prominent Western sport they hope to master. The first major sport selected was baseball, introduced in 1873 five years after the Meiji Restoration, and popularized at the turn of the century when it was clearly the preeminent American sport. Japanese sent observers to watch the strongest American teams and to undergo training under their tutelage. They invited the best players to Japan for demonstration games. It is no accident that America's most celebrated pre-World War II baseball player, Babe Ruth, received a tumultuous welcome in Japan and remained one of the great Japanese heroes. After World War II the Japanese were quick to invite to their country whole demonstration teams. Gradually Japanese teams arranged to recruit one or two American players each. To be sure, some of the American players were past their prime, but that was not the point. Their own playing might help the team only a little in the short run, but they could help to train other team members, imparting know-how that would make the Japanese teams strong in the long run. The Japanese invited the best American big league teams to Japan to play Japanese teams. In the early years the American teams overwhelmed their Japanese counterparts, but it was no shame to lose badly

at that time. It was seen as the way to build up skill. Gradually the Japanese teams lost by smaller margins, and, despite the American advantage of greater physical size, the Japanese began occasionally to beat American professional teams.

When a group of young girl swimmers from the United States dominated the Tokyo Olympics of 1964, they caught the eyes of the world, but in Japan they became a sensation. Young Japanese and their coaches made pilgrimages to the United States to study the system for developing that talent. The American girls were invited to put on exhibitions in Japan and to give occasional pointers to their Japanese counterparts. Aside from the coaching given talented Japanese swimmers, the major lesson in Japanese eyes was that the United States had developed an intensive program to single out swimmers with competitive potential at junior high school age, providing a reservoir of talent from which championship swimmers could develop. The statesmen of the Japanese sports world concluded that if Japanese grade schools throughout the country were to teach swimming, Japan could create an even larger group of talented young swimmers with an earlier start, possibly compensating for small physical size and a population base smaller than the United States' and Russia's. The government did not require that primary schools provide swimming pools, but local "PTAs," caught up in the mood, began to demand that their schools build pools and offer swimming programs. Within several years swimming pools dotted the Japanese countryside, usually alongside elementary schools, as well as urban and suburban areas. This enthusiasm began to fade somewhat when it was found that some elementary school pupils were spending too much time in swimming, to the detriment of their studies and sometimes their health, but the basic programs continued. Soon after the 1976 Olympics the East German girls who had dominated the swimming competition toured Japan not just to demonstrate their skills but to

offer pointers to aspiring Japanese swimmers and their coaches. The Japanese girls may not yet be able to defeat their East German and American competitors, but in a short span of time they have successfully climbed into the ranks of international competitive swimming in spite of their smaller physical size.

The actual decision to introduce a new sport is a complex one. No factor is more important in the timing than international popularity. Guiding the process is a kind of sports community with sports statesmen, business sponsors, coaches, leading players, sports writers, sporting-goods store owners, and allies in the government bureaucracy. The community does not necessarily have a fixed membership, but there is a recognized community of specially interested people who work together effectively and who know how best to develop a new sport. They know how to whip up the enthusiasm that makes the new sport a kind of fad, but they also know how to direct the careful acquisition of know-how that is essential for creating popularity and competence.

Interest in a new sport does not derive only from international competitive ambitions. Shortly after the war, business leaders discovered that the golf course was an ideal locale for creating informal contacts with their counterparts in different countries. Some Japanese businessmen concluded that for them to play well it was advisable to develop professional golf, for professional Japanese golfers could then give them helpful tips. Foreign professional players were invited to Japan, and before long budding Japanese professionals were on the international circuit. Once golf became popular in Japan, it took on a life of its own, with special privilege going to those who belonged to fashionable country clubs. In certain Japanese businessmen's circles, a person's golf handicap is almost as important an item of information as his company's gross sales. The stylishness only added to the seriousness with which Japanese studied golf.

Whatever the sport, the basic approach to learning has been and remains the same. For another example, one notes that bowling, learned from America, became so popular in the 1960s that for a time the world's two largest bowling alleys were in Tokyo and more Japanese were bowling than Americans. The Japanese learned gymnastics from the Soviet Union, hockey from Canada, tennis from Australia and the United States, soccer and rugby from England, skiing from Austria, basketball from the United States, table tennis originally from the United States and now from China. A newcomer to the Japanese sports repertory is American football. No country's efforts to learn football can compare with those of Japan, which has hosted entire American professional football teams that come to Japan to play one another, since no Japanese teams are yet up to American competitive levels.

While new sports are being added to the Japanese repertory, traditional sports are not ignored. Sumo, judo, karate, and aikido remain popular despite occasional faddish swings; when a new fad strikes and study of a new sport reaches a peak, the old sports nonetheless retain their niche in the expanding sports panorama.

It has been a matter of keen disappointment to the Japanese that their athletic teams have not had the extraordinary success that their companies have enjoyed in international economic competition. There has been continual self-criticism and analysis of the causes of their failure. They do not take refuge in the excuse of their small physical size, nor do they let up in their efforts at self-improvement, even though they have reached international competitive levels in virtually all sports and are not far behind the Soviet Union, the United States, and East and West Germany. Foreign sports specialists observing the Japanese expect continued progress in their mastery of Western sports.

The same ingredients found in the sports field (group

leadership, group-oriented study, humility, long-term perspective, and high ambition) are also present in other cases of learning, whether organized by the government, private companies, or the local community.

BUREAUCRATS AS INFORMATION MANAGERS

From the beginning of the Meiji period in the mid-nineteenth century, Japanese government leaders had sent abroad missions to study foreign governments and societies to prepare for a state with the most effective modern constitution, army, industry, science, technology, and agriculture. After World War II, government-sponsored study abroad extended into extraordinarily diverse fields, from philosophy to politics, atomic physics to toy making, business management to household management, and from medical science to jazz. As the spectrum of learning widened, the process of acquiring information became increasingly elaborate.

Japan's elite officials from the various ministries have the preeminent responsibility for guiding the acquisition of knowledge. They themselves are constantly analyzing information and deciding what further information needs to be gathered, playing a role that in the United States is partly played by academics and the White House staff. Within each ministry large numbers of experts spend a major part of their time following developments abroad within their respective spheres. They are expected not only to keep track of developments in general but to search for examples that Japan could usefully emulate.

The Japanese government's financing of foreign training is concentrated not on young university students but on elite young bureaucrats who have already spent at least a year or two in their respective ministries. Government officials remain in the same ministry until retirement, and therefore it pays the ministry to provide them with years of specialized training

in areas basic to their future responsibilities. Because each age cohort rises together and at its peak holds all key positions within the ministry, an effort is made to ensure that some bureaucrats in every age group are trained to tap each of the major bodies of knowledge relevant to the minstry's basic work. After receiving general training in ministry affairs, young bureaucrats within each age group are divided into separate specialties to be trained in appropriate languages, technical work, and theory in the best universities in the world, with all expenses and allowances paid by the ministry. These bureaucrats studying abroad have a clear sense of what knowledge their ministry needs and can concentrate their studies in these spheres. The system ensures that those who receive valuable training will be in key positions to make maximum use of it.

In the Foreign Ministry, for example, two or three young officers are selected each year to work on China. After a two-year tour of duty in Tokyo within the ministry, they are commonly sent for a two-year course in the language in Taipei or Peking. After Tokyo recognized Peking in 1972, the first exchange students Tokyo sent to Peking for language study were not bright university students but these young Foreign Ministry officials. After language study one or two in the age group may be sent to American universities to become familiar with Western scholarship on China and another to Moscow to become familiar with Soviet work on China. After this assignment, the officer may be sent to Peking or Hong Kong to work on analysis of current events. Although he begins work after three or four years of full-time study, he is in many respects still an apprentice until after his tour of duty in Hong Kong or Peking. Throughout his career the China specialist in the Foreign Ministry is expected to keep in touch with important research and analysis by the institutes under whom he was originally trained. This system thus guarantees

that the most important channels for potential information will remain open.

Staff preparation for other specialties within ministries is not ordinarily so extensive, but the basic approach for training elite bureaucrats is the same. The Finance Ministry sends promising young officials overseas to study tax systems, tax laws, business administration, theoretical economics, and econometrics. The Ministry of International Trade and Industry (MITI) sends officials abroad to study development of specific industries, theories of economic development, and energy economics. The object of study changes depending on an estimate of the future seriousness of certain issues. During the 1960s, for example, when Japan was reluctantly internationalizing its trade, a MITI official was assigned to France to study ways in which France had successfully resisted the advance of British manufactured goods. After 1973 the number assigned to study energy problems immediately increased.

Bureaucrats consider no responsibility greater than keeping well informed. When the scope of information gathering exceeds the ministry's span of control, they help mobilize private institutions most directly concerned to set up task forces to fill in gaps in informaton. Within the ministry considerable effort is made not just to collect information but to sift it and to ensure that key actors in the ministry are neither flooded with more information than they can control nor inadequately informed on matters of import. Within ministries, it is not the top-level who are expected to take initiatives in processing information as in America but the key bureau and section leaders within the ministry. In MITI, for example, the bureaus responsible for the respective industrial sectors all gather information that might be useful for guiding Japan's industrial development in that sector. For its respective sector each bureau wants to know world market trends, the state of tech-

nology, the likely timing and nature of new technological breakthroughs, the nature of the most successful industries in the world, and the reasons for their success. These bureaucrats erect formal and informal timetables as to when issues are likely to come to the fore, and they focus their information gathering accordingly. For example, in the decades after World War II, MITI officials considered it extremely important to develop basic Japanese industries like steel and electric power, and they concentrated their information-gathering efforts in these sectors. Interest in gathering know-how about the automobile industry began to develop in the 1950s, whereas computers did not emerge as a high priority until the late 1960s. After the oil shock in late 1973, energy problems took on top priority. Officials concerned with Middle Eastern oil, for example, recognized that paying for the oil and investing capital would not be sufficient to ensure the continuous flow of oil from the Middle East to Japan. They decided therefore to organize major technological development projects in the Middle East, which would make the oil-producing countries dependent on Japanese know-how and technological assistance. To do this well required vast amounts of information about Middle Eastern business patterns and social customs. It led to a rapid increase in the number of Japanese studying Arabic and Middle Eastern culture in general, with the goal of building a broader base of relations that would provide a more reliable source of natural resources.

When an issue rises to prominence, the Japanese do not hesitate to overlap and duplicate their efforts to gather relevant information. As James Abegglen of Boston Consulting group put it, "They smother a problem." Bureaucrats stationed abroad not only gather information directly but mobilize private Japanese who can assist in the process and identify foreign locals, be they newsmen, scholars, bibliogra-

phers, influential business friends, or free-wheeling entrepreneurs, who can open channels of information. The government helps finance research if necessary, but in most cases the gathering of information requires little or no financial support by the government. Companies finance research, and the media, sensitive to the heightened interest in the particular issue, invite academic and professional specialists to speak or write, without government financing. Informative speeches or conferences are not only reported but often printed in full in magazines. Editing may be hasty and at times sloppy, but the ideas and information are widely available at great speed.

Especially knowledgeable foreign specialists receive invitations through Japanese friends or acquaintances for attractive opportunities to speak, write, or visit Japan. Prominent Americans may be under more pressure from Japanese than American media to get their main ideas out to a broader public with great speed. Foreigners invited on such occasions are extraordinarily impressed with Japanese hospitality, generosity, and appreciation of their intellectual contributions. In the process, the information gatherer acts within the bounds of courtesy due a distinguished teacher. He listens carefully, absorbs whatever he can and asks questions, but rarely challenges or shows off his own knowledge. If anything, he underplays his own understanding of the issue.

The scope of government information gathering is breathtaking. At the height of the student turmoil in various countries during the Vietnam War, Japan's Economic Planning Agency dispatched an official to America to talk with radical American economists about various potential crises of capitalism. The purpose was to enable the Economic Planning Agency to be more sensitive to potential contingencies in drawing up its multiyear plans. A Japanese-speaking American student, the only foreigner on a mission sponsored by the Japanese government to consider developments in a third

country, was detached for part of the time to interview various local residents about their attitudes toward Japan. In the mid-1970s when it appeared that Japan might be moving toward a coalition government, a mission was sent to Europe to study the conditions under which coalition governments of European countries since World War II became immobilized and what kind of problems this created. The purpose: to explore mechanisms for avoiding such immobilization if coalition government came to Japan.

"THINK TANKS": MAXIMUM INFORMATION AT MINIMAL COST

Japanese government agencies have long supplemented their own research institutes with support to a small number of private institutes in order to obtain more specialized and detailed information. Some of these outside institutes, like the Institute for Developing Economies, with several hundred researchers studying other parts of Asia, have a staff and a collection of current materials as large as any research institute in their field in the world. However, in the 1960s as the complexity of problems facing Japan multiplied, the Japanese moved to create many more institutes to cope with the knowledge explosion. In characteristic fashion, large numbers of Japanese delegations traveled abroad to study foreign research institutes and then advise on the optimal development of Japanese "think tanks." Think tanks became a new fad and dozens of new ones sprang up, as the proverbial phrase goes, "like bamboo shoots after the spring rain." Before long there was even a federation of think tanks. Japanese observers concluded that American research centers were often too independent from the original financing organ and hence less than optimally responsive to requests for relevant information. Therefore, in Japan each research center is assigned to a certain ministry which controls the annual appropriations and super-

vises information collection. Government agencies also help sponsor other research centers with a small core of permanent staff capable of expanding through short-term contracts in order to obtain special kinds of information in their field of expertise.

By American standards many of these research organizations conduct relatively little basic research and their studies lack originality, analytic depth, and thoroughness. But the Japanese have had a different vantage point. The goal of these research groups is not to be original. It is not that Japanese lack the creativity to be unique, for in some priority areas like forecasting and analysis of energy problems the Japanese have in fact conducted high-quality original research. The task of the Japanese think tank is to serve as an information sweeper, bringing in all the best knowledge in the world on certain issues. The institutes summarize the information not to form conclusions or even to display individual analytic virtuosity but to suggest a variety of possible approaches potentially useful to their sponsoring organization. What the sponsor buys in a research center is not the beautifully prepared definitive major report but continuing access at an informal as well as formal level to relevant information on important pending issues. The researchers are generally not identified with any political point of view, and they do not defend particular intellectual positions. They accept their service role of providing all the facts, ideas, and visions that might conceivably be useful on a given issue.

One weakness of ministry-sponsored research institutes is the parochialism which stems from the specific ministerial interests. In the early 1970s the government set up the National Institute for Research Advancement (NIRA) to provide interministry coordination and to see that large issues would be dealt with in an integrated fashion, not simply from the points

of view of the specific ministries. NIRA makes an effort to coordinate the selection of topics and to guide the division of labor between various think tanks under different ministries so that all important topics receive rounded treatment.

Some think tanks are temporary creations that can be closed down depending on their performance record and the needs of government sponsors. Those with an expandable core of permanent staff are given assurance of long-term support by the appropriate government agencies. A small number of substantial research groups, most similar to large American ones, like Nomura Research Institute, Mitsubishi Research Institute, and the Japan Economic Research Institute, meet the needs for sustained quality research. They have secure private and government funding and a permanent research staff. When an issue becomes salient, competing research projects are assigned to several research institutes, but when issues become less important, the government terminates contracts with the less effective think tanks.

In short, think tanks, like most information-gathering units in Japan, draw on resources throughout the world, orient themselves to general and specific missions in defined policy-related areas, adjust to current needs of sponsors, and digest the information flowing to them to make it useful to government decision makers.

COMPANY INFORMATION STRATEGY

Individual companies sponsor information-gathering activities with no less enthusiasm than government ministries. Some American companies have programs in training and information gathering not totally different, but on the average Japanese companies collect and process information more thoroughly than their foreign counterparts. The leading Americans considered most innovative in thinking about the future, like

Herman Kahn, Peter Drucker, John Kenneth Galbraith, and Daniel Bell, are given more time and attention by businessmen in Japan than in America.

The Japanese general trading companies (like Mitsubishi, Mitsui Bussan, Sumitomo, Marubeni, C. Itoh, and Nissho Iwai) are unparalleled by other companies, Japanese or foreign, in their international information network. In part their success comes simply from their size, since most of Japan's foreign trade is conducted through these six companies, each of which is represented in virtually every country in the world. But success comes also because information gathering has such high priority. In gathering detailed economic information, private companies are superior to the Japanese government, but their superiority is especially pronounced in areas where they have a substantial economic interest. Even in political information gathering they sometimes outdo the Japanese Foreign Ministry. When a Japanese airliner was highjacked in 1973 in Abu Dhabi, for example, the Foreign Ministry relied on Mitsubishi Trading Company telexes to keep informed. And a Japanese magazine referred to one company official with high-level political contacts as the "Mitsubishi Ambassador in Washington." The trading companies' presence in small cities in major countries provides them with more detailed regional information than is obtained by the Foreign Ministry.

In 1973 the American government was shocked to learn that Soviet officials in the United States had arranged with an American company for a large sale of wheat to the Soviet Union, but a Japanese trading company was not surprised. Officials in the Moscow office of the trading company had wired the Tokyo office that several high trade officials who would make such agreements were suddenly absent from the Moscow scene. Upon request from the Tokyo office, company employees stationed in New York found that these officials were going through a New York airport en route to Colorado,

and regional trading company officials were able to confirm that they were meeting with the American company. It was not difficult to surmise what the meeting was about. The purpose of the Japanese company's research was to make some adjustments to the grain market before information about the purchase became public and caused a rise in the price of grain. Although such thoroughness is not unusual, the basic long-range effort lies not in such intelligence coups but in the continued collection and analysis of nonsecret material relevant to company interest, all the way from macroeconomic theory to the price of hog bristles in rural China.

Other Japanese companies undertake training and information gathering with comparable vigor. In middle-sized family companies, for example, it is common for the owner of the company to select one or two sons or sons-in-law for special training with the expectation that they will later acquire senior managerial responsibility, possibly becoming president of the company. Usually the father first sends the sons to a prominent private university like Keio, both to receive a general liberal arts background and to meet other future business leaders. These young men then form a network of friendships which can, among other things, contribute to the informal information flow once they assume responsibility in the company. After Keio a preferred pattern is to become fluent in spoken English and then enroll for a masters in business administration at a major American business school. The Japanese believe that American business management training is superior to that of any other country, and experience in America also helps future leaders to develop friendships and knowledge of American business. After graduating from business school the student is expected to work several years in America or Europe in companies in the same field as his father and often in companies where his father has developed some business contacts. Since the aim of this period abroad is to receive an apprenticeship

training, salary is not a serious consideration. After several years of such experience, the young man returns home, where he is expected first to reestablish himself with the workers and employees in his father's company, usually by taking on routine jobs in various parts of the company. Only later does he begin his management apprenticeship, gradually putting his training to work, all the while keeping open channels of communication with former fellow students and work associates.

In larger nonfamily corporations, officials rise slowly through the ranks. Because employees tend to remain in large corporations until retirement, it is rational for Japanese companies to invest far more heavily in training than do Western companies, where employees with such special skills would be more attractive to other employers. Employees on the management track customarily are rotated to a wide variety of departments and sent to outside training centers to acquire skills in various areas and to develop the close personal relationships that will later facilitate the flow of information needed for effective management decisions. Even if American companies can acquire new talent from the outside to bring skills to the company, the lower turnover of Japanese companies permits a more intimate nexus of personal relations between officials and other employees throughout the company.

When an issue is defined as the current top priority, the company, like a ministry, may frantically intensify its quest for information; but even in slack periods information gathering never stops. Japanese companies that have surpassed their Western counterparts in overall levels of technology and organizational know-how do not stop learning. They continuously search out weak spots where another company, Japanese or foreign, might have more strength and provide clues as to how they can continue to improve. A small dye maker in Western Japan with fifty employees, for example, follows appropriate journals to determine which dye-making plants anywhere in

the world have made the most important recent innovations. One or two employees are dispatched each year to spend a month or more observing these innovations.

Large Japanese companies hedge their bets by keeping open all potentially important channels of communication. For example, whenever a young politician becomes so prominent that he is considered to have a great future, each major daily newspaper identifies one or more young staff reporters who by reason of personality, style, and political persuasion get along well with him. This reporter may be assigned to a variety of posts, but one of his responsibilities is to retain a special personal relationship with that politician, to keep his confidence, and if necessary to become his advocate within the newspaper and in public as well. Therefore, regardless of which politician becomes prime minister or a leading cabinet member, when critical stories break, a newspaper has some reporter who can draw on a thorough knowledge of and special access to that leader. Other companies informally assign certain employees to maintain a comparable range of potentially important contacts, be they with potential buyers, sellers, suppliers, financiers, bureaucrats, or politicians, domestic or foreign.

Japanese companies also keep open channels to former senior executives who are believed to possess a priceless accumulation of knowledge and good judgment. By granting former high officials special honors and privileges and avoiding disruptive coups that would alienate them, present officials maintain easy access to their predecessors. Although ordinary workers in a large company retire at an average age of fifty-seven, the highest executives remain later. Directors and managing directors are generally in their late fifties and sixties, presidents in their sixties or even older, and chairmen of the board in their late sixties or seventies. The company board generally consists of former executives rather than outside directors as in an American company. Japanese organizations

may err on the side of granting too much authority to retired high officials, but by so doing they retain use of their advice, judgment, special expertise, and range of connections.

While most information is open, some is treated very sensitively. Where there is a danger of giving away competitive advantage to another company, Japanese company employees fight like samurai in preserving secrets. Companies prefer in-house specialists or special friends rather than outside consulting companies—lawyers and auditors, for example—to diminish the risk of passing on information to competitors. Stories of geisha passing on secrets obtained from businessmen in one company to those in another are a favorite comedy theme, but in fact geisha, like select newsmen taken into confidence by a given company, have proven to be reliably discreet. Even within a company it is accepted that certain important matters will be known only at higher levels, although the company's major goals and plans are generally widely understood by all company employees.

At the same time, competing companies are alert to opportunities where they can profit from joint study. When new management approaches were being introduced in the 1950s, all major companies, whether competitors or not, sent personnel to common study sessions. In the late 1960s when companies were introducing computers on a large scale, their representatives attended a variety of study sessions to discuss the impact of computerization on office organization and personnel policy. Joint study sessions cover an almost limitless range of issues from energy policy to government tax policy, to regional development, to welfare programs, to wage programs, to accounting procedures, to pollution problems.

In the late 1950s and during the 1960s the initiative for cooperative study sessions often came from the Japan Productivity Center, which represented government, business, and labor organizations. Sometimes the study sessions are encour-

aged by ministry officials in a given sector who want to raise the general level of expertise of companies in their sector or who, because of busy schedules, cannot brief everyone individually. Initiative may come from Keidanren (the Federation of Economic Organizations), from a trade association, from an ad hoc gathering of companies in the sector, or from think tanks or business schools concerned with promoting their own institutions. In any case, despite the basic competitiveness between companies, employees of rival companies can be perfectly cordial and even friendly as fellow students while discussing issues which, while only marginally important for competitive advantage, are nonetheless useful for all concerned. Companies have thus taken great care to distinguish when they can and cannot engage in cooperative study, for while highly competitive, they also want to cultivate every possible channel for information gathering.

To keep their employees optimally informed, virtually all sizeable companies organize study groups for senior management, middle management, new employees, and, not uncommonly, for dependents of employees. The company not only calls on in-house experts, but invites outside lecturers on topics of interest and sets up study groups focusing on new books or articles of unusual relevance. If a company cannot provide its employees with appropriate specialized training, the employees are encouraged to take correspondence courses or to take a brief leave of absence to attend proper training programs.

COMMUNITY INFORMATION GATHERING

The same kind of intensive broad-gauged information gathering takes place in a community that is undertaking a program of local development, be it a middle-sized city or a small village. Leaders of a middle-sized city considering a new transportation system, for example, are likely to study cities of comparable size to determine which have the most modern

transport systems in the world. Local government officials, local businessmen, educators, technical specialists, or, more often, some combination of the above would then form an inspection team that would travel abroad to observe the best systems in detail. The findings would be publicized in great detail in the local community through meetings of specialists and in larger public gatherings. After the community had thoroughly digested these reports, the world's most promising two or three transport systems for a city of that size would be selected for further study and the same or similar inspection teams would return to the model system for reassessment. When this team returned its findings would be discussed again. Usually one system would begin to emerge as the most promising and appropriate, although certain modifications would be suggested in order to avoid the minor problems of the best system or to adapt it to particular local needs. The result: a system as modern and up-to-date as any in the world and a local citizenry well-informed as to why a particular system was chosen.

A village considering a new swimming pool, community hall, or granary does not undertake the planning with the same sophistication as a larger community or company, but it undergoes comparable periods of information gathering and discussion, for the usefulness of information gathering has become part of the conventional wisdom of Japanese society.

KNOWLEDGE FOR CONSENSUS

The Japanese approach to information gathering did not originate entirely in Japan, but drew heavily on techniques borrowed from Western countries. These Western models were most fully developed in Japan, for it is unlikely that either the pervasiveness of general study and information gathering or the intensity of the search for focused information is rivaled in any other country.

If one examined all the research institutes, universities, and government and private research organizations in America studying any given issue, it is likely that the sum total of basic information would surpass that in Japan. But quantity alone is not the key to Japan's success in handling information. It derives rather from the long-term commitment of organizations to their employees and vice versa, for this permits a level of training and retraining that is simply not rational for organization with higher rates of mobility. And this continuity in membership means that not only is information better retained but the core of key employees are constantly reprocessing information and looking for new opportunities to add key bits of understanding. Information gathering is not an end in itself. It is a group-directed process closely linked to long-range organizational purposes, permitting an impressive range of information to be concentrated where and when the organization can best use it.

The Japanese assume that differences of opinion can best be resolved not by adversary procedures and brilliant argument but by further gathering of information. When two units cannot resolve an issue they may take it to a higher authority for resolution, but when higher authorities weigh possible courses of action, employees are dispatched to gather further data to tilt the decision in one direction or another. This increases the chance of reaching a wise decision, but perhaps even more important it reduces the need for anyone to make the difficult decisions that favor some and alienate others. People avoid posturing and advocating until the information is gathered and analyzed. The decision comes not so much from arguing, persuading, and contending but from joint efforts to arrive at the best solution, and the process of reaching the decision in this manner leaves the organization with fewer bruised egos, less contentiousness, and more good will. In decision making the Japanese endeavor to concentrate on the

overall goals of the organization, minimize polarization, and find the one solution most likely to succeed. Information gathering is ideally suited to these goals.

Furthermore, the widespread participation of all levels of a group in the process helps to increase group members' commitment to a decision. When a company decision is made to enter a certain market or start a new production line, the employee does not need to be told the explanation, for he already knows it. A citizen of a community may not expect to have as much input into decisions as specialists, but when he learns of the final decision about the new transport or construction project, he typically knows enough about the reasons for the decision that his confidence in the basic civic institutions are reinforced. When the ordinary citizen hears about an important national decision, he knows enough about the basic reasons to identify very strongly with his government and be ready to implement the decision. Japanese loyalty and patriotism are not inherited but are constantly recreated by organizational practice, and perhaps no practice is more important than the shared search for more information and the optimal solutions to which it leads.

4

The State: Meritocratic Guidance and Private Initiative

I N PUBLIC OPINION POLLS the Japanese express dissatisfaction with almost everything. The government is too dominated by big business, politicians are selfish, bureaucrats are arrogant, academics are impractical. Modern civilization is too materialistic, inflation is rampant, housing is crowded. Even at the height of economic growth, when households were polled respondents expressed dissatisfaction with the economy. But ask the informed Japanese who has traveled abroad if America and European governments have handled problems like economic growth, urban renewal, pollution control, and crime with greater success, and the reply is likely to be a sigh of benevolent sympathy, ending with a rhetorical query as to why those countries have become so decadent. Other countries are of course much worse off, the speaker reluctantly acknowledges—and then quickly returns to what really interests him: what is wrong with Japan. A foreigner can only wish his government had such problems.

What factors explain how the Japanese government handles contemporary problems with such relative success? How do the Japanese select their leaders and train them to deal with these problems so well? How do leaders avoid becoming over-extended while assuming responsibility for almost all develop-

ments affecting Japan in the entire world? How does the bureaucracy maintain the power to accomplish all this without becoming corrupt and without alienating the people? How is the central government able to control national developments without destroying local initiative?

FUNNEL TO THE TOP: HIGHEST ABILITY, BROADEST EXPERIENCE, LONGEST SERVICE

One can distinguish two key groups of decision makers in the Japanese government: the top politicians, including the prime minister and other key cabinet members, and leading bureaucrats. As in other parlimentary democracies, the prime minister is elected by Diet members, but since the conservative Liberal Democratic Party (LDP) has dominated the Diet since 1955, in fact the Diet merely approves as prime minister the man LDP leaders (mostly Diet members) choose. The prime minister in turn selects his cabinet members, almost all of whom are also Diet members, who serve also as heads of various ministries and other agencies. By custom, leading cabinet members are generally LDP politicians who have their own factions.

The politicians make many important political decisions, but compared to the American government the top politicians have little leverage over the bureaucracy. The prime minister may appoint one politician to be minister and another parliamentary vice-minister in each ministry, but there are no other political appointments in the ministry, and the person who really runs it is the administrative vice-minister, the highest career officer in the ministry. The key decisions in the ministry are made by the permanent bureaucrats rather than by the politicians of the Diet and the cabinet.

Not only is the central bureaucracy much more powerful than in the American system, but other parts of the government, like the judiciary and local government, are much

weaker. The top cabinet officials have considerable power, but the Diet is relatively weak compared to the American Congress, and most of the legislation is in fact drafted by bureaucrats rather than by Diet members.

Leading bureaucrats invariably have attended the best universities and have risen through the ranks in a carefully prescribed fashion. Tokyo University students are acknowledged to be at the apex of the two million students in Japanese universities. Entrance to Tokyo University is strictly by achievement tests that demonstrate uncommon ability and consummate determination. Within Tokyo University, the ablest students enter the Law Faculty, which in fact provides broad training for public administration, with secondary emphasis on political science and law. The top graduates of the Law Faculty enter the most prestigious ministries (Finance, International Trade and Industry, Foreign Affairs) and agencies (Economic Planning, Land, Environmental), providing they pass the ministerial written examination and demonstrate poise, breadth, and commitment in interviews. Of the twenty-odd students entering a key ministry in the elite track each year, perhaps fifteen come from the Tokyo University Law Faculty. This reflects greater openness than in the past, when that figure might have been as high as eighteen or nineteen. Now five or six might have been top students at other national universities like Hitotsubashi and Kyoto, at private universities like Keio and Waseda, or at the Economics Faculty of Tokyo University. This selection procedure ensures that elite bureaucrats are not only extremely able but are also protected by an aura of respect, rivaled perhaps only by the elite bureaucrats of France. America has elite political appointees commonly paid more than the highest paid Japanese bureaucrats, but they are not meritocratically selected, professionally trained, or subject to career discipline. Perhaps the closest American analogy would be law school graduates selected to clerk for Supreme Court

Justices, but in Japan this talent is disciplined within an organization and kept together until retirement.

The five-hundred-odd elite-track bureaucrats in a given ministry are generalists, stratified by seniority based on year of entry to the ministry. By custom they come to work as late as ten o'clock every morning, an hour or so later than ordinary ministry employees. Ordinary employees leave at five or six, but the elite rarely leave work before nine or ten o'clock at night. It is difficult to get ordinary bureaucrats to work on Saturday without special compensation, but elite bureaucrats, who are not officially required to work on weekends, rarely miss a Saturday and rarely leave before two or three o'clock in the afternoon. They are always available for extra duty, and when the work load is especially demanding, they sleep overnight at the ministry on specially provided cots. Although their salaries rise with seniority, they are paid less than their counterparts in private industry. Their offices are modest, and they have only minimal entertainment allowances. There is no statutory retirement, but elite bureaucrats invariably retire by their mid-fifties at the latest. Ordinary bureaucrats sometimes continue working even past sixty-five. Equally dedicated bureaucrats may be found in other countries, but all Japanese elite bureaucrats in major ministries are expected to display such dedication. The bureaucrats are fully aware that they are dealing with important problems, and they take pride in their successful handling of difficult issues.

The esprit that unites a ministry's five hundred or so elite bureaucrats rests on their sense of group mission. Although not immune from political pressures, bureaucrats do not hesitate to unite against politicians who obstruct their perceived mission. Responsibility for success in any important matter rests with a work unit, and all in the unit are judged by their unit's contribution to the ministry. Superiors do not promote someone who cannot win the liking and cooperation of his peers,

for an individual's value to his unit is determined by his capacity to work effectively with his peers, his superiors, and his subordinates. Each bureaucrat is personally identified with the mission of his work unit and of the ministry as a whole.

Ministries rotate all elite bureaucrats through a prescribed course, with terms of two to four years. After an initial apprentice position in the ministry, the future leaders are commonly assigned to regional posts, overseas study posts, and a variety of key sections within the ministry. After two or three terms of this kind, the elite are subdivided into ordinary elite and especially promising elite. Especially promising elite rotate through a term as a special assistant in the ministry secretariat or another highly prestigious position. By the time ministry officials reach their thirties they can identify those in their age group who are most likely to fill the top posts two decades later. At about age fifty, the top several in the age group advance to become chiefs of the most important divisions, and all others who entered the ministry the same year retire. Several years later consensus begins to jell about who would make the best vice-minister in his age group, and the administrative vice-minister chooses his successor, who becomes the most powerful person in the ministry. All remaining peers resign, not because of an official rule but because of custom and because they will receive high positions in private firms or public corporations or will become politicians. They are chosen by these other organizations for their access to the ministry as well as for their ability, and therefore the ex-bureaucrat wants to keep good relations with his former co-workers.

As an age group progresses through the ministry, the field of candidates for eventual vice-minister narrows rapidly, so that the top three or four contenders have about twenty years to prepare themselves once they know they are serious candidates for the office. Japanese bureaucrats are constantly amazed at the power the American government grants to cabinet

members and department heads who have so little governmental experience and so little preparation for the position. How can the outsider, whether he is a lawyer, academic, or businessman, know enough to do his job well? How can he successfully make use of so much authority when he lacks the intimate personal relationships in every section to ensure that absolutely reliable information will be channeled to him? Or as they put it to American visitors, not entirely cynically, "We are amazed how much talented outsiders can achieve in your system and what fresh ideas they bring to their organization."

Over the years leading bureaucrats develop close relationships with their age peers in other ministries as well as their own as they all rise simultanously. In many cases these relationships began among classmates at the Law Faculty of Tokyo University or even among classmates at the small number of elite high schools. To be sure, the intimacy among bureaucrats of different ministries is rarely on the same level as that among those within a ministry, but there are a variety of formal and informal events that enable the elite of the ministries to get to know one another. This makes possible a level of understanding and exchange of information that goes well beyond formal documents and formal meetings. It also facilitates more accurate predictions of the actions and responses of other ministries. By the time they are in their forties, leading bureaucrats in one ministry try to find occasions to socialize with leading bureaucrats of the same age in other ministries, for it makes their work go more smoothly, and this will become even more important when they reach really top positions.

In Washington, D.C., it is conventional wisdom that a new administration should appoint new department secretaries with a new vision that can overcome bureaucratic lethargy. In the Japanese view, the American president's power to make political appointments for the top positions in the departments of the American government renders them completely depen-

dent on the president and robs the bureaucracy of its daring, autonomy, and, in the long run, talent. High-level Japanese bureaucrats, having complete job security and a group esprit, are able to achieve a self-confident and dynamic leadership that, in their view, would be destroyed if they had to toady to high-level outside appointees; yielding top authority in ministries to outside amateurs would be a disaster.

How then does a Japanese ministry achieve the freshness and receptivity to public opinion for which Americans feel they must look to outsiders and periodic shakeups? First, since the elite core is relatively small, it is not bogged down in the many administrative details confronting the larger group of lower-level officials. It has the security, the ability, and an ethos that enable it to concentrate on what is good for the nation as a whole. Second, Japanese bureaucrats constantly meet with journalists, politicians, and deliberative councils, and these meetings force them to account for their ministry's performance and planning. Top leaders often gather in interministry groups like the weekly meeting of administrative vice-ministers, where they confront common problems. For their ministries to maintain prestige in such meetings, the vice-ministers must be responsive to the demands of the public and the other ministries. In general they have enough authority and success so they do not need to become defensive, but their performance in areas under their jurisdiction is constantly evaluated, and every ministry strives to be known for its achievements. With constant intimate, informal interaction, a climate of opinion develops among leaders in business, politics, and the media which bureaucrats inevitably share. They do not want to stand apart, and no one needs to threaten bureaucrats with loss of job, for the approval of others and the internal desire for achievement provide more than adequate motivation.

How do Japanese ministries assure this vigor and morale among their employees? Because retirement of the elite is at an

early age, power is invariably in the hands of young officials at the prime of their life who expect to live to see the consequences of their policies. In addition, in a small group of elite with close personal contact, the esteem of co-workers is of extreme importance, and maintenance of this esteem requires hard work and sensitivity to others. Frequent informal activities like mahjong, bar hopping, parties, golf, and weekend trips provide tension release, and fellow workers tend to offer more emotional support than in an American office, where options for pursuing one's career without going through the immediate work group create conflicts with group commitment. Furthermore, the elite bureaucrat enjoys a prestige that extends far beyond mere utilitarian acceptance of his authority. His family are buoyed by his status and share in his success, and in turn they are able to provide him with support and tolerate his extraordinarily long hours of work.

Politicians respect the ability of bureaucrats and recognize that they need their good will. Diet members have no independent research staff and rely on bureaucrats for specialized staff work. Politicians who try to work around a bureaucrat are likely to have the whole bureaucracy poised to retaliate by embarrassing the politician at the first opportunity. A Diet member may, for example, be given incomplete briefings by bureaucrats so that he can easily be made to appear foolish and ill-informed in Diet interpellation. It rarely comes to such a showdown, however, because politicians realize the advantage of maintaining the cooperation of the bureaucrat. They will want the bureaucracy to support construction projects in their locality or stand up for rice price supports. The two political appointments in each ministry, the minister and parliamentary vice-minister, have certain prerogatives on certain ministry issues like local construction projects, rice price supports, aid to small businessmen, and increase in welfare payments that are close to the heart of the politician. When it comes to the

balancing of interests between farmers and small and big business, the politicians have considerable say if it does not greatly affect the budget. However, when it comes to the basic administrative work of the ministry, politicians know they must defer to the administrative vice-minister and the bureaucrats beneath him.

Even the prime minister's office has only a limited research capacity, and while it has considerable say in large issues close to the heart of politicians, it rarely tries to second-guess the bureaucracy. Lacking the staff to make independent analysis, the prime minister's office must ally with the ministries rather than work around them. The three or four leading special assistants to the prime minister, in the fields of Finance, Foreign Affairs, and Home Affairs, are selected by the respective ministries to represent them and serve as a liaison between themselves and the prime minister. To be sure, they must be able to work closely with the prime minister, but they are not perceived as special assistants primarily loyal to the prime minister but as representatives of their ministries who provide the liaison to the prime minister in their areas of specialization. Indeed, the prime minister is not expected to formulate policy statements of his own. Rather, he works closely with the bureaucracy and enunciates what various ministries advise him to. In short, the bureaucracy is granted the prestige and authority necessary to sustain high group morale and achieve a high level of performance.

The grooming of leading candidates for prime minister is as thorough and almost as free of surprise as the grooming of leading bureaucrats. The route is not necessarily connected to university attendance, but the potential prime minister must have approximately twenty years of prescribed positions behind him. The specialized training begins when he becomes a faction leader in the LDP. The faction is, in effect, a personal support group for a potential prime minister, for faction

members are pledged to vote for him as prime minister and the leader in turn gives financial assistance to the members and helps place them in good assignments within the Diet.

People who become faction leaders are one of two types. One, the "pure politician," becomes a Diet member at a young age and rises within the Diet. By his third or fourth term, with six or more years of Diet experience, a promising young Diet member may be selected by senior leaders of the LDP to be parliamentary vice-minister of one of the ministries. After serving successfully as parliamentary vice-minister in several ministries, he may inherit a faction from its retired leader or split off and form his own faction. Although factions were theoretically abolished in 1976, old faction alignments have not disappeared, and promising young politicians now head clubs which operate like factions, looking after their members' interests while cooperating with other LDP factions against opposition parties.

The second type of potential prime minister, the ex-bureaucrat, enters the Diet later, after serving in the bureaucracy. After some years in the Diet, a promising ex-bureaucrat may inherit a faction or split off from a senior faction leader to form his own. In recent years those who have aspired to be politicians and who have the qualifications to be bureaucrats have first served some years in the bureaucracy to acquire prestige and experience. At an early age, often in their thirties, they respond to a good opportunity to become a Diet member in order to gather Diet seniority and become a major leader. Of the several faction leaders, generally the ex-bureaucrats have the greatest chance of becoming prime minister. They have a wealth of experience in the actual operations of the government as well as impeccable credentials and university training, and they are freer of the petty political obligations that weigh down politicians who rise through the ranks. Since the mid-1950s only two prime ministers, Miki and Tanaka,

were not former bureaucrats. They rose to power under special circumstances, and the experience of the Liberal Democratic Party under their leadership makes it likely that prime ministers in the near future will be ex-bureaucrats.

Whether he is a pure politician or an ex-bureaucrat, the promising faction leader must first serve a minimum of several months, but usually longer, in at least half a dozen key positions before he may be considered for the prime ministership. These positions include secretary-general of the Liberal Democratic Party and minister of the top ministries (Finance, Ministry of International Trade and Industry, Foreign Affairs, Economic Planning Agency) and perhaps some other ministries. As secretary-general of the party, he acquires experience in money raising and party affairs. As a minister, he does not direct the basic work of the ministry, which is the responsibility of the administrative vice-minister, but he must be aware of the major policy lines within the ministry, and he must work closely both with senior men of the ministry and with party leaders in affairs related to the ministry. As minister, he must be sufficiently familiar with ministry affairs to make policy addresses and answer questions in public on important issues confronting the ministry. While serving in these positions, the aspiring prime minister also gains experience directing his faction and looking after the interests of the faction members.

Which faction leader already rotated through these positions is selected to become prime minister depends on seniority and capacity to work with other top leaders as well as political considerations such as factional power and alignments, mood, timing, and public popularity. The final selection of the prime minister is de facto made by certain elder statesmen in the party, but their choice is narrowly circumscribed by these political considerations. In the past twenty years one compromise candidate has been elected: Prime Minister Miki. There had been a draw between two leading nominees, and the party

selected Miki as the third choice. Yet even he had served in each of the various positions considered to be prerequisites to high office.

By the time a prime minister takes office, therefore, he has served in all the most prestigious ministries, in the top party position, and in key Diet positions. Unlike equally homogeneous Great Britain, where party leaders and bureaucrats have virtually no informal social interaction, he will have benefitted from decades of close contact between politicians and bureaucrats. He is familiar with the issues and knows key bureaucrats and party leaders personally, having served over many of them. For informal information and advice he can draw on his former personal assistants in each ministry and on his friends in the media who formerly covered his activities and now cover various parts of the government.

By letting LDP leaders select the prime minister from among themselves, the Japanese do not risk the election of a top official who has charismatic appeal but is unable to work effectively in the central government. Rather, they choose a politically experienced and highly able leader who is a known quantity, one who can work harmoniously with the various ministries. His knowledge of policy and personnel may not be fully adequate for him to act independently in matters of important policy, but he can make excellent use of experts beneath him. The Japanese marvel that in the United States a man may be elected president who has no experience in the Washington bureaucracy, or no experience in the national capital at all, and that such an outsider can set policy and tell experienced bureaucrats what to do. Such a pattern, in their view, would destroy the pride and enthusiasm of leading bureaucrats. It could lead to amateurish decisions and to policies tied too closely to a single viewpoint. The lack of seasoned judgment and predictability that such a pattern might produce could jeopardize stable alliances with foreign countries.

Boundless Scope and Measured Encouragement: The Approach to the Private Sector

Since the late nineteenth century, when it became clear that competition alone did not sufficiently serve the public interest, the burgeoning American bureaucracy has developed and administered increasingly numerous and complex regulations designed to tame monopolies and curb the evils of business. The assumption has been that many businesses, if left to their own devices, would take advantage of the government and the people. The job of the regulatory agencies is to oversee the business community and uncover deceptions; the spirit of the regulated organization is to provide the minimum of information and to comply with as few rules as it can legally get away with. If at times former regulators enter the ranks of the regulated and the regulated corrupt the regulators, this is seen as merely an imperfection. When in industry related to the military the Defense Department encourages and strengthens certain firms, this is not considered fully legitimate, but it does not alter the fundamental stance of the government concerning business, which is to curb evils by regulation.

By contrast, the bureaucratic elite of Japan, which since the late nineteenth century has been trying to encourage modernization, tries to provide a framework that best enables business to prosper in the long run. Japan is not without regulatory agencies, and indeed parts of the American bureaucracy encourage business; but the Japanese elite bureaucrats' sense of responsibility for overall economic success is broader and deeper. Each ministry puts out one or more annual white papers which provide a tour of the horizon in each major area of the economy and society, reporting on annual developments and giving guidelines for future projects. Bureaucrats in a given agency accept responsibility for everything that occurs in Japan within their sphere of jurisdiction and sometimes

outside Japan as well. If terrorists explode a bomb at Narita Airport, the highest officials in the National Police Agency are held accountable; if the yen is revalued, Ministry of Finance officials are criticized; if a senior White House advisor makes a surprise visit to Peking, American specialists in the Foreign Ministry suffer for not knowing; if steel is in oversupply, MITI officials are blamed; if trading companies withhold goods from the market to raise prices, the cabinet is in trouble.

Japanese bureaucrats in each sphere are expected to think through all major issues in their sphere and to develop and implement long-term plans. Since 1975 the annual volume on directions for the economy published by MITI, the most important ministry supervising industry, has been called *Long-range Vision*, but the title merely formalizes what has long been a basic mission of all Japanese bureaucrats concerned with the economy. The government rarely subsidizes private business directly, but bureaucrats are relentless in their efforts to create conditions for business that are necessary to realize their long-term visions.

The constant interaction among elite bureaucrats reinforces concern with long-range issues. When they assemble, formally and informally, what they have in common is the mission of the ministry as a whole. Since they are a small group and know each other intimately, and since they are rotated frequently and interact constantly, they cannot avoid being aware of one another's responsibilities. Compared to America's Department of Commerce, for example, where an official can become lost in the work of his section without considering all relevant parts of the department, the elite Japanese bureaucrat inevitably thinks about how his work fits in with that of his colleagues he sees every day. Just as inevitably, permanent employment leads him to think about the long-range issues confronted by his ministry, and interaction between seniors

and juniors ensures stability of ministerial leadership, institutional memory, and continuity of policy.

Because political leaders also have considerable continuity and in any case rarely interfere with the main trends of ministerial policy, the continuity of policy is unimpaired by elections, cabinet shuffles, or short-range political pressures. Finance Ministry officials who make up the budget, for example, make marginal allowances for requests of politicians, but if politicians endeavor to go beyond these margins, bureaucrats are known to denounce cabinet interference, proclaiming that the budget "is not a political matter and politicians should not interfere with the government." Japanese bureaucrats yield to no one in the passion that can be generated when their jurisdictional authority is challenged. In America, on the other hand, the White House, drawing on requests from various branches of the government, puts together annual budgets that are less insulated from political pressures. The Office of Management and the Budget, located within the White House, does not have a strong independent authority that would enable it to resist political pressures that greatly disturb the budgeting process. Japanese bureaucrats, less buffeted by sudden new proposals by political leaders and special political interests, are able to provide predictable leadership for the private sector, which can then plan accordingly.

Japanese priorities for economic growth are undiluted with concern for military security. In America, since World War II military security has been judged to be of preeminent importance, consuming a high proportion of our national budget and of the time of our ablest leaders. In Japan the military has claimed less than one percent of the gross national product each year and commanded correspondingly little attention. Because of its small geographical area, Japan is the country most vulnerable to nuclear weapons, and hence Japa-

nese defense specialists have concluded that possessing weapons invites more risks than not possessing them. Of all the major powers, Japan is the only one that has constitutionally renounced the use of offensive forces and prohibited stationing forces overseas. It is tempting to argue that Japan has had a free ride in defense as a result of the American defensive umbrella, although Japan does bear a high portion of the costs of American personnel stationed in Japan. As the junior partner in a military alliance, the Japanese are appropriately deferential, but they are nevertheless convinced that Americans have assumed too forward a military posture and have spent too much on military hardware. Japan is much closer to China and Russia than the United States, but with some minor exceptions, as when the Soviet Union attacks Japanese fishing boats and its airplanes invade Japanese air space, the Japanese perception of military threat is lower than America's. For years Americans appeared more anxious to keep troops in Japan than the Japanese were to have them there. In the view of Japanese leaders, raising Japan's military expenses above the level of one percent of its GNP would not appreciably increase security. They see maintaining good relations with other countries to guarantee the flow of natural resources as more important for national security than military weaponry. In a sense Japan's military policy is a bold enterprise, an effort to be the only major power that is not a major military power. It is a boldness that has high payoffs, direct and indirect, for the private sector.

For over two decades after World War II, Japan, pursuing economic growth with a passion that America reserved for fighting Communism, turned a higher proportion of its GNP and intellectual effort toward basic internal development than did the United States. Parts of the American electronics industry, for example, found it desirable to produce for government contracts which guaranteed a certain amount of profit rather than for the consumer market. They therefore neglected the

international competition in consumer electronics, whereas Japanese firms were forced to be competitive and captured an increasing share of the market. When the American government invests in research and development, the highest proportion goes to military, space, or basic research. The Japanese government, on the other hand, concentrates research expenditure in areas where there is a high probability of a substantial return for Japanese companies but where investment costs are sufficiently great and risky as to be otherwise unattractive to private industry. The goal of the government's own research institutes is not to increase governmental control over these areas but to make the research results available to companies that can best use them to enhance the competitiveness of the economy or the industrial sector as a whole. This is true for those institutes that are part of the government, such as MITI's Agency of Industrial Science and Technology, as well as those institutes financed by other sources, such as those institutes under MITI, the Ministry of Transportation, and the Ministry of Agriculture that are financed respectively by bicycle racing, boat racing, and horse racing.

While accepting responsibility for virtually all developments in society, Japanese bureaucrats try to avoid becoming overextended, maximizing the areas where they provide guidance and minimizing the activities they manage directly. Like the United States and unlike many European countries, Japan has few government-controlled companies in basic industries. Iron, steel, mining, and petroleum are all in the hands of private companies. Furthermore, an even larger share of the Japanese economy is in private hands than in America. Even during the rapid growth period of 1955 to 1964, with considerable government investment in construction to support economic growth, the Japanese tax burden was only 18.5 percent of the GNP, compared to 26.5 percent in the United States and much higher rates in Western Europe. In 1973 it was 22 percent,

compared with 28 percent in the United States and much higher rates in Western Europe. In part this is because of the low defense and welfare budgets but also because bureaucrats try to keep government expenditures low in order to keep the Japanese economy competitive internationally.

The branches of the bureaucracy concerned with the economy all play a role in providing guidance to this large private sector. The Economic Planning Agency, established in 1955 when economic priorities shifted from recovery and control of inflation to economic growth, provides indicative planning for the entire economy. The agency's original staff included bureaucrats drawn from MITI and the Finance Ministry, and it continues to work closely with these ministries. Its multiyear plans help provide flexible guidelines for priorities of financing, foreign exchange, and technology transfer. It does not try to manage the economy directly but to provide targets reflecting long-term trends and specifying what would be necessary for balanced national development. It is in effect a point of communication, coordinating estimates of future growth made by government branches and the business community. It helps draw attention to various needs and helps shape the thinking of the Development Bank, the Export–Import Bank, the Bank of Japan, the Finance Ministry, MITI, and large corporations about what is required for a certain level of growth. Since it does not really plan the economy, it is very flexible in adjusting its estimates to changing conditions, and these changes are therefore quickly known by all concerned so they can make appropriate adjustments.

The ministry that takes the greatest initiative in guiding industrial growth is MITI. MITI officials are so persistent in their efforts to look after the welfare of Japanese industry that they are dubbed by their countrymen as *kyōiku mama*, over-anxious mothers who hover over their children and push them to study. They endeavor to push the pace of modernization

ahead of market forces by setting high standards for modernization of plants and equipment and by promoting mergers of companies that lack the capital to meet those standards. They boldly try to restructure industry, concentrating resources in areas where they think Japan will be competitive internationally in the future. As wages rose to Western levels in the late 1960s, MITI bureaucrats tried to reconcentrate resources in industries that were capital-intensive rather than labor-intensive. After the 1973 oil shock they greatly accelerated plans to push Japan into service- and knowledge-intensive industries rather than energy-intensive ones. MITI officials consider it their responsibility to assist companies in declining industries to merge or go out of business while encouraging new ones to move into the localities and employ the personnel who were laid off. If conditions are not serious enough to shut down a whole industry, they work out a "depression cartel": agreement among companies in a depressed sector to reduce production capacity, with the reduction distributed relatively equally among the companies. MITI also tries to rescue basic industries that have been harmed by some exogenous forces, like petrochemicals after the oil shock.

To strengthen Japan's competitive power and increase Japan's independence, MITI promotes oil companies that are strictly Japanese, not affiliated with "foreign majors." It encourages cooperation among Japanese companies to exploit opportunities for economic development abroad, to ensure the supply of raw materials into Japan, and to help secure markets for Japanese firms abroad. In the mid-1970s, as foreign capital became plentiful and markets for manufactured goods saturated, MITI helped form consortia of Japanese industries to undertake large construction projects and encouraged private insurance companies to provide appropriate coverage, reducing the risks of such ventures. When foreign countries demand restrictions on Japanese exports, MITI officials consider it their

responsibility to help formulate an agreement among Japanese companies in an industrial trade sector to restrict exports proportionately across the board. In areas where Japan has no choice but to liberalize, MITI officials nudge industries to prepare themselves for the threat of the international market and exert their influence to postpone liberalization in growth sectors until the companies become fully competitive on the international market.

MITI's aim is not to reduce competition among Japanese companies but to create the strongest possible companies with the greatest competitive potential. Perhaps the nearest American analogy is the National Football League or the National Basketball Association. League officials establish rules about size of team, recruitment, and rules of play that result in relatively equally matched teams of great competitive abilities. They do not interfere in internal team activity or tell a coach how to run his team, although they do try to provide information that would enable the coach to improve. MITI is divided into branches corresponding to the major industrial sectors, and firms generally specialize in a particular industrial sector. In each sector, the MITI branch tries to create the most effective league of competing companies. Through these branches, MITI considers the overall prospects of an industrial sector and the potential of companies within that sector. It helps ensure that the promising companies get the necessary capital, land, foreign exchange, technological know-how, and access to resources and markets to make best use of their potential. When necessary, MITI officials help to arrange funding from such semigovernmental organizations as the Development Bank, the Export–Import Bank, and the Asian Development Bank. More commonly, banks, whether semigovernmental or private, take the initiative themselves. MITI approves of strong, promising companies, and banks compete eagerly to give loans to the companies that have MITI's blessing. When the govern-

ment sells reclaimed land or refilled land to private companies, priority goes not to the highest bidder but to companies that can best make use of it. When foreign technology is available for purchase, MITI officials try to see that it is bought at the lowest possible price by the company that can best utilize it without overwhelming its competitors. MITI uses the same criterion in deciding which firms should be allowed to affiliate with which foreign firms.

MITI relegates to itself the right to enunciate very detailed rulings about what companies can and cannot do, but it does so only with a broad base of support from leading firms in an industrial sector. It deals with the dangers of monopolistic restraint of competition by requiring handicaps for big companies that control too large a share of a given market. So as to contain the damage to small commercial businesses and bring order to their gradual decline, it decrees how large a department store may be and where it can be located. Since pollution became an issue, it decrees whether the economic benefits of a given factory outweigh the potential harm to the environment before it grants plant construction permits.

MITI's statutory power to control these developments is very limited, and efforts to extend that authority were rebuffed by the business community, other ministries, and the Diet. It does have some statutory power in limited areas: its officials can reserve licensing for companies that meet certain standards; new plants that pollute must have MITI approval before construction; it is allowed to form depression and modernization cartels, albeit with some counterpressures from the Fair Trade Commission; it controls some research expenses; and it grants approval to licensing agreements and to companies that affiliate with foreign companies. But overwhelmingly the success of the ministry is derived not from statutory rules but from its efforts at administrative guidance and from the voluntary cooperation of the business community.

How then does MITI achieve this "voluntary" cooperation? In the first place, companies know that MITI is primarily interested in the welfare of companies in the respective industrial sectors. Second, MITI provides superior information and analysis. Third, within a given industrial sector MITI bureaucrats and company officials at a variety of levels meet constantly, formally and informally, and develop mutual understandings. MITI officials of a given rank generally interact on an equal level with company officials who are slightly older, higher in rank, and far better paid. A bureau chief in MITI responsible for a given industrial sector may be in his late forties but he may confer with company managing directors and presidents fifteen years his senior. Section chiefs and section members may meet as equals with division chiefs in a company. And while they may drink together in a comfortable private room, stretching out on the *tatami* floor of a private restaurant, the parties on both sides are fully aware that their purpose is business. The relaxed, intimate atmosphere is a means to achieve frank exchange of information and views. A mid-level MITI official not uncommonly spends three or four evenings a week in such informal gatherings with appropriate business representatives. In America, a private company's footing the bill might be considered conflict of interest, but in Japan it is clear that these MITI officials are not in collusion with a specific company. Rival companies entertain them similarly, but officials do not base their ultimate decision on the quality of the entertainment or their personal preferences. They are human and admittedly not immune from tilting close decisions, but decisions are made by groups in consultation with the industrial sector organization so that favoritism is difficult; the main criterion for all decisions is the long-term contribution to Japanese industry as a whole. Many leading MITI officials go to work for private companies after retirement, and while outright collusion is difficult, they can be very

useful in facilitating communication between MITI and companies in need of improved channels.

Fourth, company officials know that when they request licenses, permits, choice locations, and tax breaks, MITI will respond more favorably to cooperative companies. Even if MITI eventually grants the necessary permissions to an uncooperative company, the harassing tactics of delaying, requesting more information, raising new questions, and creating uncertainties are ordinarily enough to inspire companies to be more cooperative.

Finally, MITI generally works in harmony with the consensus in an industrial sector or in the business community as a whole. In a given industrial sector there exists a social community of leading firms whose opinions carry great weight in many circles—with politicians, bankers, and other businessmen. Everyone asumes that the companies in an industrial sector and the corresponding branch of MITI have sufficient continuity in personnel to maintain, in effect, an institutional memory. Cooperative companies are eventually rewarded, uncooperative ones punished. Through cooperation with the Finance Ministry, MITI may determine a company's allowable deductions and the amount of depreciation permitted. Also in cooperation with the Finance Ministry, which directs the Bank of Japan, which in turn lends money to commercial banks, MITI maintains leverage over lending. Banks could refuse to extend loans to a company not supported by MITI and a trade association. However, banks rarely need to consider the ultimate sanction of recalling loans, MITI rarely needs to consider refusing permits, and an industrial sector organization does not often need to consider threatening a company with expulsion. Whatever implicit sanctions are conveyed in granting or withholding goodwill, it is the maintenance of goodwill that consciously motivates the company leaders. Since MITI generally acts in concert with the industrial sector organization or the business

community, it can ordinarily count on the support of the majority of firms in disciplining an unreliable member. Indeed, many decisions made by MITI might more properly be viewed as MITI enunciation of a consensus among the most significant actors.

To provide feasible goals and issue such detailed decisions intelligently, MITI officials regularly collect an extraordinary amount of information. They keep up with foreign developments, especially in business, technology, and economics, reading not only foreign publications and government reports but unpublished papers by foreign scholars and researchers at think tanks. In addition to basic financial statements and other regular reports of developments in Japanese firms from various sectors, they require knowledge of the personal, social, and political relationships within a company and between companies. The agreements they promote among companies in a given industrial sector require a higher level of trust than can be achieved through formal contacts. When a specific issue arises, interested parties schedule even more informal gatherings than usual. When necessary, bureaucrats from other ministries join these meetings and other knowledgeable experts and men of influence are called in. Businessmen convene parallel meetings on related topics without bureaucrats present to reach understandings to be presented in later meetings with MITI officials. As a result, American government officials and businessmen negotiating economic matters feel at a great disadvantage because Japanese officials are much better informed, not only about Japanese companies but often about American companies, which are more reluctant to share information with government officials who may be more interested in regulating than assisting.

Some of the most intensive interaction between MITI and companies in a given sector occurs when a declining industrial

sector needs help or a growing industry needs financing and other resources for modernization. In both cases, because companies alone cannot solve the problem, MITI officials naturally think of mergers as part of the solution. The process of exploring various possible mergers and organizing several strong companies from many smaller ones commonly takes several years and may take more than a decade. This kind of process requires very detailed knowledge of and constant interaction with all the key personalities involved. Even in the end MITI is not always entirely successful. It tried valiantly, for example, to reduce the number of major auto companies to two or three rather than the present six: Toyota, Nissan (Datsun), Honda, Isuzu, Mitsubishi, and Tōyō Kōgyō (Mazda). The primary question is how well the personnel, capital, and plants of the various companies supplement one another and how these resources can best be combined. Although MITI may help arrange tax breaks, capital funds, and technology transfer for merging companies and create obstacles for companies especially resistant to a reasonable merger, in the end companies merge only when they consider it in their interest to do so. In the course of this process, MITI encourages companies within the sector to hold discussions about possible merger and prods companies toward merger faster than they may wish to go. MITI officials generally approve any reasonable mergers worked out by the companies themselves. But the strong ties within a Japanese company make it difficult to discharge excess personnel even at a time of merger, and the fusion of two formerly tight-knit companies can result in cleavages between the two groups of personnel that remain for years or even decades. Personnel in a smaller company, naturally wary of being absorbed by a larger company, may offer formidable resistance. A foreigner observing the interaction between MITI and a resistant company would be hard put to describe

the process as part of the cozy government–business partnership of "Japan, Inc.," and mighty MITI is not always victorious.

Whatever the issue, MITI officials do not approach their task legalistically. Their view is that rapidly changing conditions require more adjustment to individual predilections and special circumstances than is permitted by relying on legal precedent. They may draft a host of specific regulations that are later approved by the Diet, but such regulations serve as guidelines for standards and procedures without greatly restricting the scope of bureaucrats' decision making. They want to avoid too many minute regulations that might hamper their effectiveness and distract attention from the major issues affecting the larger purposes of their ministry. Important issues therefore are not resolved by courts or even by legal criteria but are settled on the basis of more complex judgments about world trends, market potential, political and financial support, and individual company capacity. Whereas in the United States, regulatory functions are usually independent of departments like commerce and work at cross purposes, in Japan the combination of regulatory and advisory functions within MITI helps ensure that regulations are administered in a way consistent with the ministry's overall purpose.

The pattern of relationships between MITI and the manufacturing sector is also found in the relationship of other ministries and the private sector in their jurisdiction. Other economic ministries like Finance, Construction, Transport, Posts and Telecommunications, and Agriculture, Forestry, and Fisheries accept broad responsibility for all developments in their sectors. The relationship between the Finance Ministry and banks and security companies is very similar to that between MITI and manufacturing companies. Its "window guidance" is analogous to MITI's administrative guidance, and it supervises a major league of twelve large commercial banks

(city banks) and a host of smaller regional banks. Among the responsibilities of the Construction Ministry, for example, is ensuring that there are several strong companies to offer attractive bids for civil engineering and other construction projects.

The Ministry of Transport is mandated to develop modern air, railway, shipping, and motor transport. Japan Airlines, All-Japan Airways, and Toa Domestic Airlines monopolize air travel, but they operate as private companies, and government bureaucrats constantly encourage these airlines to provide efficient and modern domestic services at low costs, despite their strong support for Japan Airlines in international negotiations. In the 1950s a number of the private railway companies competed to become private airway carriers, but the Ministry of Transport determined that the domestic airline market (aside from special helicopter services, sight-seeing planes, and the like) was too small to support several competing companies and that one major international and two major domestic carriers could meet the demand with the greatest effectiveness. The Transport Ministry later established another international airline when Taiwan refused to permit Japan Airlines to service both Peking and Taiwan, but the Japanese airlines are essentially monopolistic. However, Japan Airlines requires the close cooperation and support of the Ministry of Transport, which therefore is able to encourage the company to supply inexpensive and efficient service.

The superiority of Japan's rail service to that of the United States cannot be attributed to superiority of government planning alone, although the programs of technology importation, research, planning, and construction required impressive coordination. Japan's population concentration, the high volume of intercity travel, and the interest in public transportation compared to American preference for automobiles permits a capital investment in rail services that the American public is not prepared to support. But even given

this financial support, the Shinkansen bullet trains are a model of passenger transportation that may yet influence American patterns as energy problems affect passenger car travel.

A number of Japanese private railway companies (like Tōkyū, Seibu, Tōbu, Hankyū, Meitetsu) compete with the national service in regions where there are large numbers of commuters. The Ministry of Transport helped plan these regional systems, which are parallel in organization and purpose. The same company owns not only the individual railroad but real estate along the route, a department store, and sometimes hotels located at the main terminal. The company is profitable, even if it loses money on the running of the passenger line, because of the many passengers it carries from outlying areas to the main terminal where the department store is located. Compared to American private railways, this structure has helped to maintain effective and reasonably priced rail transport over the long term. The role of the ministerial elite lay not in managing the system but in devising the system and providing the facilities and encouragement so that private companies could make it work. Now that costs of rail transport are rising, the National Railways is also considering a series of money-making schemes in large terminal buildings to keep down costs.

The Ministry of Transport also oversees tourist and freight information. By 1970 the ministry had linked travel agents to all inns and hotels throughout the country by a single on-line or teleprinter reservation system. A computer system also keeps track of cargo assigned to each freight train throughout the country.

The modernization efforts of the Ministry of Agriculture, Forestry, and Fisheries are constrained by the government's policy of maintaining the small family farms in order to stabilize the rural family, the village, and the political support base of the Liberal Democratic Party. In the late 1950s, when farm

technology first enabled the average rural family to farm far more than its own land (averaging about three acres), the government discouraged the consolidation of farms that would have permitted more efficient agriculture. Therefore, many rural men and women who might otherwise have moved to the city remained in the rural areas but began commuting to work in nearby towns and cities. This left farm work to the elderly. In an effort to make small-scale farming attractive and profitable during rapid economic growth, the government used the mechanism of high rice price subsidies, since almost ninety percent of the farm families were engaged in rice growing. The ministry bureaucrats, with the support of Diet members from rural districts, have maintained barriers on agricultural imports. But given this framework of small family farms and artificially high prices, the ministry has assisted in introducing modern fertilizers, hand cultivators, rice transplanters, and insecticides, and in educating farmers about the proper timing of such techniques. The result has been rapid diffusion of modern technology and a rapid rise in productivity per acre. The development and cultivation of new fruits and vegetables and the growth of dairy and beef farming have been rapid and extensive.

In the 1950s the Japanese government gave top priority to economic growth, to the neglect of wages, consumer goods, housing, welfare packages, and pollution control. However, in the 1960s capital for these social overhead expenses began to catch up and in the early 1970s sometimes grew more rapidly than the gross national product, albeit from a lower base. The leaders sometimes neglected these problems until they became intolerable, although one could defend their general strategy of first concentrating on the economic base and then, more recently, attacking these issues with the same gusto and creativity they previously concentrated on issues related to economic growth.

For example, the government leaders were initially slow in dealing with the issue of pollution. They had identified so much with the purposes of growth that initially they were reluctant to consider problems which would slow down growth. Death and disease from mercury poisoning were serious problems recognized by some Ministry of Health and Welfare bureaucrats long before most bureaucrats deigned to act. Local governments were concerned about air pollution in Tokyo, Yokkaichi, and elsewhere before the central government began to give the issue serious attention. By the early 1970s, however, central government bureaucrats mobilized to attack the problem with vigor. Japanese auto companies originally were no more eager than their American counterparts to accept the stiff auto pollution standards demanded by the government, but when Honda announced it was prepared to meet them, its Japanese competitors had no choice but to follow quickly. As a result, Japan has auto emission standards that meet rules as strict as those of the original Muskie Law proposal in the United States. America has yet to achieve these high goals. Similarly, after consultation with appropriate industry leaders, Environment Agency bureaucrats created standards for smoke emissions from newly opened plants that are the most rigid in the world.

One of Japan's most imaginative pollution control plans is built on the principle that requires automobile producers to pay an emission tax and polluters to pay the cost of medical care and compensation to victims. Since the number of pollution victims in a given area is commonly more than public health or court officials can examine individually to determine precisely the source and amount of pollution, bureaucrats worked out a system to determine disaster areas with geographic boundaries. All polluters in the area are required to contribute to a fund to compensate victims certified by local health officials as suffering from a pollution-related disease.

In this way, the Japanese avoid the complex litigation, investigation, and expense required in America when individuals sue insurance companies to provide compensation. As a result, companies are eager to control emission to avoid both monetary payments and adverse publicity. Some Americans concerned with pollution are beginning to urge that America consider similar measures.

When the costs of pollution control are particularly expensive in industries considered basic to the economy, the government helps to arrange low-interest loans to facilitate modernization. To hasten progress in confronting pollution, government bureaucrats in the past have also worked closely with the business community, which has contributed financially to basic research on pollution control and borne the major share of pollution abatement costs.

A 1975 OECD report estimated that Japan was spending about three percent of its GNP on antipollution expenses, several times as much as any other member country, and noted that "anti-pollution investments have been much more important in Japan than elsewhere." The report concluded that "Japan has undoubtedly reversed rising pollution trends for a number of pollutants, particularly in the fields of air pollution and of toxic chemicals." And, despite the higher concentration of industrial production, "By now the air breathed in the main Japanese cities is quite as 'clean' as the air of American, French, British, or German cities," an impressive accomplishment given the highest concentration of industry in the smallest space.

Bureaucrats are concerned with issues as diverse as modernizing fisheries and shipping fleets, redistricting and consolidating geographic administrative units, equalizing standards of living, maintaining social equilibrium, and elevating educational standards throughout the country. Yet the elite corps has remained small in size. Bureaucrats conceive visions, but whenever possible they pass the implementation to the private sector,

where concern for profit heightens motivation and increases efficiency. They place key former bureaucrats in high positions in these public corporations and retain budgetary supervision, thus ensuring that they remain responsive to bureaucratic initiatives. They monitor developments and provide nudges when necessary, but their role is more specialized. Like conductors, they know what music they want to hear, they worry about everything it takes to make good music in the end, and they try to work with each player to give his all while staying in tune with the other players. They do not try to be players themselves. In short, the bureaucratic elite neither reign nor rule but conceive, discuss, persuade, encourage. They bring the entire society within their scope of concern, but their genius lies in avoiding managing while creating the conditions for strong private players.

GUARDING THE GUARDIANS

Postwar bureaucrats are no longer above the political fray as sacred servants of the Imperial Way. But their extraordinary talents and contributions have provided them with an aura of authority that insulates them from the crudest of attacks. Big business leaders depend on them and politicians who reach high office are close to them, having succeeded by following the rules of a game that requires close cooperation with the bureaucracy. With elite bureaucrats thus protected from political pressures, how does Japan avoid a problem that has, as Michel Croizier shows, devastated France, the other country with a comparably elite bureaucracy: formation of a disruptive chasm that isolates various strata, dividing the elite bureaucracy and the people?

Japanese bureaucrats do have considerable authority, and they are not above flaunting their status. They may make powerful businessmen wait to see them, and few ordinary citizens would be so brash as to make direct requests of arro-

Japanese Successes: The State

gant senior bureaucrats without some help from their local political representative. They can be abrupt when giving explanations of policy, impatient when asked their opinion, aloof when receiving a request. Yet their authority is not sufficient for them to give orders. In their search for information, for example, they depend on the voluntary cooperation of the private sector and they therefore must be more sensitive than French bureaucrats to their views.

The willingness of the private sector to cooperate with bureaucrats derives not so much from the formal authority of the bureaucrats as from the public's belief that the bureaucrat is doing the job properly. This in turn owes much to the activities of the Press Club located in each ministry, usually near the minister's and vice minister's offices. Here more than twenty reporters, one or more from each of the major Japanese papers, news agencies, radio, and television networks work full-time to cover the ministry. They are usually assigned here several years after starting work, and their term is commonly two years. At the ministry, they attend occasional official briefiings and keep track of ministry activities. They have access to major officials almost every week and may have special briefings daily. Through reading ministry reports, interviewing and socializing with officials, and exchanging information in the Press Club, the reporters soon develop a highly detailed understanding of affairs in the ministry. The reporter in the Press Club does not necessarily report everything, for he is constrained by the opinion of his colleagues in the Press Club, the ministry officials, and his editors, who weed out peculiar interpretations. But the editors expect him to report accurately the thinking of the ministry as a decision is being made. Bureaucrats notify reporters as they narrow down their options, and the journalist is able to prepare his readership for the ministry's final decision. In this way the reader follows the reasoning of the bureaucracy, and, as in the community decision on a trans-

port system, he anticipates and understands the final outcome. In addition to articles reporting ministry thinking, the newspaper also publishes editorials concerned with the content, and the editorial writers do not hesitate to criticize bureaucratic decisions that are not in accord with public opinion. Editorials, unlike reporting, often have an antigovernment thrust, for everyone recognizes that some controversy and criticism of the government is necessary to sell newspapers.

Ordinarily the reporter must not publish "leaks" prematurely, but the bureaucrat must also play by the rules and disclose important developments. Japanese readers, more than American readers, expect the newspapers to present detailed information on the thinking of the bureaucracy, and if the bureaucrats clearly neglected the public interest, members of the press are expected to use their intimate knowledge or contacts with nonofficial sources to gain information. The long-term close relationship with officials leads to an undesirable lack of independent by-lined criticism in major newspapers, but reporters are also able to write more informally under a pseudonym in the numerous weeklies without jeopardizing their relationships with ministry officials. The weeklies carry gossipy criticism that bureaucrats can easily dismiss, but they also contain serious criticism not so easily dismissed when bureaucrats clearly depart from the public's perception of national interest.

Most of the public opinion polling in Japan is conducted by the newspapers or by the various ministeries and the prime minister's office. In the case of newspapers, this ensures widespread diffusion of poll results and makes it more difficult for newspaper articles and editorials to veer far from public opinion. The polls conducted under the guidance of the ministries and the prime minister's office survey opinion on major questions relevant to national policy. They provide a more direct input from public opinion to the bureaucracy than any

mechanism in the United States and make it more difficult for bureaucrats to veer too far from the polls, the results of which are readily available to the public.

Diet interpellation is another mechanism for guarding the guardians. This gives opposition party members an opportunity to question LDP leaders on legislative matters, but since most legislation is prepared by the bureaucrats, they regard it as an examination of their work. Although Diet members are ordinarily reluctant to appear uninformed and may even consult with acquaintances in the bureaucracy about questions they should ask in public, the interpellation is by no means a sham. Bureaucrats are indeed worried about the fate of their legislation at the hands of the Diet. They complain of the long hours they must spend in the Diet and of the audacity of Diet members who disrupt or threaten to disrupt their well-reasoned plans, but they take the responsibility of appearing in the Diet very seriously. The Finance Ministry officials, for example, are always tense until the Diet has finally approved the annual budget, and as soon as the Diet passes the budget, it is announced on the Finance Ministry loudspeaker, whereupon the employees throughout the ministry break into applause. Opposition parties commonly use Diet interpellation to challenge and embarrass the LDP and the bureaucracy, and bureaucrats must therefore worry not only about their bill's passing but also about possible weak points that will delay passage and leave the bill open to criticism. As a result, even though Diet members may not be well-informed on all legislation, interpellation requires that each bill prepared by the bureaucracy be more or less acceptable to the public and defensible as a rational program for meeting national interests.

Deliberative councils (*shingikai*), composed of well-known private citizens to consider important issues confronting the country, serve as another check on the bureaucracy. They are analogous to presidential commissions or executive-branch

advisory commissions in the United States, but they are used much more extensively. Every ministry except the Foreign Ministry has at least one deliberative council, and in most cases several, to deal with everything from current policy issues to broad questions such as government structure, industrial structure, and tax policy. There are over two hundred standing councils and in addition numerous ad hoc deliberative councils to consider special issues. By the time an issue reaches a deliberative council, bureaucrats prepare carefully by analyzing the basic issues, discerning how key groups stand on the issue, and anticipating major lines of criticism. The councils bring together some of the best informed and most interested parties in a particular sphere. Officially, deliberative council members are selected as individuals, but in fact the "individuals" are systematically selected from the major relevant organizations and interest groups. Councils concerned with wages, for example, include representatives of management and labor and also well-known social critics or professors representing the neutral public. These neutral participants in fact constitute the crucial swing-vote in determining the outcome of council deliberations.

The deliberative council officially acts only in an advisory capacity. It makes recommendations to the bureaucracy which in turn presents its proposals to the Cabinet or the Diet. But the conclusions of the deliberative councils are usually not too dissimilar to the views of the bureaucracy, although there is a great deal of variation in the power and independence of the various deliberative councils. Since the bureaucrats preparing the materials for the deliberative council often have in mind a fairly clear notion of the conclusions they would like the council to draw, they may select the kind of data and make the kinds of presentations that would tend to lead to these conclusions. They select the members of the council, who, though of different persuasions, are likely to be cooperative in reaching

a conclusion without undue delay. Once the council has had its meetings, it is the bureaucrats who write the council reports. Ordinarily council members do not go over the final drafts of the report with great care, in effect granting the bureaucrats considerable leeway in choosing how to summarize the oral deliberations of the council.

Nonetheless, the deliberative council officials are qualified and respected individuals who would by no means agree with everything the bureaucracy might propose. When several possible solutions are almost equally plausible, the deliberative council is usually given the alternatives to debate. Even if it is easy for the bureaucracy to convince a majority of the council to support its viewpoint, there is always the possibility that another member of the council might take his case to the public. During the debates a council member has an opportunity to express his views on television and in the press, and a persuasive case against the bureaucracy's proposals could be embarrassing.

However cleverly bureaucrats might try to manipulate the process, the public airing ensures that their proposals be defensible when subject to public scrutiny. Even if deliberative council members do little more than choose between options outlined by the bureaucracy, public participation forces the bureaucracy to prepare these conclusions with great care. After the debates of the deliberative council are published, the public is able to understand the logic of the advice offered the bureaucracy. When the bureaucracy then makes its decision, the public has been prepared carefully for the conclusion and has a clear understanding of the reasons behind it; at this point it is not easy for Diet members to raise idiosyncratic objections. The public may have no particular respect for the politician who enunciates the conclusion in a policy speech, but it knows that the conclusion has been carefully prepared by the best

minds of the country. For most of the public, the outcome appears not as something a narrow group of bureaucrats decided but something "we Japanese" decided.

CENTRAL DIRECTION AND LOCAL ACTION

Until 1868 the Japanese government was far more decentralized than the United States had been after 1789, but Japanese leaders after 1868 chose a course of centralized coordination and planning as a means to rapid modernization. The American-led Occupation after World War II introduced democratic reforms like the local election of governors, but central direction in guiding local developments, now modified by democratic practices, has continued to be widely accepted.

As in the private sector, much of the actual administration is left to local governments. Compared to America, a high proportion of tax income flows through the central government to the local government. This pattern provides leverage for maintaining high overall standards within national plans and still gives flexibility to the local government. Special legislation in the 1950s has permitted the government to consolidate local communities and to redistrict local administrative boundaries to make them more rational. This has permitted more effective regional and metropolitan planning. It allows the national government to develop consistent, integrated plans for redistributing wealth to poorer areas, for raising standards in education, for standardizing local public transport systems, and for standardizing rules about commerce and industry.

So as to equalize local financial resources and yet give local areas flexibility in choosing their own programs, the national government gives larger equalization grants to poorer local areas. In the United States, because the national government gives out a much higher proportion of funds for specific projects, the local governments try to obtain as much as possible for each project; but in Japan, where the local government

receives a general grant which it can use for many purposes, it makes greater efforts to conserve funds in each area and it has more flexibility in seeing that programs are not suddenly started and suspended by central government fiat. This Japanese plan of equalization of local resources was in fact conceived by an American professor, Carl Shoup, and introduced during the Allied Occupation as the most rational plan for providing equalization of resources while encouraging local initiative and economy.

The grand vision for redistributing the population and industrial facilities to less crowded parts of the country was embodied in the 1972 Tanaka Plan for Remodeling the Japanese Archipelago, a plan actually written by MITI bureaucrats. The plan was designed to provide tax and other incentives for redistributing industry and population to less crowded areas to reduce excessive concentration. It included construction of rail, bridge, and road transport in less developed areas to stimulate their economies. The plan was just out when the oil crisis caused the government to lower interest rates to stimulate the economy. As funds became readily available, the Tanaka Plan led to land speculation and contributed to runaway inflation. As originally formulated, therefore, the Tanaka Plan proved disastrous and, with subsequent retrenchment to control inflation, unrealizable. But the basic program for reconcentrating industry and growth in middle-sized cities and backward areas and for providing tax incentives and low-interest loans to encourage this has continued to guide the work of bureaucrats in relevant government ministries like MITI, Finance, Construction, Transport, and the Land Agency.

With the amalgamation and redistricting of local communities, Japan has been able to undertake concerted metropolitan planning that is not possible in the United States. The National Land Agency is still analyzing long-term population

and economic trends with a view toward consolidating administrative districts where it is desirable to do so. Japan's metropolitan transport systems can cover a broader geographical area and be integrated into national systems. Japan can distribute industrial, commercial, recreational, and other facilities throughout the metropolitan area according to certain guidelines and principles. It can equalize the tax burden between richer and poorer communities and reduce the differentials of public service between rich and poor suburbs, thus creating a more homogeneous nation.

In addition to administration, most of the actual plans for regional development come from the local community. Various parts of the national bureaucracy must cooperate in order for the local community to realize its potential, but the national government makes its guidelines well known. Although the Japanese government takes much greater initiative in defining the desirable course of local development, local communities are given room for initiative. Local business leaders, political leaders, and bureaucrats can do a great deal to remake their area and, through consultation with national politicians and bureaucrats, receive considerable national help. In short, the national government deals with local areas much as it deals with private businesses. It sets up a league, establishes the rules, provides guidance, and reserves the right to make certain decisions, but the key actors are the local leaders.

The maintenance of a centralized authority permits Japan to avoid the overlapping, entangled, inconsistent, unequal, and sometimes totally inadequate programs maintained by American states in matters of welfare, education, crime control, and the like. The variations among American states require an additional layer of national bureaucracy that tries to minimize or go around these inconsistencies. Japan's clear, forthright steps to centralize leadership in these areas in the latter part of the nineteenth century has permitted smoother planning and more

rational administration while reducing excessive bureaucratic overlap. It has not ended local experimentation, and indeed the national government has encouraged it. One wonders whether the United States, in an era of such complex problems requiring such a high level of coordination, is still best served by a pattern of government that places such extensive powers in the hands of the states, a pattern that grew out of premodern agrarian conditions, and whether the entangled web of varying state regulations is optimal for achieving the overall goals of the society.

It requires no great effort to discover instances when Japanese bureaucrats made important errors of judgment. In 1951 the head of the Bank of Japan refused to extend a loan to create the first modern postwar steel plant, arguing that Japan could not hope to compete against America's steel industry. Sony had to postpone for two years its efforts to import transistor technology because government bureaucrats considered the company unable to make good use of the technology. After the first oil shock, bureaucrats overstimulated the economy, causing runaway inflation. Just prior to the first yen revaluation shock, officials confidently predicted yen revaluation would not take place and exchanged yen for billions of dollars. In the 1960s bureaucrats pushed the rapid construction of the Narita International Airport, which then stood idle for a decade because they had vastly underestimated public resistance. This was compounded by delays in constructing local transport facilities and inadequate preparations against terrorists. Jurisdictional disputes between ministries have led to inaction. Yet in balance, the bureaucracy has been remarkably effective in guiding the country.

If one factor stands out in keeping such errors to a minimum and providing relatively rapid self-correcting devices, it is the involvement of all relevant parties in the decision-making process and their thorough commitment to the resulting de-

cisions. In English, this process is sometimes referred to as "decision making by consensus," but this does not adequately describe the Japanese decision-making process. In Japanese the term used is *nemawashi*: root binding. The term originally comes from gardening, where it designates the careful untangling and binding of each of the roots of a tree before it is moved. The Japanese bureaucracy provides vigorous direction on many major issues, continuing over a long period of time, and during this process they are in close touch with all relevant groups to make sure they understand the evolving decisions, that their roots are bound. The press clubs and deliberative councils ensure that wider circles of the interested public are similarly informed of these decisions. The relevant groups are not expected to agree with all decisions made by the bureaucrats. Sometimes a group's interests are not in keeping with the emerging decision, and this group must be made to understand the necessity of the decision and the well-considered impartiality of the decision. If that group is disadvantaged by this decision, then it is understood that they will be given special consideration now or in the future. The long-term continuity in bureaucratic leadership, unimpaired by changes of politicians, ensures the reliability of bureaucrats in carrying through future commitments. The disadvantaged group's roots are thus bound and do not impede the effective moving of the tree. Not all a tree's roots can always be smoothly bound, but a majority is not enough, and a serious effort is made to include as many roots as possible.

An important part of root binding is to give each group ample time to adjust to the emerging decision, to explain the goals of the decision and let them understand the information that leads to this conclusion. If all groups are in order, then the tree can be moved with extraordinary rapidity, but if not all groups are convinced or are not prepared, then the decision

is delayed. Some Westerners working with the Japanese bureaucracy have complained that the slowness of the process can be exasperating. Occasionally top Japanese bureaucrats talk enviously of their Western counterparts who can simply give out orders or directives or plans, but when pushed they acknowledge that the Japanese system works better in the long run. The final administrative decision or Diet bill or pronouncement coming from the Japanese bureaucracy is not a tidy, tightly knit, clearly reasoned, lawyer-like brief that might emanate from the White House. It is evasive, indirect, even inconsistent in points, not because Japanese bureaucrats like evasiveness but because they want to maximize the level of cooperation of all relevant groups.

An example of the results of root binding can be seen in what may be the most critical problem for both countries in recent years, the energy shortage. The Carter Administration put forth a brilliantly argued, thoughtful plan for dealing with the problem of energy, but it lacked the consensus and support of relevant groups, and its key parts could not therefore be implemented quickly and vigorously. The Japanese bureaucracy, in contrast, consulted closely even with oil companies, working out in conjunction with leaders of the private sector a series of programs for energy conservation. They increased the cost of gasoline about twice the rate of increase in America, gasoline mileage in new cars expanded rapidly, solar energy units were installed in many homes, and companies developed fuel economy programs.

The result was that Japan basically kept petroleum imports constant despite economic growth, while American oil imports were growing rapidly despite lower economic growth. Large Japanese trees cannot be moved automatically, and in the 1930s, despite cultural homogeneity, they were often moved by intimidating potential opposition. They are helped

by homogeneity, but they make the best of it by highlighting a sense of common national purpose, working closely with key groups whose cooperation is needed, and preparing the general public. The public may complain about imperfect plans from arrogant bureaucrats, but in the end it is not "their plan" but "our plan," and the roots stick with the tree.

5

Politics: Higher Interests and Fair Shares

IF THE TERM "DEMOCRACY" is used to signify the expression of diverse interests in the political arena and the capacity of the government to satisfy these interests, it could be argued that Japan is now a more effective democracy than America. The interests of the Japanese are expressed not by specialized groups but by basic multipurposed groups—like villages, towns, firms, professional associations—that are generally better organized and disciplined and more systematic in representing the wishes of their membership than the more ephemeral American special-interest groups. Groups in Japan interact with one another more frequently, so that they are particularly effective aggregating interests—engaging in joint political activity for a broader common purpose. And at all levels in Japan, people make a conscious effort to provide a balanced though not equal "fair share" to all recognized groups in the society. The distribution of fair shares, like the aggregation of interests, is made possible by the solidarity of these multipurpose groups.

GROUP SOLIDARITY

The solidarity of Japanese communities is hardly unique. Traditional New England villages and the villages in Europe

from which many American immigrants came also had strong group ties, enabling them to work for common goals and to discipline community members. What is unusual is that the Japanese have been able to retain this sense of community— to keep what George Lodge termed their "communitarian values"—in a time when group consciousness attenuated in many nations.

One could argue that Japan's success in perpetuating a sense of community stems from its late transition from feudalism directly to modern corporate society, without an intervening period of individualism lasting hundreds of years as in Western Europe. But whatever its historical roots, group solidarity remains in Japan because people work at it. Whether in villages, towns, urban neighborhoods, or work places, leaders exert themselves to retain the loyalty of group members by responding to their needs. Children are taught the value of cooperation for everyone's benefit, and, however annoying they may find group pressures, adults remain responsive to group attitudes for they are convinced that everyone gains from restraining egoism.

Even today, a Japanese tends to maintain primary loyalty to one all-embracing group in which he expresses all aspects of his personality, from private and personal to formal and businesslike. Membership is not casually begun or terminated, for mutual obligations are strong and enduring. The American tends to belong to no such basic group but to express different aspects of his personality in the various special-purpose groups to which he belongs. The Japanese may belong to as many groups as his American counterpart, but one primary membership stands out, and the others are clearly secondary. The farmer, for example, may belong primarily to the local agricultural cooperative, and this becomes the basic reference point for him and his family even when he participates in other groups. An employee of a company is known by his

affiliation with that company no matter in what groups he participates. This primary identification with the company is reinforced by other groups, for they want members who are trusted by the company. It is further reinforced by national organizations, for they choose to work through the primary local group to distribute their political favors and economic benefits while seeking local bases of support.

Now that young men living on farms earn most of their income in nonagricultural pursuits, commonly commuting to work, the power of the village over the family is no longer as great as it was. Nonetheless, the people in the village not only share a common Shinto shrine and hold common celebrations but often meet in the village recreation hall. They are quick to organize for road improvements and other beautification and modernization projects for their community as a whole, as many villages did in building swimming pools after the 1964 Tokyo Olympics. The local agricultural cooperative is still able to make available less expensive seed, fertilizer, agricultural equipment, insurance, and charter trips than farmers could attain individually. The cooperative may also arrange investments that are more reliable and profitable than individuals could have made on their own. Although the richer people in the village may in fact have more influence in the outcome of these activities than the poorer, they are also obligated to make a much greater financial contribution to the common good, a pattern not unlike that in traditional European and American villages.

In urban and suburban neighborhoods, especially in older, established neighborhoods, but even in new public apartment projects (*danchi*), local residents belong to neighborhood associations. In the university, students commonly have one predominant activity club to which they belong. The club does engage in a specialized activity like skiing or English speaking, but it is far more all-embracing and requires more loyalty and

continuity than the typical extracurricular activity on American campuses. Perhaps the nearest analogue is the American fraternity or sorority, but in a Japanese university virtually everyone belongs to such a club. The Japanese activity club is strong on nostalgia and sentimentality, celebrating farewells, taking pictures for commemoration, singing and drinking together. Essentially the same type of primary membership group exists among small shopkeepers on a street of small stores, among employees of larger organizations, and among independent professional groups such as doctors and dentists.

In Japanese villages there is a high degree of family continuity spanning several generations. In urban neighborhoods also family home sites turn over less frequently than in the United States. In large companies, peers who enter the company together remain close throughout their working career and sometimes later as well. This continuity helps to strengthen group opinion, and if this leads to excesses on such superficial matters as how members talk and dress, it does help make members more responsive to one another's opinions.

HIGHER AGGREGATION OF INTERESTS

These multipurpose groups spend a great deal of time talking and thinking about their long-range interests and are therefore much better informed about matters relating to their interests than the more ephemeral interest groups in America. Village leaders, for example, are well-informed about prefectural and national programs for which they might qualify and, when dissatisfied with the response of bureaucrats, take their case to a prefectural assemblyman or Diet member. They will probably have endorsed him and contributed as a group to his campaign funds to ensure a receptive hearing when they visit him with proposals on behalf of their community. Interest in political affairs is high: about seventy percent of voters turn out for local elections, compared to about fifty percent

in the United States. The assemblyman or Diet member knows that each village in his constituency is watching his behavior in other villages, and he must therefore develop a strategy of either helping all to a comparable degree or concentrating on certain communities where he has an especially strong following. He may work with a village separately on local issues, but on complicated issues affecting other communities he knows he must side with large groups that have aggregated their interests to form the largest pressure group. This process of combining interests is by no means unique to Japan, but what is unusual is how consistently all villagers in a village vote as a bloc, how much they discuss candidates and issues with each other, and how much time representatives of different villages spend with each other in trying to find common interests that they can jointly pursue at higher levels.

The group to which an individual owes his primary loyalty is the basic building block for aggregating interests. Since this basic group unites people with a common source of income—fellow employees of a company, farmers in a given community, fellow professionals, or fellow shopkeepers—the main interests aggregated tend to be those most affecting members' pocketbooks. This contrasts with America, where special-issue groups dealing with the environment, civil liberties, and abortion, for example—groups that unite people from diverse occupations and diverse communities—are much more important. In Japan the group with income from a certain source may be linked with like groups elsewhere or with diverse groups in the same locality. Local communities can then aggregate their interests in progressively larger geographical areas, and at the national level some associations link many different occupational groupings from many different localities.

Despite Japan's small size, there are three important geographical levels between the nation and the municipality. One

is the "large region," of which there are nine. The next level down is the prefecture, of which there are forty-seven, including two urban prefectures (Osaka and Kyoto) and one metropolis (Tokyo). Of the three levels, only the prefecture has corresponding government institutions. The third and lowest level consists of smaller planning areas, many of which more or less correspond to some of the roughly two hundred and fifty feudal fiefs of the Tokugawa period. National Land Agency officials and other bureaucrats have found it fruitful to work with these areas, which are somewhat larger than a municipality, in a variety of area development programs. Since local community consolidation in the 1950s, the only formal governmental level below the prefecture is the municipality.

Corresponding to the nine large regions are nine regional associations of large business enterprises, each of which promotes its respective interests. These associations meet to work out concrete plans for regional development, but they also engage in social activity as well, thereby reinforcing the sense of community, especially among regional leaders. Over the years these leaders have developed a set of informal rules to ensure the success of their associations. For example, so that the head of the association could not use this post to enhance his own company's interests, he should not be from a prominent regional company with competitors of comparable size. Yet he should be an important, successful, and respected person of sufficient age for his personal authority to reinforce his official authority, enabling him to mobilize cooperation when necessary. He thus tends to be a company president or chairman who has already handed over some company responsibilities to younger men, permitting him to devote perhaps half of his time or more to the region as a whole. He tends to be from a company so dominant that the enterprise has no regional rival or from a small but highly respected locally based company so he cannot misuse his position. There is a neat and

popular solution to the problem of headship which derives from the post-World War II splitting of the government-owned electric power monopoly into nine private electric power companies, each servicing an area corresponding to one of the nine regions. Since electric power is the major business without competitors in the area, since its scope of interests corresponds precisely to that of the region, and since business-men want to be on good terms with the power company, the chairman of the electric power company is commonly elected president of the regional businessmen's association. Other important businesses, like metropolitan-area railways, regional banks, and industries with a main office in the region, also play a major role in regional organizations, and vice-presidents of the regional association are chosen systematically to represent major sectors and industrial groups, for they have a prominent role in working toward regional agreements. Local leaders of large national companies with facilities in the region are represented in regional business associations, but because of national interests they cannot be expected to fight vigorously for regional interests; they are therefore rarely chosen even as vice-presidents and have less power in regional associations than the size of their business would otherwise warrant. Young growing companies that have not yet had long years of co-operation with other regional leaders are not given prominence equal to their economic power until they have proven they can work well with others.

Since each of the regions plays a major national role, leaders of their business associations regularly see not only prefectural politicians and Diet members from their region but all leading Tokyo politicians and bureaucrats concerned with major national problems. Their constant contact with national politicians assures that national leaders are alert to local sensitivities and well-informed about weak spots in regional development. Although much of the contact is informal

and social in order to develop a relationship of trust, the participants are aware of their respective responsibilities to the region and the nation. In a sense their respective roles make statesmen of the participants because business leaders in this context cannot speak of their individual company's interest. They are selected because of their sense of responsibility to the region as a whole, and they value the personal and social relationships that come from fulfilling regional responsibility. They do not solve big problems in these meetings alone, for interaction occurs at many levels. The Kansai business leaders, for example, ordinarily meet with the prime minister once a month at an exclusive restaurant for informal discussion of Kansai problems. The leaders in these meetings discuss only general issues, leaving to association staff members the problem of working out the details with bureaucrats in Tokyo, which the leaders then approve. Without the agreement and participation of their underlings, however, the top leaders do not have the leeway to make final commitments. Regional business leaders work with regional labor leaders, newspaper and television representatives, and university faculty in similar pursuit of regional interests. Although American regional leaders may occasionally meet informally for similar purposes, in Japan each organization spends more time considering details and working out agreements so that when high-level officials meet, they do so as representatives expressing carefully considered regional plans with a high level of consensus among participating companies and with the understanding of local politicians, newspaper editors, and labor and farm groups as well.

In Tokyo the forty-seven prefectures each maintain a large meeting center (*kaikan*) with many conference rooms and offices and appropriate staff to represent prefectural interests. These prefectural offices are in constant contact with national politicians, bureaucrats, reporters, and businessmen in an effort to monitor all recent developments of interest to

the prefecture. They value informal contacts to keep one step ahead of formal announcements and thereby better represent their prefecture. The prefectural representatives are concerned not only with annual budget allowances for schools, hospitals, welfare establishments, and construction projects but with virtually every major project affecting prefectural activity. Representatives of prefectural groups of all kinds constantly visit Tokyo, checking in at their respective prefectural offices and talking to appropriate politicians and bureaucrats in their respective spheres. Many maintain dual residences, one in their home prefecture and one in Tokyo. Because there is a government office in the prefecture, prefectural initiative is more often in the hands of the government than in the case of the large regions, which lack government offices and therefore must rely more on big business associations. Nonetheless, the prefectural Chamber of Commerce looks after prefectural business interests, and their representatives systematically work out priorities for economic development just as government officials do. If anything, there is greater camaraderie and information exchange at the prefectural level than in the large regions.

Some local politicians of particularly great power represent the interests of their constituencies more effectively than others, and stories of major politicians arranging for a train stop to be built in or near their hometown are not without foundation. The project for building a bridge to Shikoku was long-delayed because three effective local politicians were vying for location. But each prefectural government and prefectural business community is well organized to look out for the interests of their locality, and this forces Diet members and bureaucrats to work out even-handed policies for balanced development and to formulate a convincing rationale for selecting certain localities for certain projects. It ensures well-organized prefectural groupings and forces the national gov-

ernment to be sensitive to local problems and to evaluate the overall impact on regional development when considering a particular project. Interested national officials know they can turn to the prefectures for well-considered plans. And this pooling of common interests makes idiosyncratic solutions virtually impossible.

Below the prefectural level the sense of solidarity going back to fiefs of the Tokugawa era sometimes lurks in the background, but the emphasis in contemporary organizations is on present-day economic development. Local business associations parallel to those at higher levels look after the interests of their municipality or other sub-prefectural unit. Although leadership may be less sophisticated than at higher levels, thorough-going organization and careful consultation results in the same approach for evaluating overall interests.

Although associations of functional specialties such as farming, medicine, dentistry, and industry are represented at the regional, prefectural, and lower levels, these sectoral groups are generally branches of national associations, and the strongest representation of each sector tends to be at the national level. Virtually every industrial, professional, and agricultural sector is well organized to represent its special interests. Labor associations work together to create the united front that leads to an annual rise in wages. Agricultural associations, with the Agricultural Cooperative (Nōkyō) in the lead, cooperate to maintain high price supports for rice. Fruit growers of various kinds meet to aggregate their national interests, aware that their individual interests will easily be sacrificed at the national level unless they band together. Indeed, the reason Japanese politicians are reluctant to open Japan to free import of cherries and citrus fruits despite trade imbalances and American pressure is that Japanese farmers are so united that a politician showing flexibility on any agricultural product runs the risk of strong, well-united farm op-

position. These special-interest groups make their case strongly to leading politicians and Ministry of Agriculture bureaucrats, who defend them. Medical and dental associations also coordinate their efforts to obtain adequate fees for service, but consumer organizations and insurance companies similarly represent consumer interests, leading to constant bargaining between representatives of the practitioners and consumers.

Virtually all major Japanese firms specialize in a single sector like banking, trading, real estate, department stores, heavy industry, electric appliances, petroleum, and textiles. This pattern—developed partly through bureaucratic guidance —to encourage the expertise and long-range technical development necessary for the most competitive performance is very different, for example, from American conglomerates, which spread over several sectors and leave and enter various industrial sectors with relative ease. Given the specialization of Japanese firms in a given industrial sector, the aggregation of interests can take two directions. One is the organization of all firms from a single industrial sector, which maximizes the cooperation that comes from looking after their common interests in building up their sector. The second is the organization of firms into "groups" consisting of one firm from each sector. A firm in a group has the advantage of special affiliation with companies in different sectors. *Zaibatsu* (literally, "financial clique") groups (like Mitsui, Mitsubishi, and Sumitomo) link firms formerly united under their prewar holding company, and non-*zaibatsu* groups (like Fuji, Sanwa, Daiwa, and Dai-ichi Kangyō) center around large banks.

In addition to these two types of organization, a third type combines virtually all firms of a given size in all sectors: Nikkeiren (Japanese Federation of Employers), for example, deals with labor problems of all large firms, Keidanren (Federation of Economic Organizations) and the eight other regional associations deal with all issues aside from labor confronting

big business, and the Chamber of Commerce (composed of all companies) includes all firms but now particularly represents small business.

Depending on the issue and the extent of common interests, trade associations, or ad hoc groups of companies in a sector, look out for a range of interests impossible to represent in the United States, where antitrust laws are more rigid. To make sure that they have entrée when politicians consider issues like tax rates, consolidation and rationalization of firms, industrial and safety standards, and protection against foreign industrial threats, they make regular collective political contributions as a sector. On more detailed issues they deal regularly with the bureaucracy, and major trade associations include staff members who were elite bureaucrats in big ministries, creating smooth relationships with the bureaucracy. The associations discuss virtually every issue considered by MITI in their sphere, for even if MITI eventually resolves the issue, it would not do so without fully understanding the dominant views of the sector. In a declining industry, it is the trade association that helps shape the depression cartel with apportionment of quotas for reduced production. When the United States demands that Japan limit exports to the United States, this association, in cooperation with MITI, apportions quotas for reducing exports, although paradoxically the kind of restraint the United States demands is prohibited in America by antitrust legislation. Similarly, in times of growth, because of the danger of "over-heating" the economy and of creating excess capacity, it is this industrial sector organization that works out with the appropriate MITI branch a fair system for restraining expansion.

Sectoral associations sometimes develop special projects which they administer directly. The banking association, for example, developed the system that permits deposits to be transferred by a centralized computer, operated by the bank-

ing association, from any regular commercial bank to any account in any other commercial bank. The steel sector, interested in keeping down the cost of electricity and fuel, takes an active role in securing stable sources of energy for the entire nation and in lobbying within Keidanren and the government to limit the inflationary pressures of electricity and fuel costs. Similarly, the automobile sector seeks to keep down the cost of steel as well as electricity and fuel so it may continue to compete internationally.

After the consolidation of the Nippon Steel Corporation in 1969, counterpressures to check oligopolies, monopolies, and sectoral cooperation grew rapidly. These pressures rose to new heights in 1973 after some companies took advantage of the oil-embargo jitters to corner certain markets and restrict the flow of goods, profiteering from artificially high prices. The Fair Trade Commission, then fueled by popular sentiment, drew on long-standing American trust-busting efforts to fight sectoral cooperation and monopolies. Not long after these oil shocks, Japan passed some antimonopoly legislation, but the stricter provisions advocated by some groups were not enacted, partly because of effective representations by the business community. Most Japanese companies acknowledge that profiteering from cornering markets should be prevented, and many business leaders did condemn the offending companies. Some business leaders undoubtedly cooperated only to escape political pressure for a more virulent antimonopoly law, but the capacity of the business community to restrain such practices by a combination of social pressure and threat of legislation is quite possibly more effective than legislation itself, with all the attendant problems of regulation and litigation.

Although business sector associations are naturally opposed to strong antimonopoly legislation and a trust-busting Fair Trade Commission, they tone down public expressions on

this issue to avoid public indignation. MITI officials are, if anything, more open than the business community in opposing the Fair Trade Commission. In part it is a classic jurisdictional dispute, but in part it is because MITI's approach is so directly contrary to that of the Fair Trade Commission. MITI officials believe in the ultimate value of the marketplace, but in the short range they think it advisable to gain the cooperation of companies in a sector in cushioning economic fluctuations, thus reducing disruptions to the specific industries, their employees, and the economy as a whole. They are confident that their administrative guidance with the sanctions at their disposal can contain the dangers of oligopoly. The public supports sectoral cooperation, for they want their companies to avoid the dangers of sudden layoffs and unemployment. Furthermore, both the bureaucrats and the public believe that improvement of safety and pollution standards as well as economic prosperity require sectoral cooperation.

The foreigner is struck with the paradox of extraordinarily competitive relations among firms in a single sector whose leaders nonetheless genuinely enjoy each other's company when working for the sector as a whole. Officials who fight to increase their company's market share can seem totally relaxed in the camaraderie of drinking with counterparts in rival companies. Sector association leaders at times fight almost as arduously and effectively in the interest of the sector as a whole as the individual company leaders fight for the good of their own businesses. Indeed, they cannot understand how Americans can keep their individual companies abreast of modern developments without the kind of cooperation that American antitrust practice forbids.

Cooperation within a *zaibatsu* or non-*zaibatsu* group is even easier than within a sector association, for the companies have many business interests in common and few in competition. The *zaibatsu* groups date back before World War II,

when a holding company at the top of the *zaibatsu* had direct control over the range of *zaibatsu*-related companies. In the postwar period, holding companies were outlawed and dispersed by the Occupation, and even after regrouping, the companies are much more independent and group ties weaker than before the war. A non-*zaibatsu* group is organized similarly, although these groups are of more recent origin and are even more loosely structured. The companies in a group are bound together by friendship and regular meetings among top leaders as well as by loans, some mutual stockholding, interlocking directorates, information sharing, division of insurance risks, and, in case of trouble, mutual assistance, but all these kinds of relations may, to a lesser degree, extend across group lines.

Within the group, the bank or the trading company commonly plays a predominant role, for both have maximum contact with other group companies. In new fields like computers, petrochemicals, and atomic energy, other group-affiliated companies help finance the growing company, thereby tying it closely to the group, but the older, well-established company with its own funds enjoys virtual independence. A company in a declining industry may place some personnel in a group-affiliated company in a more prosperous sector. Companies in the group may collect funds jointly for political leaders, making use of these contacts, for example, to get necessary approval for large group projects abroad. The projects are not always undertaken solely at the request of the group; in some cases, Japanese government officials, spotting an overseas opportunity for Japanese companies, encourage the group to work out a program to compete effectively with project proposals from other countries. Sometimes government bureaucrats help arrange low-interest loans (as, for example, through the Export–Import Bank) and necessary insurance to reduce the risk and make the project financially

appealing. These projects require complicated cooperative efforts which companies with group affiliation can achieve more effectively and easily than nonrelated companies. The Sumitomo project in Singapore, the Mitsui project in Iran, and the Mitsubishi project in Saudi Arabia are notable examples.

In aggregating interests at the national level, the Chamber of Commerce speaks for small business. By law every company in Japan is a registered member of the Chamber of Commerce. The majority of companies are naturally smaller ones, and as a result the Japanese Chamber of Commerce has come to represent the interests of small- and medium-sized enterprises. At the prefectural level and below, because there are few large company headquarters, the Chamber of Commerce branches commonly serve as the focus for the entire local business community. It is not unlike local American Chamber of Commerce branches, but on the whole the Japanese Chambers of Commerce are better organized and more active and work more closely with government officials in planning the development of their region. This is evident in projects like filling in land along the ocean, reclaiming land, and planning for local industrial sites. Because the total business conducted by small companies cannot compare with that of large businesses, and because their diverse interests are not so easily aggregated and many of them are dependent on large companies, their aggregation of interest is less effective than that of large businesses. Nonetheless, in the spirit of "fair share," an effort is made by government bureaucrats as well as Diet members representing local business interests to provide special programs of financial aid, low-interest loans, insurance, and security for small businesses. Although sizeable numbers of individual small businesses have gone bankrupt in some "recession," large numbers of new firms have started and the small-business sector has remained strong despite the rapid growth and concentration of very large companies.

Keidanren, composed of the seven-hundred-odd largest Japanese companies, is organized to represent big business with a thoroughness without peer in the world. Its role might be compared to that of the National Association of Manufacturers if that association enjoyed the regular and active participation of the very top business leaders working closely with a large professional staff to forge agreements on behalf of big business as a whole. In the mass media Keidanren is termed the "main temple" and its chairman the "prime minister" of the business community. Although there is no other regional association of top businessmen for the Tokyo area, it is really a national organization, and all major corporations in Japan, regardless of location of headquarters, belong. Keidanren occupies a large fourteen-story building in the heart of Japan's Wall Street, Otemachi, and here each day there are dozens of meetings for the leaders of the largest companies to study and discuss issues of interest to their sector or to some substantial part of the business community. On the first floor is the Press Club, with desks for the reporters from major papers and networks who work there full time covering the business community.

In a sense Keidanren also acts as the Foreign Ministry of the Japanese business community, sponsoring meetings with foreign businessmen and sending abroad specialized missions of business leaders to find solutions to trade problems with key countries. When threats of European and American protectionism arise, Keidanren consults broadly in Japan, does the careful root binding with foreign business leaders, and if necessary sends out delegations to conclude the agreements. In dealing with communist countries, especially the Soviet Union, Keidanren organizes joint projects and deals with communist trading companies to assure that state monopolies do not take undue advantage of rivalries among Japanese companies. As for the very largest overseas projects such as those currently

underway in Brazil and the Soviet Union, Keidanren itself sponsors the project because it alone has the capacity to represent and work with a wide variety of Japanese firms that cross industrial group lines.

Because it represents numerous and diverse companies with so many different interests, Keidanren cannot express its view on every small matter even if its study groups and committees do discuss every important issue and most minor issues of interest to the business community. It cannot be partial to any single group or any industrial sector, although it can give special attention and aid to needy sectors. Keidanren concentrates on issues of interest to the business community as a whole, and rather than express its views to the outside, it discusses issues in broad national terms, taking, for example, a firm stand in favor of stimulating the economy in opposition to prime ministers like Fukuda who tend to be more concerned about inflation. In this Keidanren represents the predominant view of most businesses. Similarly, it tries to design tax proposals that represent a compromise between the interests of the various companies but still provide encouragement to business as a whole. It only sponsors study missions that will affect many companies in different areas; other study missions are sponsored by groups, sectoral associations, or ad hoc groupings for special purposes.

Keidanren is, of course, criticized in the press for pushing the interests of big business while slighting the interests of small business and the public at large. To be sure, Keidanren officials do pursue the interests of big business and do so vigorously, but the top leaders are themselves convinced that they are moved by broader goals. They achieve fame and wealth in their own company many years before assuming leadership in Keidanren, and once there, they see themselves as playing a grander role as business statesmen, with visions benefiting all Japanese. When these leaders of the business community

first began to meet with businessmen from the United States, many confidentially expressed surprise at the extent to which American businessmen thought only of their own company and were ill-prepared to consider business problems from a broader perspective, let alone negotiate agreements on complex issues. Many senior American business leaders have been impressed with the statesmanship of their Japanese counterparts like Keidanren leader Taizō Ishizaka. Many of these senior leaders have not only a broad training in European history and literature, Chinese classics, Japanese history, Marxist and "modern" economics but a bold vision for the future and an overarching philosophy.

Keidanren uses a uniquely Japanese method of collecting political contributions from the business community. Beginning in 1955 when the Liberal Democratic Party was formed, Keidanren has developed and modified a system to assess each of the large industrial sectors for a political contribution. The largest business sectors such as steel, electric power, and banking have been the pacesetters, giving the largest contributions, and the other industrial sectors are assessed proportionately. The automobile sector, for example, which originally gave less than steel, has now grown so substantially that its contribution is roughly the same as that of steel and electric power. Within each industrial sector the major companies are expected to give in proportion to their size and profitability. Keidanren distributes the funds it collects from the big business community primarily to the Liberal Democratic Party through an intermediary citizen's group (long called the National Association), but some is also given to various opposition parties. Political representation from the business community concentrates on the most general issues: that the country maintain a private business economy rather than a socialist one, that the LDP select leaders who can maintain stability, and that governmental policy encourage economic growth and stability.

It tends to favor basic industry necessary for national development. Compared to Japan in the 1930s or present-day America, its efforts are not distorted by a large defense industry strongly protected by one part of the government. The big business community does not expect a precise quid pro quo. It expects only a sympathetic understanding of conditions necessary for general business health.

This large centralized financial contribution tends to tilt the government toward big rather than small business, but it also tilts it toward the interests of the business community as a whole rather than toward the interests of any particular industry or company. If one company or one industrial sector tries to pressure the government in its favor, the government is likely to be cautious in responding because of the considerable support of the rest of the business community. This higher level of aggregation of interests within the business community tends to ensure that the highest level politicians also think in comparably broad terms of the interests of the country rather than of peculiar, sectarian interests. Although big business does not fully speak for farmers and laborers, big business reaches its conclusion only after fully understanding and accommodating to their views, for it realizes that its own success depends on the active cooperation of these groups.

The aggregation of interests is no casual process. It includes an exhaustive discussion of issues by all relevant parties from the outset, so that any conclusion reflects a thorough understanding of the issues. Every single group can turn to several associations in pursuing its interests, but it is constrained by the resulting cooperation. It is too facile to describe the result as a consensus, for everyone's best interests are not necessarily served, but the conclusion is acknowledged as a considered view that represents the best long-term interests of the largest part of the business community. The Japanese believe that the American system—wherein individual contributors

pressure individual politicians to their own ends, and some groups are better organized than others—leads to haphazard results that do not necessarily reflect the major interests of the largest number. They perceive America as making political decisions that are inadequately considered, subject to idiosyncracies, and lacking in constancy and breadth of vision. It is not that Japanese politicians have broader visions than their Western counterparts but that the private sector's constant interaction, mutual consultation, and hammering out of common understandings creates a stronger support base for the political leader and the bureaucrat with broad vision to respond to. It makes it infinitely easier for national leaders to respond to the general interest against narrow special interest groups. Dismissing this as Japan, Inc. vastly understates the struggle between different Japanese groups in the course of achieving agreements. In contemporary societies so rent by disruptive centrifugal forces, it also vastly underestimates the value of groups' being sufficiently aware of larger interests to be willing to sacrifice short-range egoistic interests for the long-term general good.

Fair Shares

At the risk of oversimplification, one may say that a fundamental underlying rule of American political life may be characterized as "fair play," contrasted with a basic rule of Japanese political life, "fair share." In America one must follow the rules of the game; if the game is fought fairly, the loser, being a good sport, congratulates the winner and to the winner belong the spoils. In political elections, as in many other spheres, the winner takes the pie. In Japan, aside from sports tournaments, there are rarely such clear-cut contests. Even before the contest is concluded, the Japanese may look at the pie to see if it can be expanded, to see how many ways it can be cut, to see what acceptable rules can be devised for

apportioning it. However, they are interested not only in rules but in results, and rules may be changed to accord with a sense of "fair share." After the contest everyone must receive some share. If there is reasonable doubt as to how one contest was decided or if an indivisible pie is given to one party, the disadvantaged party has a standing claim to a larger share of the next pie.

In the elections to the lower house of the Diet, each district selects three to five representatives, almost assuring that some opposition parties and members of rival factions in the LDP will have representation. LDP politicians may scheme to keep their party in the solid majority, but they do not believe it desirable to eliminate opposition. When the largest companies apportion their political contributions, they try to ensure good connections with every political leader who has a reasonable chance of becoming prime minister. To this end they contribute more heavily to the most promising factions of the Liberal Democratic Party but they also give some to all major opposition parties, with the possible exception of the Communist Party, where there is no clear evidence of such gifts. If in fact the Communist Party receives no contributions from such large companies, it is not because companies refuse but because the Communist Party wants to remain independent and can do so from the money it earns from its publications. Similarly, after the Liberal Democratic Party selects the prime minister, he in turn must assemble a cabinet balancing the different LDP factions and ensuring that each is represented. Although opposition party leaders have not yet been included in the cabinet, they are nonetheless consulted to bind their roots before important measures are considered in the Diet. Grandstanding by LDP leaders is carefully resisted. If public rhetoric is dull and almost inarticulate, it is nonetheless carefully worded to minimize the danger of giving offense to anyone, including opposition leaders. Measures that pass the

Diet are, like the rhetoric, often filled with vague generalities which reduce the offensiveness to various groups. Most bills pass the Diet unanimously, supported by opposition parties as well as the LDP.

When the national budget is apportioned, there is an implicit assumption among interest groups that each will in some way receive its fair share. For example, in the case of international expositions, consideration is given to those metropolitan areas deserving modern construction. The first such project—the 1964 Olympics—was naturally located in the capital and the largest metropolitan area, Tokyo. Since the winter Olympics that year had to be hosted in the northern island, there was no choice but to make Sapporo the headquarters, although there were larger metropolitan areas that otherwise should have received their turn first. The next huge project, Banpaku (Expo), was naturally held in the second largest area, the Osaka-Kobe-Kyoto area. Now it is understood that the next time such a large event occurs, it will be in the next largest area, although since the Nagoya and Fukuoka areas are comparable in size, each might be able to present a plausible case. But the loser would then get the next round. Regional location of national construction projects is decided according to the same principles.

In apportioning the annual budget, the Finance Ministry generally allows major recipients, prefectures, and ministries to retain about ninety-five percent of their previous share of the budget without making a special case. Assuming that each unit needs to have considerable security over its own funds to plan effectively for the future, old organizations are rarely surgically removed but merely allowed to wither. The margin of five to ten percent of each ministry's share of the budget is up for reallocation for new projects. In this marginal area, each ministry must compete to develop new and especially promising projects. Thus, although all government branches are as-

sured a sizeable share, there is also the possibility of financing new projects and pressure to rationalize and economize on existing ones. But each ministry is given the freedom to carry on its own retrenchment for the five to ten percent each year, thus avoiding the antagonism between the regulator and the regulated that develops in America when the often poorly informed outsider arbitrarily and hastily chops up programs, creating management problems for those inside.

Income distribution statistics for Japan indicate that the gap between the highest and lowest quintile is among the smallest in the world. The ratio of income of the highest quintile to the lowest quintile in 1970, for example, was 4.3, while in the United States it was 7.1. And, according to recent figures on students entering Tokyo University, the most competitive national university, roughly thirty-five percent came from families whose incomes fall within the top twenty percent, and fourteen percent from families in the bottom twenty percent. The success in income distribution derives not simply from a booming economy with full employment but from conscious policy. In national polls about ninety percent of the Japanese public consider themselves middle class.

As the nation began to recover from World War II, government leaders recognized that capitalists, company white-collar employees, industrial laborers, farmers, and government workers should share in the fruits of economic growth. Since the 1950s there has been an implicit understanding in many circles as to how these different groups would share in the benefits—not through a welfare system but through adjusting wage increases to balance improvements among various segments of the population. Consumer organizations have been weak, but people organize groups to improve their circumstances by raising their income through their place of work. Each spring labor unions compare figures and then formulate

their demands for wage increases. Similarly, management associations jointly declare the necessity of limiting wage hikes to avoid ruining the companies. Although representatives of large associations present general and specific arguments to prepare the climate of public opinion, the final decisions are made in individual companies. Companies are not bound by rigidities imposed, for example, by the Swedish system, where national ratios of wages are set for various kinds of work. Although each company retains some flexibility, statisticians who have analyzed wage increases in various companies are able to predict final wage settlements with a high degree of accuracy, using a formula that takes into account productivity increases, cost of living increases, and profitability. This testifies to a widespread consensus among workers and management in the various companies as to what constitutes an equitable share of the profits. Each company knows that to maintain the enthusiasm and support of its workers it must be roughly as generous as other companies of the same kind. The constancy of considerations does not preclude some changes as, for example, when the gap between young and old workers began to narrow in response to the shortage of beginning workers. Over the years, however, as information has spread, the differentials between people with the same level of skill in different industries has declined.

There are differences in public and private sector salary increases in a given year, for government employees tend not to receive such large increases in the years of excellent business as do workers in the private sector, nor such slight increases in the more difficult years. However, over several years the average increase in the two sectors is remarkably close. National and local governments also raise their salaries at about the same rate, with only minor variations. Since government employees watch the wage increases in private industry

very closely, the government recognizes that to maintain a devoted work force it must increase salaries at roughly the same pace as private industry.

The same sense of fair share applies to increases in the standard of living of farmers, whose income has also kept up with nonindustrial salaries. Adjustment of rice prices is the single best way to affect farm income because rice is the most staple crop, being produced by about ninety percent of all farmers. Each year the government determines rice price subsidies so as to keep the income of farmers in line with the rising salary of private and government workers, an aim that was codified in 1961 in legislation drafted by the Ministry of Agriculture. In a given year there may be marginal differences of two or three percent between the increase of nonagricultural salaries and the increase in farmers' profits from rice sales. This differential is determined by such factors as the extent of the obligation of LDP leaders to farmers in the most recent election and the sufficiency of the rice supply in meeting demand. If there is a great shortage of rice in a given year, rice subsidies rise slightly more than nonagricultural wages, and, conversely, if there is a surplus of rice, rice subsidies rise slightly less. This minor differential gives the government some leverage for adjusting the rice supply to meet demand.

The balance between government benefits to big business and small business rests on a long-term acceptance of change and modernization which generally favors big business, but an effort is made to provide a fair share to small business until the people dislocated are placed in other lines of work. The government has encouraged the rapid modernization of industry, sometimes requiring the merger of small plants that cannot meet its new standards for modernity of facilities. It has not opposed the transformation of many small industrial plants from independent units to subcontractors of larger plants for it often leads to modernization of the subcontractors.

But in certain light industrial sectors in which small business remains competitive, the government has helped make loans available to the smaller firms. In the retailing sector it has established limits on the construction of new department stores, discount houses, and shopping centers, thus slowing down the impact they have on small retail stores. It is acknowledged that in the long run the share of the market of small private shops will decline, but the government tries to make the process orderly. Bureaucrats argue that small business should get a fair share, and the fair share should decline at a moderate, predictable pace so as to prevent sudden disruption, but they cannot halt the tide of progress.

The balancing act between big business and agriculture rests on the fact that LDP political funds come mostly from big business at the national level and from small business and farmers at the local level. Because of the size of contributions from big business, politicians cannot afford to alienate it in basic policy formation. But the LDP depends on votes as well as funds, and it relies on small businessmen and especially on farmers for those votes. Since farmers in a locality tend toward bloc voting more than the floating urban voters, their interests are strongly represented in the Diet. Because Diet members support the interests of the farmers, the Ministry of Agriculture cannot stray from the interests of the farming community.

Labor unions and their allies in the Socialist, Democratic Socialist, and Communist parties can also create difficulties in delaying and disrupting Diet progress if some effort is not made to accommodate their demands. The implicit sense of what constitutes a fair share takes account of relative power, but there is public sympathy with the underdog and this provides a balance wheel if rewards are in danger of becoming too one-sided. Despite symbolic gestures of vehement disagreement from these opposition parties, in fact there is considerable compromise underlying most Diet action. In large part this is

because government leaders and even their business supporters recognize the advisability of granting them a fair share of the rewards of growth to ensure that they too have a stake in the system.

These broad levels of agreement about equitable shares reduce the threat of strikes because special interest groups are unlikely to receive much more than their fair share no matter how much they struggle and leaders are unlikely to give them much less. The system provides security and predictability without removing the flexibility of companies to respond to special problems of economic fluctuation and to special opportunities for investment. Because all other affected groups can be mobilized to prevent one group from getting an undue increase at any one point, inflation control becomes immeasurably easier than in the United States and helps explain why the Japanese economy recovered so quickly from oil-shock inflation and why it has maintained an inflation rate significantly lower than America's in recent years. Japanese homogeneity may make it easier to forge these understandings, but it is the constant effort, mutual awareness, and discussion that make it work, precedures which are not inherently impossible to achieve in other societies.

THREATS OLD AND NEW: OVERCONFORMITY AND CHAOS

From about 1935 to 1945 the information reaching the Japanese public from abroad was for the most part highly restricted and heavily filtered. Only a small percentage of intellectuals, bureaucrats, and people of culture could be considered sophisticated in understanding developments and thinking in the West. At the same time, with the expansion of Japan into Korea, Taiwan, and later into Manchuria and China proper, the military came to have a dominant role in the society. The democracy that had begun to sprout in the Meiji

period and had expanded rapidly in form and substance in the 1920s proved fragile under pressure from the military. The average citizen, having grown up in an extremely close-knit society, found no basis for resisting a military dictatorship and a controlled press.

The transition of the average person from a subject to a citizen with an increased awareness of government activity and a greater sense of his rights to be represented in the decision-making process has thus taken place quite recently. Compared to the citizenry of other countries, the Japanese citizen has in fact been relatively passive. The elder generation, trained in the 1930s and 1940s, has not entirely outgrown the experience of docile acquiescence in matters of great import to the nation.

This has led many Japanese intellectuals and Western scholars of Japan to worry about the strong pressure for conformity that could restrict dissent and stifle individualism, perhaps even returning Japan to prewar totalitarian patterns. The fear is not without foundation. In the newspaper world, for example, despite the thoroughness of international news reporting and the coverage of internal Japanese developments, the range of opinion expressed in the three major dailies is narrow, and certain important stories may be suppressed. It is generally accepted that government bureaucrats are extraordinarily honest, but there are occasional instances of bureaucratic indiscretion known to reporters that are not published for fear of tarnishing the image of the bureaucracy. For example, it is widely believed that if the Lockheed scandal had not occurred just after Watergate, when so many Japanese were filled with admiration for America's capacity to root out difficulties at the highest level, the affair would have been quieted much more easily. In late 1972 a long article appeared in *Bungei Shunju*, a well-known literary magazine, detailing the indiscretions of Kakuei Tanaka, then prime minister. How-

ever, for several weeks after it appeared this important article was not discussed, directly or indirectly, in any of the major Japanese papers or on television. At that point Tanaka appeared before the Foreign Correspondents Club, which led to many foreign newspaper articles about his indiscretions; only then did Japanese papers feel compelled to write about these problems, which in turn triggered Tanaka's downfall. To be sure, once news of the scandal had appeared in the press, it was no longer possible for newspapers to avoid divulging many of the details, but many are convinced that the press never thoroughly explored all aspects of the story.

It is understood that politicians receive funds from people seeking favors and that they have some obligations to respond to these requests. Although their activity in this regard is not totally unlike the activity of politicians in America and elsewhere, by any standards Japanese politicians and newspaper reporters receive an impressive number of gifts and entertainment from those wishing favors. The distortion of public policy to favor certain vested interest groups on the basis of political contributions is probably not great, but there have been several well-known incidents of such manipulation, all publicized only later, and it is generally assumed that there are more cases known by reporters and key business leaders that are suppressed.

Because of the strength of group ties, people tend to adapt themselves to their group, accepting its viewpoints on specific issues rather than developing individual opinions. Even if a vote is held, the vast majority commonly follow the group position without developing a separate position of their own. At the local level, whether in the village, town, urban work place, or neighborhood, certain leaders tend to set the tone and define the framework in which issues are considered. What passes as village or community consensus therefore may in fact reflect not agreement but the reluctance of many ordinary

people to express their views for fear of offending these leaders. At the national level, the power of big business has often stifled dissenting opinion. The sense of community among top leaders tends to exclude those who do not meet their standards—whether size of firm, nature of business, or personal style—and this often makes it difficult for outsiders to get a fair hearing in influential circles.

These pressures for conformity are inextricably linked with the capacity of those groups to maintain their cohesiveness. No one would advocate limiting the variety of views expressed or suppressing stories. It is doubtful, however, that the limits to expression of variant opinion imposed by group cohesiveness still constitute a serious threat to Japanese democracy. The prewar totalitarian state dominated an unsophisticated public that had no choice but to follow blindly a militaristic government because so few of its members had the sophistication to know otherwise or the opportunities to say otherwise. With the explosion of foreign movies and later television shows since World War II, the sophistication of the Japanese public about foreign and domestic affairs has reached a level that precludes a return to prewar ignorance. The experience of the Japanese in forming and voicing their own opinions has grown immeasurably. Similarly, the level of involvement of millions of Japanese in business overseas and the constant electronic contact with the outside renders next to impossible the threat of communication restriction and thought control of the population. One might imagine that even sophisticated people with constant contact with foreigners could somehow be nationally controlled under an extraordinarily powerful military, but the possibility of a strong military appears remote. In addition, the public has grown much more accustomed to free expression of ideas. In short, it is hard to imagine that the control of thought by a totalitarian leadership is a viable threat to Japan.

In the opinion of many thoughtful Japanese leaders, the greatest threat to Japanese-style democracy comes not from the possibility of external aggression or the potential cutoff of raw materials or foreign markets. Nor does it come from committed rightists, Marxists, urban guerrillas, or the Red Army. The real threat, in their view, is the dissipation of group cohesiveness. During the university disputes of 1968-69, faculty and university officials were unable to bargain with the New Left. That group was not well organized, it did not have a defined constituency nor a precise point of view, and there was no means to assure that any agreement would stick. Some citizens' groups are equally ephemeral or nebulous. They protest, prevent construction projects, and disrupt ongoing organizations, but they are not sufficiently organized to represent a constituency nor are they empowered to reach agreements. With the old left, including Socialists, Communists, and even their student affiliates, there is opposition but there is also structure for negotiation. There are arguments and counterarguments, demonstrations and manipulations, but in the end an agreement or at least a modus vivendi with tacit understanding is reached. With unorganized groups there is no way to reach an understanding.

In the view of most Japanese, their style of democracy rests on the ability of groups to retain sufficient power over their members to maintain solidarity and ensure that agreements are honored, since both the higher aggregation of interests and the distribution of fair shares is accomplished through group solidarity. The increase in urbanization, physical mobility, and apartment living rather than independent housing all threaten to weaken group organization. The growing affluence that permits young people to buy motorcycles and cars and to worry less about their sources of income, combined with the new cultural systems, in part imported from abroad, create a new type of modern youth much less

susceptible to group organization. In the view of many Japanese leaders, this constitutes the most serious threat to their democracy.

In balance Japan has been more successful than modern Western countries in stemming the tide against egoism and nihilism. There is enough flexibility in the Japanese political scene to allow new loose groupings to form where other established groups do not adequately represent their interests, and most civic leaders try to develop relations with them; but to become effective, new groups must go the way of more structured groups, carefully cooperating with others while defending their own interests. It could be argued that in the complex modern world the dangers of chaos from centrifugal force is a greater threat to most countries than the threat of overly tight control. Japan, which has put great emphasis on cooperation, is in a fortunate position at this juncture in history when coordination of diverse groups is so difficult. Japan's success derives not from a carefully enunciated ideology but from a strong commitment to what George Lodge calls communitarian values and from the determination and imaginative efforts of group participants at all levels to maintain their cohesiveness. Convinced that it is difficult to respond to loosely organized citizens' movements on a national scale, business and government leaders have endeavored to institutionalize relationships with local protesters. They try to identify consumer advocates who can carry on the dialogue while retaining the respect of their fellow protesters. Although this might be criticized as co-opting the movement, businessmen and politicians know that in the end they will have to share a portion of the pie with these new organizations. If necessary, they are even prepared to adapt their own way of operations, for they are eager to absorb new ideas and to make constructive use of the energy of capable young people who might otherwise be alienated.

While political participation continues to expand broadly

and rapidly to include vigorous new groups, leaders are cautious not to make concessions that would weaken the capacity of their organizations to maintain their inegrity. Within organizations, officials insist on retaining the flexibility to reward those who cooperate, even if the short-term reward is approval and honor rather than money or high office. An organization's institutional memory ensures that this short-range symbolic approval will be translated into long-range material benefit. Members know that others will not quickly or easily forget if they should be remiss in responding to group expectations. An individual approaching higher levels with requests is powerless if he does not come with organizational backing, for higher-level politicians and bureaucrats are aware above all of the petitioner's group membership. An individual cannot expect to have a share in the spoils unless he stays with his group, because it is through groups that the fair share is distributed. In short, even in Japan the threat of chaos may be greater than the threat of overconformity, but by Western standards chaos does not seem imminent.

6

The Large Company:
Identification and Performance

AFTER TOURING automobile assembly lines in both countries, a visitor observed, "The American factory seems almost like an armed camp. Foremen stand guard to make sure workers do not slack off. Workers grumble at foremen, and foremen are cross with workers. In the Japanese factory, employees seem to work even without the foreman watching. Workers do not appear angry at superiors and actually seem to hope their company succeeds."

Japanese workers' pride in their work and loyalty to their company are reflected in their capacity to produce goods that are not only competitive in price but reliable in quality. Some workers, especially younger workers in small plants, may be alienated from their company, but compared to Americans, they are absent less, strike less, and are willing to work overtime and refrain from using all their allotted vacation time without any immediate monetary benefit. The average Japanese laborer may accomplish no more than a loyal hard-working American counterpart in a comparable factory, but loyalty to the company is typically higher and hard work more common. Many an American businessman, after touring a Japanese company and inspecting figures on time lost from absenteeism

and strikes, has expressed the wish that he had such a labor force.

It is tempting to account for the differences by historical tradition, but American workers have become less disciplined in recent decades, albeit with the same Amercan tradition, and modern Japanese employees of large companies are far more loyal than, for example, Japanese textile workers at the turn of the century. It is common to assign American labor problems to our affluence, but discipline has remained strong in affluent Japan. Furthermore, Japanese companies establishing plants in America have achieved with a few years of modified Japanese-style management a level of employee devotion on the average higher than in comparable American plants. Before resorting to an explanation that centers on a semimystical "Oriental spirit," one might consider whether Japanese success bears any relationship to company management and treatment of workers.

THE EMERGENCE OF THE JAPANESE COMPANY SYSTEM

The Japanese company system as we know it today began to emerge only late in the nineteenth century. Craft shops, with paternalistic masters and their apprentices and journeymen, date back centuries, but these "feudalistic" shops are not totally different from the kind of paternalistic shops of Paul Revere's America or preindustrial Europe.

Modern Japanese corporate paternalism drew on the recent feudal past, but it emerged in industries that borrowed modern industrial technology and organization and required a high level of skill. In new industries with lower skill requirements like textiles, no long training was necessary. Here, young, dexterous employees were, if anything, more useful than older experienced ones with less dexterity, and young women were at least as agile as men. Late nineteenth- and early twentieth-century Japanese textile manufacturers, therefore,

offered wages based on a piece rate system without significant salary increases for seniority. Wages were so low and factory conditions so unsatisfactory that most workers left before completing two or three years, and in some factories turnover was even more rapid.

Modern industries requiring a high level of skill faced different problems. As Ronald Dore has shown, the resulting late development pattern, unlike other industrialized countries' earlier indigenous development, relied on more concerted planning, training, and investment. In sizeable companies that manufactured steel, machine tools, electric equipment, and the like, companies needed to train both a group of highly skilled laborers and a group of white-collar managerial personnel. Because these skills were not based on experience with indigenous developments, it took considerable time and capital investment to train them. And since these new companies were in basic industries that were well-financed and ultimately backed by the government, the companies were in a position to guarantee long-term employment. They therefore developed a seniority system of wage increases such that the newly trained employees in whom the company invested so heavily would be motivated to remain. The system of seniority and permanent employment was by no means universal in Japanese industry, but it became the predominant pattern in the large-scale modern industrial sector and has since spread to the large commercial organizations as well. As the modern industrial sector expanded, a higher proportion of company employees has gradually been brought into this seniority and permanent employment pattern.

The modern form of the Japanese company has evolved considerably since the early 1900s. In the 1930s and during World War II Japanese companies were brought under increasingly tight government control. During the Allied Occupation, the large *zaibatsu* firms were split up into smaller

independent firms, but they gradually recombined into the present-day loosely organized groups after the end of the Occupation. During the 1950s and 1960s under government guidance many smaller firms were consolidated in order to modernize, and new American technology and management were introduced. For a time companies even considered copying the American pattern whereby workers could be dismissed and laid off more easily and hired in midcareer: it might get rid of employees with low performance, reward bold, innovative employees held down by the system, increase flexibility, give employees stifled in one company more options elsewhere, and reduce costs in a declining sector. By the late 1960s, when Japanese businesses started outperforming companies in the West, Japanese management intellectuals were satisfied that their seniority system was preferable to the dominant Western pattern, and they began to articulate a new philosophy of management.

The new philosophy incorporates many concepts from modern Western management and has much in common with large companies of American origin such as IBM, Polaroid, and Kodak. There is attention to basic business strategy, to product life cycles, to market surveys and marketing strategy, to accounting, to econometric models, to modern advertising, to up-to-date information processing. But some basics of the pre-World War II Japanese system remain: long-term perspective, permanent employment, seniority, and company loyalty. In addition, certain features gradually developed have recently been articulated to a higher degree: separation of rank and task, low differentials in pay and status for workers of a given age, "bottoms-up" management, and small-group responsibility.

The Japanese firm is less interested in short-term profits and more concerned with the long run. Executives may disparage their success in planning and forecasting, but they con-

tinue their best efforts and, when appropriate, boldly sacrifice profits for several years to build the groundwork for later success. They take care in cultivating good relations with institutions that might potentially be useful. They provide extensive training for personnel in skills that might be needed in the future. They invest in technology at seemingly high prices if it might later pay off. They invest heavily in plant modernization even when present plants meet immediate demands. As products become competitive, they conduct extensive preparatory work to lay a solid grounding for markets.

The company's capacity to think in long-range terms is made possible in part by their relatively greater reliance on bank loans than on the sale of securities to meet their capital requirements. Since stock now accounts for less than one-sixth of a company's capital needs compared to one-half in the United States, stockholders lack power to pressure for showing a profit each year, and banks are as interested in a company's long-range growth as the company itself. When companies are able to pay interest, the banks want to continue to lend them money, for banks are as dependent on quality companies to lend to as companies are dependent on the banks for borrowing. Indeed, when quality companies with their own capital want to cut costs by repaying loans, the banks try to make it attractive to continue borrowing.

Despite their interest in the future, most Japanese companies have not considered it profitable to invest heavily in basic research and development. It has made more sense to purchase foreign technology, for even if costs seemed high at the time of purchase, in retrospect the technology was obtained at bargain prices. The company concentrates research on adapting the technology for large-scale production, sometimes in such a way that it no longer needs to pay royalties on a particular patent. Japanese laws are such that processes, not functions, are patented. Thus, the company can buy technol-

ogy, make new inventions that meet the same function as the original patent, and end their dependence on foreign technology. Until the 1970s many Western companies sold technology cheaply. Some did so because it was a perishable item likely to become obsolete or to be pirated, but often they were short-sighted in licensing patents—eager for a quick profit, ignorant of the long-term Japanese competitive threat, and unwilling to take the trouble to invest in developing the Japanese market. In recent years, as foreign companies are more clearly aware of the potential value of patents to Japanese mass producers, the prices and terms of technological transfer have become much higher, and the Japanese companies have therefore begun to move selectively into more research and development. Having caught up with much of Western technology, Japanese research is more concentrated in innovative rather than adaptive areas, and in areas with high potential economic payoff. Japan now has about as many people engaged in nonmilitary research as does the United States.

Just as MITI has tried to reorient industrial structure toward industrial sectors that can compete more effectively on world markets in the future, so each individual company tries to concentrate on product lines or segments that are likely to be more profitable in the future and to reduce its activity in declining sectors well before it is no longer profitable to continue.

It is not that Japanese are not interested in profitability, but that they are prepared to defer maximizing immediate profits in order to increase market share. Beginning in the late 1970s when the Japanese growth rate started leveling off, most Japanese companies have been trying even harder to find ways to cut costs to maintain profitability. But they tend to judge their company's success less by annual profit than by the annual changes in the market share their company has compared to other companies in the industrial sector. As the Boston Con-

sulting Group has demonstrated, profitability is closely related to market share, for as firms expand they have more low-priced young labor and more modern plants. Therefore the companies' emphasis on market share has been well-placed.

The company's interest in the long term is also related to the system of permanent employment whereby an ordinary employee remains in the firm from the time he first enters after leaving school until he retires, which in most firms averages about fifty-seven or fifty-eight. The firm is committed to the employee and provides a sense of belonging, personal support, welfare and retirement benefits, and increased salary and rank with age. Barring serious long-term depression, the employee expects that he will never be laid off, and even if the company were to disband or be absorbed by another company, he expects that a new job elsewhere will be arranged. Companies are able to offer this kind of security despite economic fluctuations for several reasons. In times of temporary growth, additional temporary employees may be hired. For example, housewives may be added to the work force with the clear understanding that they will remain only while business needs them. Employees retiring from the company may be offered special short-term assignments in the company, usually at a lower salary than before retirement. Work may be subcontracted to small companies with the understanding that these contracts imply no permanent relationship.

If a large, reliable company should encounter economic difficulty, it will not go out of business because it is backed by banks, and behind the banks are various government institutions. Japanese companies have large debts to banks, but virtually all major companies are considered important for the economy as a whole, and therefore the Bank of Japan, backed by the Finance Ministry, stands behind the city banks that lend to the companies. Every company borrows from a main bank and then from other banks. If the company should be

badly in debt and need to be bailed out, the main bank arranges a new management team for the company, often from its own staff, thereby strengthening lines of control over the company, which had previously been essentially autonomous. To the company officials replaced, this is not only a loss of power for them and their followers but a disgrace, something to avoid at all costs. Similarly, even in a declining industry, management and unions consider consolidation and consequent loss of power a last resort, something to fight against as long as possible. Every large company that has collapsed in Japan had resorted to questionable practices and behaved improperly toward its main bank. There is virtually no danger of a reliable major firm collapsing, but this security does not lead companies to relax their determination to perform at a high level.

The Japanese company with a given amount of resources has much greater security than an American firm in making bold efforts to modernize and undertake new activities. In addition to financial backing through banks, the company can be sure that key government ministries are concerned with their success and will help out in unpredictable emergencies in finding land, getting resources, gaining crucial technology. They know the government will be unlikely to undertake antitrust or other legal action that will greatly upset the company's overall capacities. The Japanese company signs fewer contracts and works more with other firms with whom there is a high degree of mutual trust, especially within the same group. They can therefore make more flexible adjustments in case of unpredictable outside forces, greatly reducing legal risks which American companies would have to bear regardless of new circumstances.

A company that encounters economic difficulties has many ways of adjusting without sacrificing the permanent employment system. Usually in addition to monthly salary, the company pays sizeable semiannual bonuses amounting to

several months' salary. The size of the bonus depends on company profits, and therefore in times of depression it may be reduced without affecting basic monthly salary. In the spring, when basic monthly salary is determined, salary increases can be reduced or eliminated. The company can request employees to take an immediate vacation with partial rather than full pay or to reduce working hours, or to take minor salary cuts while requesting high officials to take larger salary cuts. If the difficulty is more severe, a company will reduce its entering class or even take in no new employees, adjusting assignments within the company so that jobs that would have been done by new employees will be done by others. Since companies follow long-term trends very closely, in industries that are expected to level off or decline, as for example in family electronics products which are increasingly made in Taiwan and Korea where labor costs are lower, companies will have anticipated the decline and admitted fewer employees in the years preceding the decline. Temporary employees will be released and permanent employees reassigned to their tasks. If the situation is very severe, the products formerly made by subcontractors will be made by regular permanent workers when contracts with subcontractors are terminated. Some individual subcontracting firms may be in trouble, but until now there have been enough new opportunities that few workers still in their prime are unable to find new work. If the recession is so severe that this kind of remedy is not adequate, then the company may move into some product line where it can keep people busy, for it makes sense to the Japanese to employ steadily a devoted work force and to take a small loss in order to provide work opportunities for one's permanent staff. As a further remedy, a company may encourage its workers to retire somewhat earlier by providing special benefits. If all these strategies are insufficient, some employees may be transferred from a company in a declining sector to affiliated companies

in growing sectors. In fact, however, the number of cases of permanent employees being transferred to other companies in hard times is small. The system has so many cushions that permanent employees in large companies have ample reason to feel secure. Japanese companies may trim around the edges but they are not about to abandon the system.

Because an employee has job security and knows his salary will rise with seniority, he is willing to accept moderately low wages during his first few years in the company. Also, since retirement age is normally in the late fifties, salary increments can go up fairly rapidly without a company's worrying about having very high-paid elderly employees for many years. Although the system is designed to provide incentives for the young person trained by the company to remain loyal throughout his career and to have a sense of advancement, one of the important side effects is that it creates great pressure on a company to hire young people. Companies are reluctant to hire a midcareer person not only because his sense of loyalty would be questionable but because it is to the company's advantage to employ him during his low-priced younger years. In boom years, school and university graduates usually have had several positions to choose from, and even in relatively depressed years unemployment among young people leaving school is virtually nonexistent, much lower than the general figure for unemployment, which escalated to over two percent in the late 1970s.

The seniority system in the company works much as in the bureaucracy. Although there are pay differentials later in the career based on performance and responsibility, these are small compared to those accounted for by seniority pay. Responsible executives consciously try to keep pay distinctions among those with the same seniority no larger than, and if anything smaller than, what most employees consider appropriate. New employees ordinarily receive precisely the same

pay for the first several years in the company; when differentials begin to appear later, they are minor, having more psychological than monetary significance. Equal pay tends to dampen competition and strengthen camaraderie among peers during their early years. If anything, the peer group recognizes that the ablest of their group are not being fully compensated in salary for their contribution, and this tends to dull any envy of peers toward the fastest rising in their group. Even those who rise more rapidly after differentials come into play can be promoted only if they enjoy the respect and approval of their associates; this prevents the growing distinctions from being overly disruptive. In a basic social sense, all those with the same seniority are considered as equals.

Those with higher positions continue to dress like others, often in company uniforms, and peers retain informal terms of address and joking relationships. Top officials receive less salary and fewer stock options than American top executives, and they live more modestly. It is easier to maintain lower pay for Japanese top executives because with loyalty so highly valued, they will not be lured to another company. This self-denial by top executives was designed to keep the devotion of the worker, and it undoubtedly succeeds.

It is understood that no one in a management track will be skipped over in advancement and no one will serve over another who entered the company at an earlier time. The same is true for technical track personnel and for laborers. Japanese executives at times considered increasing incentives for young people by allowing them to rise more rapidly and serve over their elders, but this caused undo strain in personal relations. The embarrassment for a person serving under a younger person is greater than in the United States. A person's official position can only rise until his retirement, and this eliminates any anxiety over the possibility that a worker will be relieved of his job or dropped to a lower position. After the first several

years the able person begins to take on positions associated with the elite course inside the company and gradually rises to more important posts. But the differentials among age peers in title as well as pay are slight. A very able person might become section chief a year or two before his peers, or he might become section chief at the same time as his peers but be chief of a more important section.

As with elite bureaucrats, those who come up an elite course within the company have a broad range of experience in all parts of the company. The high official therefore has detailed understanding of issues in all sections as well as close friendships that ensure continuous frank communication. The highest officials just below the level of president have members of their peer group at all other important positions in the company, which makes for unusually effective communication and mutual understanding. It also makes it more difficult for younger men to break into the inner circles if they were to advance more rapidly than others of their age group and requires that they wait until their peer group holds the top positions. This also ensures classmate linkages with other companies and the government bureaucracy, where elite rise in pace, so that contacts with every important institution at every level can be conducted through long-term intimate channels. Managers of a large American corporation commonly have at least as broad a range of experience, and American companies can acquire some know-how by hiring workers with certain skills. However, with more turnover American employees lack the close personal connections within the company and with peers in other key organizations that contribute so much to Japanese company effectiveness.

As in the bureaucracy, only the top handful of officers work beyond normal retirement age, and when one man in an age cohort is chosen president, all his peers resign, usually to assume a high position with a subsidiary or subcontractor. One

man therefore stands alone as the senior person concerned with daily affairs in the company, although the chairman of the board, usually the previous president, and board members or consultants, also former chief executives, may carry great weight on major issues or other issues in which they have special interest. It is conventional wisdom in Japan to concentrate the most experienced men at the top, in part because they have mature judgment but also because other senior people do not have to suffer the humiliation of serving under people younger than themselves and will wholeheartedly accept authority from those older who are also competent.

How is it possible for a unit to work effectively when a mediocre senior person is serving above an abler junior person? The answer lies not only in the senior person's lack of worry about being replaced by his junior but in the differentiation between task and title or position. The essential building block of a company is not a man with a particular role assignment and his secretary and assistants, as might be the case in an American company. The essential building block of the organization is the section. A section might have eight or ten people, including the section chief. Within the section there is not as sharp a division of labor as in an American company. To some extent, each person in the same section shares the same overall responsibility and can substitute for another when necessary. The abler younger person knows that he cannot surpass his senior in rank and salary now, but that all concerned informally recognize that he is abler than his superior. He also knows that he will eventually rise higher than his present senior, but that he must cooperate with his present senior for his section to accomplish its tasks and for him to be considered promising. Similarly, the head of the section is held responsible for the successful work of the section. He knows that he needs to take advantage of the talents of the abler person under him, and he therefore eagerly gives him responsible work. He is in

no fear of being upstaged by his underling, for they are lumped together when their accomplishments in the section are evaluated. Within the general work of a section, one's assignment to a task at a given time is affected by one's general abilities, skills, and aptitudes more than by one's title within the section. The section is, in a sense, an organic unit composed to match a variety of talents rather than a team with clearly distinct, independent role assignments. The section has a responsibility to perform, and each is expected to help out by dividing up what needs to be done, substituting for someone who is absent, or assisting another when necessary. The assignment is flexible, for the position and tasks are two different systems: the position rises with seniority, but the work depends on the tasks of the unit and the talents and complementarity of the individuals. Work is not determined by a specifically defined position.

When asked to describe a Japanese company, most Japanese managers list as one characteristic the practice of "bottom up" rather than "top down." The lowly section, within its sphere, does not await executive orders but takes the initiatives. It identifies problems, gathers information, consults with relevant parts of the company, calls issues to the attention of higher officials, and draws up documents. Of course the section acts within the context of the wishes of higher officials and is in constant communication with them. Proposals are not usually sent to higher levels until the section has consulted broadly with other sections and has formulated detailed plans. Nowhere in the process is there a fully organized presentation of several options to higher officials, and nowhere is there a neat package of conclusions flowing from higher levels. Good decisions emerge not from brilliant presentations of alternatives but from section people discussing all aspects of the questions over and over with all the most knowledgeable people. Some senior executives in companies play a central role in making decisions, but ordinarily they do so only after appropriate

section leaders lay the groundwork through close consultation with other sections and only when lower levels cannot themselves resolve their differences. Section people take great pride in their work because of their initiatives and because they have a chance to develop their leadership and carry great weight within the company on matters relating to their sphere. Consequently, the morale of young workers in their thirties tends to be very high.

For this system to work effectively, leading section personnel need to know and to identify with company purposes to a higher degree than persons in an American firm. They achieve this through long experience and years of discussion with others at all levels. Company aims are not canonized into documents but continue to fluctuate with the changing environment, and therefore section leaders must avoid being locked into a specific list of aims but rather adapt to overall opportunities for the company as a whole. Section leaders are sufficiently tuned to the overall thinking of the company for them to in fact achieve this, and they are given the leeway to act accordingly because higher officials know that section leaders are thoroughly committed to their company, where they will remain until retirement.

With so much authority concentrated at low levels and with so much discussion between levels, how can the company leaders make the bold decisions that have led to Japanese success? First, they operate in a climate of much greater security than the typical American firm. A company receives advice from well-informed bureaucrats, banks, affiliated trading companies, and other companies in its group. It is backed by banks and ultimately the government, which when necessary will assist it in obtaining special resources and facilities and will not pursue it in ways that create uncertainties and costly law suits. Second, because rivals are striving for market share and because the seniority system and bank lending require expansion, it

becomes more dangerous to stand pat than to move ahead with bold modernization and innovation. Further, stockholders do not constrain executives with demands for short-term profits. As a result, Japanese companies have consistently been bolder than most of their Western counterparts in modernizing and expanding their capacity.

GROUP SPIRIT AND PERSONAL INCENTIVES

In addition to providing the employee with the economic incentives for long-term loyalty, company officials do their best to reinforce employee identification wth the company. They provide elaborate annual ceremonies for inducting the new employees who enter as a group shortly after the end of the school year. The official training program may be any-where from a few weeks to years, and includes not only useful background information but emotional accounts of company history and purposes. For spiritual and disciplinary training the employee may go on retreats, visit temples, or endure special hardships. To strengthen the bonds of solidarity, the new em-ployee may be housed in company dorms while undergoing training, even if it means being separated from his spouse or parents. But even after the formal training program is over, the young employee continues to be treated as an apprentice for some time. He continues to receive training and super-vision, and he is expected to behave with appropriate deference to his seniors. In American terms it is perhaps like a combina-tion of the behavior of the fraternity pledge, without the hazing, and the young doctor in residency training.

Companies commonly have their own uniforms, badges, songs, and mottos. Each company has a special lore about the spirit of a "Matsushita person" or "Sumitomo person" or "Sanwa person," but to the outside observer the spirit sounds strikingly similar: enthusiastic, loyal, devoted. Company recep-

tion halls are available to employees' families for receptions and celebrations. Resort houses in the mountains and on the seacoast can be used by company employees who have put in the appropriate years of loyal service. Dormitories or apartment projects are available to employees of many companies. Unlike America, where mortgages are commonly obtained directly from banks, in Japan a high proportion of mortgages are obtained from the workers' company at subsidized interest rates. The company supplies gifts for many occasions in addition to the large semiannual bonuses. Special discounts of company products are available to employees and their families. Many companies have daily ceremonies—for opening the store, commencing work, or starting physical exercise. Parties large and small bid farewell to the old year, send off employees transferred to another city, welcome them home, congratulate people on promotions or honors, greet visitors, and commemorate retirement. Weekend group trips celebrate the coming of cherry blossoms, fall foliage, or holidays. For family members there are parties, special-interest clubs, courses, lectures, and exhibitions.

In addition to providing gymnasiums and swimming pools, a large company usually has sports teams well-equipped with uniforms and often with showcase facilities. So they can do well in their leagues, many companies recruit talented athletes as company employees, much as American colleges do, and they are given only minor work responsibilities. Outstanding professional sports teams that in the United States would be privately owned and associated with a particular city are in Japan sponsored instead by companies. The very highest officials in the company commonly take off from work to attend important sports contests with their rival companies.

During Prime Minister Tanaka's time companies even tried sponsoring political candidates, but this was abandoned

because they had limited appeal, even within the company, and it proved embarrassing for companies to have their candidate lose.

Executives generally want their employees to spend a certain amount of off-duty hours together, preferably under company sponsorship. One company, troubled that too many young employees had their own cars and sufficiently high salary to go off on their own rather than use company facilities, surveyed employee interests and, finding that bowling was then the current rage, provided very attractive uniforms, bowling balls, and other equipment. It also bought a regular block of time for workers at the most luxurious nearby bowling alley. By ensuring that more leisure time was under company auspices, the company reinforced group solidarity.

Loyalty in a large company is a many-layered overlapping labyrinth. Employees have layers of loyalty to the group with which the company is affiliated, to the particular factory or store, to the section, and to the immediate work group. Younger employees who are in a given specialty or career line may also enjoy a special link with senior sponsors in the same career line. Even with the immediate work group, one kind of group spirit thrives when the superior is absent, another when he is present. Part or all of the peer group assembles to commemorate earlier times and gossip about current events. Informal socializing, celebrations, and farewell or welcome-home parties occur at all of these levels.

At times a senior's concern about younger colleagues borders on what Westerners would consider "mothering," for Japanese of both sexes accept personal solicitousness that in the United States would ordinarily be considered unmasculine for men to give or receive. To avoid embarrassing an individual in public, criticism is commonly expressed in private in the spirit of a superior siding with a junior to help with a problem certain to cause him trouble.

With so much security and warmth, how does the system ensure high performance? In initially hiring employees, the company aims to be as merciless as entrance examinations in selecting people of quality. In preparation for selecting among employees of a peer group for more responsible positions, key line officers spend an enormous amount of time informally evaluating the performance of juniors, for decisions about personnel are considered too important to be left to personnel specialists. Employees are generally reassigned every two or three years, and each person knows that the quality of his over-all performance is being evaluated to determine his next assignment. Those who rise to the top are chosen because in addition to high innate ability they have the capacity to see the big picture, to analyze problems clearly, to convey poise and confidence, to inspire support from fellow employees in all parts of the company, and to form successful relationships with top-level people in other companies and in the government.

The Japanese company makes it clear that its substantial benefits to employees are not guaranteed. Benefits are not distributed automatically by contractual agreement to anyone simply because he is a company member or because he falls into a certain category of age, status, and length of service, for leaders believe flexibility of rewards is needed as a critical leverage to maintain discipline. Bonuses, sick leave, and use of company facilities are offered to the hard worker, but signs of disapproval to the dilatory cause doubts about how superiors will respond when they come with their next request.

For motivating the worker, superiors rarely need to talk directly about benefits. Since employees have such long-term personal relationships with each other, small systematic differentiations of treatment by superiors have great psychological significance. Those who receive subtle hints that they are likely to rise eventually to the top positions are tremendously motivated because there is sufficient continuity and predictability

to ensure that the hints can be translated into reality. When peers become overly solicitous to see if they can be of help, the worker knows that others consider his performance below par, and he may be devastated. He will rise by seniority alone, but to be at the bottom of his age group is extremely embarrassing and to be at the bottom and disliked for not trying as well is something to be avoided at all costs. But unlike students at the Harvard Business School and members of the United States State Department, for example, those at the bottom of the Japanese peer group do not need to worry that they may become castoffs as long as they exert themselves; the threat of banishment is often implicit but rarely used.

The most important single criterion for assessing quality for regular term promotions is the capacity to work well with others. The person who rises more rapidly is not the one with the original ideas but the one who can cooperate with others in finding a conclusion satisfactory to everyone. Personal achievement cannot be separated from the capacity to work effectively in groups. Eventually the reward for performance and effort include salary and position, but the proximate reward which foretells the eventual success in salary and position is the esteem of colleagues. In an American company without a strong group spirit and without expectations of permanent employment, an employee might come to feel that the only significant reward is salary and position, which in his view ought to be finely tuned to match performance. In the Japanese view, this custom, like tipping which they still avoid, cheapens the sense of service and contributes to contentiousness. In a Japanese company with strong group spirit and a long time frame, the really significant reward, the thing an employee strives for, is the esteem of his colleagues.

THE COMPANY MAN: HARD WORK AND SELF-ESTEEM

Earlier generations of Western social scientists like Durkheim and Parsons thought that occupational specialty could

provide the means for integrating the individual in modern society. However, the pace of modern technological and organizational change renders occupation specialty training too rapidly outdated to provide a stable source of life-long identification and basic social integration for the society. No structure in the West compares with the Japanese firm in its capacity to introduce rapid change and to provide identification for a substantial portion of the population(The young American employee hired as a specialist is not interested in learning as broad a range of things about the company as the young Japanese employee, who is more of a generalist. A Japanese employee who knows he will be kept and retrained in midcareer is less likely to worry about innovation and resist technological change. Featherbedding and the reluctance of American workers to be flexible in performing various jobs in a company are problems for American industry not only because workers are afraid of losing their jobs but because they want to protect their skill level. The Japanese worker concerned about the long-range future of his company eagerly seeks technological change and, because his status and future is less related to a special skill level, he is more willing to perform miscellaneous tasks and to assist fellow workers in different tasks as the need arises. The employer gets fuller and more flexible use of employees, and employees find the varied work less monotonous than their American counterparts who stick to the same work.)

Like paternalistic craft structures in premodern America, Europe, and Japan, the large modern Japanese company is committed to the whole individual, not simply to the task-related part of the individual. Alfred Sloan once boasted that General Motors continued to pay dividends to stockholders right through the depression even though it had to lay off workers. A Japanese business leader would never say such a thing and, if he did anything remotely resembling it, he would try to hide it, for valuing profits above his employees would destroy his relationship with his workers. The primary com-

mitment of a Japanese firm is not to its stockholders but to its employees.

Japanese workers reciprocate this commitment, for they prefer a company that is not simply "dry," cool, and calculated, but "wet" with human emotion. The American employee with specific assignments and responsibilities and strictly calculated pay per hour is not inclined to work beyond stated time or to do extra personal things for his colleagues, but a Japanese employee is. Every five years, beginning in 1953, there have been public opinion polls in Japan asking if people would prefer to work for someone who made specific assignments and provided help within the confines of the work or someone who expected extras beyond specific assignments but was prepared to offer personal help beyond the regular rules. The Japanese public, by a substantial majority, consistently prefers the supervisor who has personal relations going beyond the work requirements. Americans overwhelmingly prefer the opposite.

Even without company-sponsored activities, employees find time in the evenings or on weekends to have good times with one another without work in front of them. They often socialize on the way home from work. In many companies with a five- or five-and-a-half-day week some employees at almost all levels come in on Saturday and stay later to play mahjong, *go*, *shoji*, or to go drinking. Even among more "modern" employees who, like Americans, want to spend weekend time with families, couples often spend their time with other couples connected with the same company. Socializing is partly for sheer fun, but many consciously try to have good times together to make it easier to work together during the week. Because employees know they have to have each other's goodwill until retirement, they are not as likely as Americans to become righteously indignant with each other. They look for ways to subdue tensions and rivalries and rein-

force camaraderie.)Inner feelings of competition, anxiety, and annoyance may be at least as strong as in American companies since relationships are so close and since escaping difficult problems by leaving the company is not ordinarily a realistic option. Informal sociability is not only an end in itself but a way to contain these potentially disruptive tendencies.

The success of Japanese companies in avoiding disruptive labor unrest must be understood in the context of long-run individual identification with the company, but it has been reinforced by company handling of labor unions. After World War II, when the Allied Occupation ordered a rapid expansion of labor unions, Japanese company executives moved quickly to make employees members of labor unions. Labor unions were thus born not from virulent struggles led by bitter union leaders but from the initiative of company leaders. Nonetheless, the labor movement, at first protected by the Allied Occupation, became a powerful and sometimes violent political force. Management moved to encourage faithful employees to take part in union activities with the hope of moderating the potentially devastating strikes. They encouraged white-collar employees to join the same company union as the blue-collar employees and provided rooms and other facilities for union activities. These same white-collar employees, after serving their stint in labor unions, then returned to their managerial career line without loss of seniority. When unions became too militant, companies sometimes used questionable tactics to break the union and sponsored a second union that was more sympathetic with company goals. Management realized that simply co-opting unions could not be successful, and they eagerly sought feedback from unions to find opportunities for meeting worker complaints in order to create better working relations and a more satisfied labor force. Japanese unions are organized by the enterprise, and national craft unions tend to be weak. Nonetheless, unions do energetically represent the

interests of the workers in pushing for benefits. Otherwise, union leaders would lose the support of workers. Unions also play a role in aggregating worker opinion on issues directly affecting them as part of the root-binding process in the firm. Though very worried about the danger of unions in the late 1940s, management has come to regard their unions as friends in helping stabilize the company. To avoid an excessive adversary relationship and create a proper climate, management finds time to socialize with union leaders without waiting for disputes that engender an atmosphere of controversy.

Because Japan is a rapidly modernizing country, with a dual economy of a modern and less modern sector, workers in larger companies are elite, with better training, more security, and better working conditions than workers in small companies that are less modern. Employees in large companies therefore have felt privileged to be there. Furthermore, since companies were mostly formed by managers rather than independent owners, workers have no rich capitalist class above them but only a managerial class whose style of life is not so different from their own. Japanese executives feel that not only American company owners but managerial staff have given themselves too many emoluments compared to what they gave the workers. This modest differential between managers and workers of a given age tends to reinforce the worker's sense of identification with the firm.

In some areas unions have engaged in long disruptive strikes, but in all such cases workers were not afraid of company losses through strikes. Local government employees, public school teachers, national and private railway workers, workers in government monopolies like tobacco, and, in the early postwar period, mine workers have fought militantly, but they all share a common characteristic: they are convinced that disruptions will not endanger the future of their organization. Government employees know that taxes can be used to

raise their wages and improve their conditions regardless of the effectiveness and efficiency of their government unit. Private railway workers know that company income is determined by the rate structure, which can be adjusted if wages are increased. And in the early postwar period, when coal was the main source of energy and the government provided necessary subsidies to private coal companies, workers were not afraid that militant struggle would weaken the competitiveness of their company. In the late 1950s, when coal companies were going out of business because of the decline of available resources, miners struck because they knew they wanted the best possible settlement, backed by government support for a declining industry. In ordinary companies, where workers identify with the long-run interests of the company, strikes have been virtually unknown once the Occupation ended and the economy returned to normal in the early 1950s.

With growing affluence and full employment in the late 1960s, many young Japanese became confident of their ability to earn a living even if they should leave their present company, and this attitude threatened company discipline. Many worried managers therefore fought harder than ever to maintain company solidarity. At the height of rapid growth, when unemployment was less than one percent and many company employees could have found work elsewhere, they still remained in their company. Since the oil shock of 1973, with renewed fears of a depression and increased unemployment, workers have felt especially dependent on their company and discipline has improved further. Although the Japanese standard of living is now on a par with that of the most advanced countries in the world, affluence has not ended hard work.

Even in the public sector there have been few debilitating strikes in recent years. Strikes in the public sector are officially illegal, and when some unions tested this legality in 1976, the strike was stopped before the announced termination date by

public opinion and not the law. Employees from private companies who worked hard and accepted what they considered reasonable salary raises would not tolerate the government providing more favorable conditions for striking workers in the public sector. Newspapers that initially had taken a somewhat favorable attitude toward strikers changed quickly with the vehemence of public reaction. They began reporting, for example, that children of striking workers were ridiculed by classmates for what their parents were doing to the general public. It would not be politically feasible for workers in the public sector to use their capacity to stop the operation of public facilities to raise salaries higher than their counterparts in the private sector. It is not simply that the majority of Japanese workers are basically satisfied because their interests are being served, but that the workers in the private sector who do not strike because of devotion to their company exert public pressure strong enough to contain strikers in the public sector.

Perhaps more important than the success of companies in mobilizing workers for production and avoiding disabling strikes is the impact the system has on the self-esteem of the individual. The American who is fired or laid off as soon as the company's financial statement is in the red and who must go on unemployment insurance finds it hard to maintain great self-respect for his capacity to work. The worker who knows he will then be out of work understandably might demand more salary now, but in so doing he begins to measure his contribution and even his own worth solely in monetary terms. Even a high American official who is dropped or demoted because his division is unprofitable or who is hastily removed when dissatisfaction rises about company performance cannot help but have doubts about himself as well as his company. Unless caught in a horrendous well-publicized scandal, no Japanese official would be comparably disgraced by his company, and even if an official were caught in such an extreme

case, other company officials find a way to cushion the blow if he has indeed performed well for the company. Officials who must be demoted to take responsibility for a public problem are often given substitute rewards and honor within the company so that they may not feel especially distraught. Success and failure come from group effort and are never laid on the shoulders of a single person. At worst, if an official performed badly, his term would be brought to a close slightly more rapidly or he might not be promoted to the next post quite as readily. Former officials do not need to be discredited by new officials and generally remain on good terms with their successors. Japanese workers who feel they do more than is required and feel they are appreciated by fellow workers enjoy a greater sense of individual worth than do those who merely get by with the minimal effort, a more common American pattern.

In short, the large Japanese company, an institutional structure that originated not in traditional Japan but in the mid-twentieth century, has developed a very effective modern corporatism well adapted to the needs of the latter part of the twentieth century. It has not eliminated problems. There are bad managers as well as good ones, and workers feel unhappiness with boring assignments, anxiety over personal difficulties, disappointment at not being more appreciated. But by international standards the large modern Japanese corporation is a highly successful institution. It is successful not because of any mystical group loyalty embedded in the character of the Japanese race but because it provides a sense of belonging and a sense of pride to workers, who believe their future is best served by the success of their company. The pride and stability that so many Japanese have because a family member works in a large company helps stabilize the political process and set a tone for the society at large.

7

Basic Education: Quality and Equality

AMERICAN REPORTERS in Tokyo have expressed envy of their Japanese counterparts for the sophistication of the reading public and the resources of the major newspapers. Crocker Snow, former *Boston Globe* correspondent in Tokyo, observed that the Japanese reporter can assume that the typical reader of the three major dailies (combined circulation, about sixteen million) is better informed about international affairs than the reader of America's east coast elite dailies. News commentators on Japanese national commercial television can assume that the audience has sufficient scientific understanding to use various chemical formulas when discussing pollution, nuclear plants, or other scientific questions. As Richard Halloran, former Tokyo correspondent of the *New York Times*, acknowledges, because a large Japanese newspaper "can smother a story with more manpower than any ten American papers," these large dailies are able to carry detailed information about international developments that compares with Americans' elite papers. They have more analysis of their own government's planning and policy options than even the *Washington Post* carries about the American government. These newspapers are highly competitive commercial operations, and they include such

thorough coverage because the general public has sufficient knowledge and interest.

Beyond such subjective impressions, it is difficult to find a meaningful quantitative measure to compare the educational level of the adult population of different countries. Probably the most meaningful cross-national comparisons can be made in fields like mathematics and natural science, where cultural and historical factors play a relatively smaller role than social science and humanities. Where data is available for such cross-national comparisons, no country outperformed Japan overall. Nathan Glazer points out that on the 1964 twelve-nation achievement tests in mathematics for thirteen-year-olds, Japan scored second to Israel. However, these were selected samples, and when adjusted to estimate the average in the age group, Japan ranked third, although the first and second place countries edged Japan by only an insignificant amount. When adjusted to estimate the top three or four percent of the entire age group, Japan was first both for mathematics majors in the preuniversity group and, by an even larger margin, for non-university majors.

In the 1970 international science test given to ten-and fourteen-year-olds in nineteen countries, Japanese youth performed comparably well. Among ten-year-olds, the Japanese were first in the subtests for earth sciences, chemistry, and biology. Although they ranked fourth in information, they ended overall in first place because they were first in understanding, in application, and in higher mental processes. Fourteen-year-old Japanese scored second to their Hungarian counterparts in biology but first in physics, chemistry, and practical science. Although they ranked only second in information, they were also first overall because of their test results in understanding, application, and higher processes. These findings are not unrelated to the fact that Japanese middle schools have science labs, and ninety-three percent of the science teachers were trained in science at universities, a record

unrivaled in other countries. In grand total score America ranked fifteenth of nineteen countries.

Only a handful of American children, even among those living in Japan, have ventured to attend regular Japanese schools, whereas thousands of Japanese children have attended American schools. It is commonly understood that those Japanese who attend elementary and junior high school in comfortable American suburbs will be a year or two behind their grade level in mathematics and the natural sciences when they return to Japan. The same is true even for the physical education skills stressed in Japanese schools, to say nothing of Japanese and Chinese history.

Lest it be assumed that music and artistic skills in Japan are neglected, William K. Cummings, who has done the most thorough cross-cultural study of Japanese and American elementary education, comments as follows from his observations of music classes in Japanese schools: "By the sixth grade, most students are able to switch readily between at least three different instruments. The first time I saw this level of achievement, I could not believe my eyes. But after the fifth primary school, I had to recognize that it was widespread. While the members of the orchestras and bands in American primary schools achieve this level, most of the remaining students are musically illiterate. Comparisons in art are nearly as dramatic." When a foreign television producer's delegation observed Japan's NHK television concerts, they were surprised how little time is spent by the television staff in rehearsing for the program until it was explained that producers, cameramen, and other support staff all used the same musical scores for cues, reflecting a capacity of everyone to read music that could not be assumed in an American television studio.

Some of the differences might be accounted for simply by the fact that the Japanese attend school about one-third

more than Americans, for 240 days a year compared to 180 days a year in America; and, as Cummings notes, attendance rates in primary and junior high school are much higher in Japan.

What is perhaps even more remarkable than the high quality of Japanese education is that such an insignificant percentage of Japanese do not achieve a high standard of literacy. Whereas the United States Army must reject a sizeable proportion of applicants because of illiteracy, the inability to read and write is virtually absent in Japan. Although precise cross-cultural comparisons are almost impossible, illiteracy has been estimated by some to be as high as twenty percent in the United States, but in Japan illiteracy rates are generally estimated to be below one percent.

The Japanese drive to extend formal education has been as vigorous as their efforts to increase their GNP. In 1955 only about one-half of Japanese youth entered high school and less than ten percent postsecondary institutions. By the late 1970s over ninety percent of both Japanese girls and boys were completing high school, compared to approximately eighty percent of all American youth. Virtually all Japanese who enter a school complete it. In 1975, for example, ninety-seven percent of those entering high school completed it, compared with seventy-nine percent in America. At the postsecondary level in Japan, approximately the same number of males and females enter colleges, but females more commonly complete two-year courses and males more commonly four-year courses. Although approximately thirty-five to forty percent of college-aged youth were attending a university both in the United States and Japan, because of sizeable numbers of American drop-outs Japanese more often complete their training. Almost forty percent of Japanese males in their mid-twenties have completed four-year colleges compared to about twenty percent

of Americans (although the American figure rises to about thirty percent by the late twenties). Very few Japanese attend graduate school. However, the desire for higher education in Japan is greater than enrollment figures suggest, for university openings are still not adequate to meet the demand. In America virtually any high school graduate can find a college or university to attend, but in Japan there are roughly three openings for four applicants. Even after students have completed their schooling, an extraordinarily high number continue taking a variety of correspondence courses and special study programs in their place of work, whether or not they are required to do so by their company. A very high percentage of the Japanese continue to read serious books and to master new bodies of knowledge.

Japanese education is not without major problems. Universities have an important function in certifying students, but faculty devotion to teaching and to students is limited, student preparations are far less than prior to the entrance examination, analytic rigor in the classroom is lacking, and attendance is poor. University expenditures per student are unreasonably low, and the level and variety of advanced research are highly limited. The Japanese student in his essays is more likely to follow guidelines than to develop his originality. Entrance examinations to high schools or universities can be so competitive as to cause students to restrict their intellectual breadth, eliminate extracurricular activities, neglect their social development, and, in case of failure, become psychologically depressed.

Americans are not about to import these problems, which show deep failures in Japanese education. Yet the maintenance of high motivation for learning, the uniformly high quality of the nine years of compulsory education, and the wide scope of educational television in Japan are remarkable achievements worthy of emulation.

THE DRIVE TO LEARN: EXAMINATIONS AND GROUP RESPONSIBILITY

Japanese are not satisfied just to attend school more hours per day and more days per year than Americans. Over half of Japanese youth at some time attend supplementary schools (*juku*) during their elementary or secondary school years. Supplementary schools come in all shapes and sizes, but the vast majority are to improve the students' chances of passing an entrance examination to a slightly more desirable high school and college. Most students have a good idea af what institution they might qualify to enter by entrance examinations if they prepare thoroughly for one or two years. Yet after entrance examinations are over, about eighteen percent of the men and a somewhat smaller percent of the women who fail to pass an examination to their desired institution remain for one year or more as *ronin* (masterless samurai), without institutional affiliation, preparing for another try at entrance examinations.

The pressure surrounding entrance examinations derives from the fact that they are the exclusive means for determining admission to institutions of higher learning and for obtaining that all-important first position. In fact, the American student who attends a good university and receives a good first job is likely to be significantly more successful than one who does not, but there is somehow an American hope that one will have many opportunities to move throughout one's career. In Japan the widely acknowledged importance of the university attended for determining later success concentrates life-long career ambitions on the entrance examinations.

The entrance examinations measure acquired knowledge on the assumption, widely accepted, that success depends not on innate ability, IQ, or general aptitude but on the capacity to use innate ability for disciplined study. It is acknowledged that native ability may affect the capacity of an individual to

absorb information, but in the Japanese view there is only one way to alter the result: study. Those who spend a year or more going through special cram courses in order to enter what they consider an acceptable institution are not criticized for plodding but are praised for perseverance.

Entrance examinations are much maligned for causing excessive tension, rote memorization, and one-sided intellectual development, and for eliminating extracurricular activities and destroying the joy of youth of preexamination students. Horror stories of examination preparation receive ample publicity, although extreme cases are in fact small in number. There are suicides over exam failures but these have declined since the late 1960s, and the overall Japanese suicide rate is not high by European standards. Educators have urged and undertaken a variety of reforms to reduce examination fever, albeit without appreciable success, for the desire to achieve through entrance examinations remains unabashed.

No one defends extreme cases of "examination hell," and if the system were imported to America, it would probably not be carried to such extravagant lengths. It should be noted, however, that entrance examinations have a great deal of logic in their favor. They are highly predictable so that schools, students, and their parents know what to prepare for. The teacher's authority in judging a student's record is negligible, since grades or written recommendations are unimportant for college admission. It is unmistakably clear to students that their future depends on meritocratic performance as measured by entrance examinations. Motivation comes from the inside, and the student, mindful of his responsibilities to parents and school and concerned about his future, wants to learn so that he may be prepared for the entrance examination. As shown by the questionnaire returns accompanying the science achievement tests in nineteen countries, Japanese children enjoy school more than students in other countries. The teacher becomes an ally

who is trying to assist the student in facing the examination. The Japanese teacher has a broader sense of responsibility for helping the student outside classroom hours and is typically available in school many days during summer recess.

The motivation for achievement through examinations is increased by the tight-knit membership of a variety of groups. Families are, in a sense, competing with other families, and the child's success in examinations is seen as directly reflecting on a family's success. As Thomas Rohlen has shown, the small, intact family does much better in preparing the child for entrance examinations than the large family, the broken family, or the family with one parent deceased, for the intact family exerts itself, sending the child to supplementary classes, assisting him at home, and arranging family life to ensure the sanctity of study. Parents, and especially mothers, take a great interest in how well the school prepares their student for the examination. Through the junior high school level it is unrealistic for most parents to send their children to schools other than their local public school; therefore parents take an active role in local school activities, supporting teachers of excellence and school administrators who try to maintain quality education.

Furthermore, there is intense competition between schools to place their students well. Just as villages compete to erect the best most modern buildings, so schools strive to get a higher share of their graduates admitted to the best schools at the next higher level. Since teachers are responsible for their students' personal and motivational life as well as for classroom behavior, they feel responsible for the success rate of their students.

The system thus reinforces the key actors—students, teachers, and parents—in their identification with the student preparing for the examinations. Given the tendency to relax that comes with affluence, schools in Japan, as in other modern

countries, face the danger of lax standards. From his interviews in various Japanese schools, Rohlen concludes that having the entrance examination system in the background is necessary to maintain discipline and high standards.

Compared to examinations that would certify high school graduation—an idea now being considered in America—entrance examinations have clear advantages. With certification examinations, it is unlikely that many students, teachers, and parents would be positively motivated since only those close to the margin of failure would be at all concerned. On the other hand, entrance examinations make sense to the Japanese because they are not simply arbitrary evaluations by authorities but a legitimate demand by educational institutions that those who enter meet a certain standard. Most of the ninety percent of the age group who wish to enter high school and the fifty percent who wish to go on for higher education are highly motivated to prepare for entrance examinations to be able to enter an institution of their choice. Once a student enters an institution, examinations do not end, but he does not need to worry about being terminated for academic failure, and this allows the student to develop a feeling of belonging in a mutually supportive group environment.

By the time the Japanese student enters a good high school or good university, he has internalized attitudes about hard work. He may not have enjoyed the pressure of examination hell, but he has learned discipline as well as mastered a body of knowledge. For all the excesses of the entrance examination system, the desire to succeed on them maintains group solidarity and the motivation to study. In entrance examinations a student's competition is not with a small circle of intimate friends but with thousands of unknowns who want to enter the same institution. The strong attachment of the student to his peer group in school, to his family, to his teachers, and they to him, greatly reinforces the motivation to study. All want the

student to succeed. In later life, it is again in large part the individual's attachment to the work group and his long-term time perspective that makes him want to master materials that might someday prove useful to him, his work group, and the company at large. As a result of the examination system the nation acquires a large reservoir of well-trained people with a substantial core of common culture, people who are curious, teachable, disciplined, and sensitive to humanistic and civic concerns. Despite complaints, no one has moved to weaken entrance examinations, for no one has yet devised a better system to maintain motivation, hard work, and family and school solidarity.

UNIFORM NATIONAL STANDARDS

Until the end of World War II, the Japanese Ministry of Education wrote the textbooks for each subject in each grade. After the war a new set of guidelines was established by the Allied Occupation to provide a more democratic orientation for compulsory education. Compulsory education in Japan is measured not by age but by completing the ninth grade, although in fact virtually all students complete it at age fifteen. Some of the guidelines for course content were influenced by American educators from states like California and New York which had similar statewide guidelines. After the Occupation, the Japanese Ministry of Education kept the democratic thrust but prepared even more detailed, book-length guidelines for the essentials of the curriculum (*gakushū shidō yōryō*, officially translated as "Course of Study") of all elementary, lower secondary, and upper secondary schools in the country.

In the elementary schools the Course of Study includes Japanese language, social studies, arithmetic, science, music, arts, handicrafts, homemaking, and physical education. In junior high school it covers Japanese language, social studies, mathematics, science, music, fine arts, health, physical educa-

tion, industrial arts, homemaking, and foreign language. The curriculum is quite comprehensive by American standards, including political and moral issues, physical training, the arts, vocational information, and world affairs as well as basic academic subject matter. In preparing the Course of Study, twenty of the nation's leading educators for each subject weighed various alternatives to determine the nature of skills that students should be expected to acquire. In addition to setting overall objectives and listing for their subject specific topics to be covered, they provided suggestions for teaching methods. The Course of Study was first completed in 1958, and the revisions were made in 1968 and 1978. (The 1968 volumes have been translated into English). Other specialized handbooks provide suggestions for the use of audiovisual and other materials.

For example, goals for the second grade student include the following: "To listen with delight to a story or juvenile tale; to hear a story, considering the sequence of the matters involved; to convey a message without missing its vital point; to speak to all of the audience with a clear voice; to speak, considering the sequence of the matters involved; to speak in response to the content of the other party's statement."

A common practice for developing confidence in speaking positively in front of a class begins by asking students simply to call out "present" in a loud, firm voice, then at a later time to go on speaking loudly and clearly on small matters they are certain to know the answer to, and then move on to slightly more complicated matters.

The objectives for the study of geography for lower secondary schools are:

(i) Through studies of various regions of Japan and the world, to have the pupils seek foundations for geographical views and

considerations, take cognizance of our country from a broad viewpoint and understand the importance of making advanced and rational use of the land, thereby cultivating an attitude of endeavoring to develop the country.

(ii) To have them realize that there are both regional peculiarities and common features in every geographical phenomenon, consider the geographical conditions accountable for them, and establish foundations for proper understanding of each region and the peoples' lives.

(iii) To have them understand that there are various types of regional groupings, large and small, in Japan and the world, which are mutually interdependent, and think about the role of Japan in international society, thereby deepening their realization as a member of the nation and the world.

(iv) To have them understand that the relations of human beings with nature and social conditions have been undergoing ceaseless changes due to human activities and that each region has also been transforming correspondingly. And, to have them understand the importance of the proper development and preservation of nature.

(v) To foster the ability necessary for proper consideration of geographical phenomena through direct contact; the proper handling of maps and charts, the writing of reports, etc.

Some examples of the topics to be covered in lower secondary history are as follows:

(v) Emergence of "Buke" (warriors' class) Government
Through studies of the administration of the Kamakura Shogunate, life of warriors, culture during the Kamakura period, invasion by the Mongolians, and so forth, the teacher should have the pupils understand how the Kamakura Shogunate came into existence and how the "Buke" (warriors' class) government replaced the "Kuge" (court nobles) government.

(a) Formation of Europe

Referring to Greek Culture and Roman Culture, the teacher should have the pupils understand that these, coupled with Christian Culture, formed the basis of the European world in later years.

(b) Contact with the Islamic World

The teacher should have pupils understand the outline of contacts between the European world and the Islamic world, while referring to the natural features and advancement of the Islamic world.

(c) European peoples' overseas expansion

Referring to the Renaissance and Reformation, the teacher should have the pupils understand that the Europeans had been expanding overseas since new sea routes were discovered. In addition, the pupils should be led to take note of the expansion of the Netherlands and Britain in later years as well.

(xvi) Development of Modern Japan

Through studies of international relations and Japan's external policy, development of Japan's modern industries and social changes, formation of modern culture, revision of unequal treaties, etc., the teacher should have the pupils understand that, since the early Meiji years, this country had, amidst complicated international relations, established her national structure on the basis of political, social, economic, and cultural developments, gradually elevated her international position and grew up as a modern state. And also, the pupils should be led to realize that many problems emanated from the posture of overtaking other powerful nations rapidly.

Similarly detailed outlines are provided for other topics in history and all other subjects.

The number and location of vocational courses are determined by and adjusted to estimates of manpower needs. In certain fishing communities near Sendai, for example, modern

courses on fishing techniques are offered that are not paralleled by courses in any American fishing communities, and it is not surprising that the skill levels and technology of American fishing communities have fallen far behind those of Japanese fishing communities. Vocational training suffers from many of the same problems as in the United States, in that it tends to attract the less diligent, the less motivated, and less able students. However, the Course of Study provides detailed quality guidelines for home economics, agriculture, industrial science, business, fishing, and nursing.

As in many European countries, textbooks are published by private companies and approved by boards of leading educational specialists chosen by the Ministry of Education. In fact, usually there are only four or five approved textbooks on a given subject for a given grade. Although they are generally bland by American standards, in order to be approved the books must be well written, must be filled with the best scholarly information available, and must cover all the topics in the Course of Study. The price of textbooks is very low, but the market is large and the leading textbook publishers compete keenly to develop high-quality books. In a sense, textbook publishers in a given field, competing first for Ministry of Education approval and then for sales to local schools, are like manufacturing companies in an industrial sector competing first for MITI approval and then for successful markets. Only a small number of publishers have the resources to meet the very high standards involved.

Textbook certification in social sciences raises difficult questions of judgment. Until 1945 the single textbook approved for each subject had strong nationalistic biases. Since then leftist intellectuals who are concerned about the concentration of power in government hands have worried that the Ministry of Education might favor conservative texts, and traditionalists have worried that traditional moral training is

inadequate. In fact, textbooks generally avoid controversy by presenting objective information or, where opinion was sharply divided, by offering several differing views with some context for each of the views. In one difficult case, a textbook written by a famous historian Ienaga Saburo was judged by other historians to be overly one-sided, and when Ienaga refused to include alternative positions in the textbook the Ministry did not approve it, arguing that in such controversial matters Ienaga's views could be presented but that other views should also be presented. William K. Cummings, who was originally skeptical of the claims of textbook objectivity, concluded after his study that although there are debatable cases concerning certification of controversial texts, as a whole social science textbooks "presented a remarkably open-minded, even a progressive picture of Japanese society . . . The social studies texts enabled the students to reflect on their own social situation."

The success since World War II in maintaining fair-minded social science texts rests on the balance of political forces and the independent professional ethos of educators and Ministry of Education officials. Whatever pressures educators might feel from a conservative government are balanced by the pressures from the leftist Teachers' Union, and this balance of power helps ensure that educators have the independence to maintain quality and objectivity.

When an American state or a European country or Japan sets educational standards, there is a risk that the approval of textbooks may lead to political bias. It is not easy to maintain high national standards without some such risks, but given the balance of political forces in North America, contemporary Western Europe, and postwar Japan, and the exposure of youth to a wide variety of ideas through television and other media, the danger of narrow thought control as in prewar Japan and prewar Germany seems small. If anything, in the United States, which has no national standards and no stan-

dards in many states, the danger is that teachers might provide incomplete training or that, having so little supervision, they might impose personal biases. In Japan every parent can be assured that his child will be presented the knowledge and well-considered ideas of the best educators, that noncertified textbooks are widely sold, and that television (with average viewing time comparable to that in the United States) will provide his child with considerable diversity.

The Course of Study plays an important part in the curriculum of education majors in the university and of teacher-qualifying examinations in each prefecture. The seven-to-ten-day prefectural training program commonly given new teachers is financed by the Ministry of Education and draws heavily on the Course of Study. After a teacher has about five years of experience, and again after ten years, he undergoes similar programs to update his knowledge. Finally, if a teacher is to be promoted to a higher administrative position such as Dean of Studies (*kyōtō*), he is given another round of orientation and upgrading. Ministry of Education officials are not necessarily satisfied with the typical teacher's level of awareness of the Course of Study, but these training sessions undoubtedly help assure that teachers have a clear idea of the goals of education.

In addition to the periodic training of teachers, every ten years when a new version of the Course of Study is issued, special programs introduce them to the teachers. The Ministry of Education first invites leading educators from each prefecture to national centers for two days of discussion. These leaders then carry the program back to their prefecture for two days of similar discussion with local school leaders, and the final round of meetings occurs at the local school level.

Thomas Rohlen, who has perhaps conducted more detailed study of Japanese educational practices at the secondary level than any other American, has concluded that the supervision

of teachers by colleagues at the local level is more important than national guidelines in maintaining standards. In their beginning years teachers are not embarrassed to seek guidance from more experienced teachers about how best to respond to various classroom situations in order to keep the students positively motivated and to ensure that they all clearly understand the material. Their frequent informal study meetings after school provide, in effect, an ongoing supervision and mutual support system that greatly raises the quality of teaching.

Although the teachers must cover certain topics and tend to follow the advice of their seniors, they do have flexibility in the particular ways in which they teach the material. American teachers are given more encouragement to be creative in the classroom, but it is questionable whether most teachers' colleges train students adequately in subject content to create their own materials and whether the typical teacher in fact has the energy to engage in original preparations, given classroom discipline problems and the typical teaching and paper-grading load. Cummings observes that the Japanese teacher seems more secure in knowing what he is expected to cover, whereas the American teacher is often uncertain about what is expected of him because of experimentation and innovation.

From 1961 to 1964 students throughout the country were given achievement tests so that Ministry of Education officials could know how each local school throughout the country performed. Objections from the Teachers' Union over the possible use of such tests in hiring and discharging was sufficiently strong for the Ministry of Education to discontinue comprehensive national testing, but sample testing was continued in order to determine general performance level. Even if the national sampling service does not test a local school, the number of graduates of that school who pass examinations to the select schools at the next higher level is known, and it is therefore possible to have a judgment on the success of each

school in inculcating the basic skills. Higher level educational administrators can thus provide special help to schools that fall below standards. In the United States there is no federal agency that sets standards or even attempts to define what all students of a given age should know. To be sure, some American states set standards for students to graduate, but in general there is a less complete system for assuring that students are given adequate training to meet these standards. Americans are now concerned about the decline in the quality of preparation in primary or secondary schools, but no national data is ever collected in such a way as to tell how well a given school is training its students.

It is impressive how well schools throughout Japan ensure that virtually every pupil achieves minimal standards. No student is failed, and all students of the same age proceed together up through grade nine. The threat of failure or of being held back is considered neither desirable nor necessary to encourage students to maintain minimal performance standards. Approximately ninety-five percent of lower secondary students attend public institutions. There is no tracking, and all students are expected to acquire the basic materials of that grade. Some teachers have complained that this system slows down the more talented students and that some of the poorer students still do not catch on to many things in the class. However, the assumption that everyone can and will get through puts pressure on the teachers and the poorer students. Americans are much more prepared to accept that some students are unteachable and to give up on difficult students. Japanese teachers exert themselves to see that every student in the class has achieved a certain level before the end of the school year. They mobilize other students and parents to work with students with difficulties, for they are responsible not just for presenting the material and giving the students an opportunity to learn but for making sure that they do learn.

To assure that every school has the financial resources to provide a minimal level of compulsory education, the Japanese government provides subsidies to poorer prefectures and isolated school districts. A good part of the educational budget is met by the prefectures and some by the local community, but the national budget constitutes about one-fourth of the budget for the nine years of compulsory education. In a relatively wealthy prefecture like Tokyo, about eighteen percent of the public funds for the elementary school budget comes from the national budget, but in a poor prefecture like Aomori about thirty-three percent of the elementary school budget comes from the national government. Within a prefecture an effort is made to supply equal facilities for all pupils, and therefore in isolated rural areas with a smaller number of students the expenses per pupil are actually greater than in the metropolitan areas. As a result, there is much more uniformity in school facilities and expenses between school districts than in the United States. In most American states, where major costs of education are still met by local taxes, rich suburban schools can sometimes spend twice as much per pupil as poorer suburbs or urban areas. Furthermore, in America dollars spent per pupil in the poorest states are substantially lower than that in the richest states despite special programs of federal aid.

Even in Japan there are some differences in salary and teacher qualifications between localities, but they are modest. Special subsidies and salary incentives attract teachers to remote communities, and the resulting shortage of teachers in the urban areas forces cities to reduce the large differences in qualifications to a much smaller level than those between school districts in the United States. Certification of teachers is by prefecture, but general qualifications are closely monitored by the Ministry of Education, which does not allow the disparity of standards between prefectures to become very large. Cummings' analysis of cross-national science achieve-

ment data suggests that less than one percent of test score results in Japan is explainable by urban–rural differences.

In the United States, because there are no national standards and because of much greater variation in courses, it is more difficult to determine overall quality of training, although Educational Testing Service examinations and Stanford Achievement Tests do provide measures of performance in scores on such tests. At best, American average scores, as measured by international tests in mathematics and science, are well below Japan's, and the range of scores is also much wider. In short, the schools of America do not come as close in providing equality of training.

The uniformly high quality of training provides Japan with an unexcelled supply of generally competent labor power prepared for company life and receptive to learning more specialized skills at the workplace. If anything, the high level of education has overtrained students for their jobs and has created shortages of blue-collar workers. However, the Japanese do not share the disdain for physical labor found in some countries. Japanese schools, for example, use fewer cleaning personnel than America, and because teachers and all students share the "dirty" cleaning work in the schools, students learn to take physical labor for granted, not as something to be done only by those at the bottom of the social scale. Japanese students also learn the value of saving, as every pupil in every elementary school saves a few yen each week over several years to finance the sixth grade school trip (ordinarily to Tokyo for non-Tokyo residents).

Japanese schools, like the Japanese home, also teach self-discipline. They teach it at a general level in ethics and society courses, in an exemplary way in accounts of great men in reading classes, and in a practical way through the handling of classroom situations. All students are expected to be courteous and considerate to their teachers and to other students.

Expected standards of behavior are high, but explicit punishments are used less than quiet but clear expression of disapproval. Students, in their regular group sessions for self-reflection, are expected to talk about their inadequacies, as when they are insufficiently considerate of each other and of the school. On matters considered to be serious, like smoking cigarettes, teachers are likely to visit the student's family or to call the parents in to the school to discuss the seriousness of the problem, pointing out the importance of not having black marks on a student's record and their desire for the student to be the kind of person who could get a good job later. The school thus prepares the student for the work organization and the community, for they also rely less on regulation than on inner discipline and sensitivity to others.

Much of a student's study time, outside as well as inside the regular classroom, is spent in group study. Through group projects, group trips, classroom organization, and above all through close-knit activity clubs with membership lasting several years the student is not only allowed to enjoy group life but taught to be sensitive to his peers and to restrain personal egoism. Indeed, student organizations themselves play a major role in advising a student about ways to gain the respect of his peers. This prepares the student for life in a modern organization, where he is expected to develop a long-range commitment to work peers and to be considerate of them.

Not only does this high uniform standard of training strengthen social cohesion and provide a labor force with superior training, but it also eases the problems of spatial mobility. In the United States, which has great variation from one school district to another, a child who is transferred to a new school when his parents move may have great difficulty adjusting to the academic level of various subjects. At best, many of the things the child has learned are not in step with the curriculum in other schools. The mobile child in a highly

mobile society such as the United States is therefore caught in confusions, disruptions, and inefficiencies. In Japan, movement to different offices of the same firm is frequent even if interfirm mobility is not. But Japan's standardization of curriculum makes spatial mobility of pupils a much less serious problem than in countries with more heterogeneous school systems, although preparation for entrance examinations makes it difficult to transfer schools at high school age.

Some Americans believe that certain disadvantaged groups should be allowed to receive certification even if they have not met the same standards as others and that certain minority youth should be allowed to attend bilingual schools. The Japanese approach would be different. They would not allow a school in a second language but would provide supplementary courses until minority students entered the regular track. Japanese traveling to French Canada, Belgium, New York, and other areas with dual cultures are surprised that minority groups are required to know so little of the dominant national language and culture. In their view, it is ultimately damaging to minority groups not to provide and require the same high level of training as that of the majority, for without it minority groups would have lower standards of performance and would not be able to compete effectively in the marketplace, and regulations could not entirely overcome market forces. The Japanese problem with Koreans, *burakumin* (descendants of outcasts), and other minorities is admittedly much smaller in size than the American problem with minority groups, but their approach is fundamentally different: they have more confidence in the necessity of training the entire population to meet a high level of educational standards.

It is often said that the Japanese population is highly homogeneous, and by contrast to the American population, which came from many more diverse sources, this is certainly true. But Japan in the mid-nineteenth century was more a

collection of diverse fiefs than a single culturally unified nation. Japan has become a homogeneous country not only because of the new national media like radio and television but also because there is a common core of culture transmitted to virtually the entire population. The Japanese encourage diversity in culture, art, cuisine, and style of life, but it is to be in addition to a very substantial common core. This core reduces the danger that cleavages will disrupt the social fabric and increases the chance that the populace will work together against crime and disorder and pull together when the national interest requires it. Japanese homogeneity did not result from tradition alone, for up until shortly before World War II regional accents in certain parts of the country were mutually unintelligible and regional variations in culture substantial. Homogeneity was created and is maintained by social policy, and educational policy is one of the pillars of this social policy.

Homogeneity results in a high common base of general knowledge, so that education can proceed to even higher levels, whereas in America, which has not pushed so hard for a homogeneous cultural base, a teacher must spend more time helping students of diverse backgrounds catch up to a lower basic level. In Japan standardized opportunities and uncompromising uniform standards of performance make it more difficult for students to explain their poor performance as being caused by extraneous factors; the burden of performance is theirs. In turn, it becomes infinitely easier for work organizations to later demand the same high standards of performance as that required in the schools.

TELEVISION FOR EDUCATION

Educational television in Japan has existed only since 1959, but by 1977 its national network broadcast some fifty-two hours a week of educational and cultural programs. Each

week it transmits ninety-six programs to schools, from 9:00 to 12:15 and 1:00 to 3:15, Monday through Friday, and from 9:00 to 12:00 on Saturday. As of early 1976, programs were used by more than 10,000 of Japan's 13,000 kindergartens, over 23,000 of Japan's 24,600 primary schools, and 4,700 of Japan's 10,700 junior high schools. Schools decide whether and how much to use these various programs, which are designed to supplement regular classes.

There are special courses for students with various disabilities and for those who need supplementary work to keep up with their grade level, but there are also regular programs for the public. In contrast to programs offered by America's Public Broadcasting System, which are often, in effect, high-level entertainment, the programs transmitted to Japanese schools are basically informative, primarily including illustrated lectures for the general public. Although there is an effort to make these programs appealing, they are selected not on the basis of popularity but on the basis of meeting educational needs and conveying informative content.

The two channels of national public television (NHK and NHK Educational Television) are financed through a user tax, a small fee paid by every household that has a television set. These funds enable NHK to have complete autonomy, for the Diet and other politicians have no control over how the funds are to be used. The Diet cannot even propose rates but only approve rates proposed by NHK.

Along with the television programs, NHK Educational Television makes available special textbooks. Ordinarily textbooks sell only twenty to thirty thousand copies, although the text to accompany *Sesame Street* (offered to increase the English abilities of small children) sells about forty thousand copies and the largest selling basic English textbook sells about five hundred thousand copies per year.

There is a continuous program of research and consulta-

tion with schools to build up new and better programs. Every August and September the educational television station carries out investigations into selected sample schools in each prefecture. Then in November there is a meeting of the high-level Central Consultative Conference (*Chūō jimon iinkai*), ordinarily composed of four leading scholars, four broadcasting specialists (one each specializing in kindergarten, elementary school, junior high school, and senior high school), and four people from the Ministry of Education. They meet throughout November and December to make final plans for the next academic year, which begins in April.

There is a separate committee, the Program Development Committee (*bangumi kaihatsu iinkai*), that engages in testing every August and September to assist in planning the development of completely new programs. The committee is a part of NHK and consists of a team of around ten people with the varied skills required for planning a new program. It takes about two years to develop a program. Each year, in addition to the survey data collected for annual programs, there are special meetings with teachers in the various prefectures to hear their opinions about desirable programs for meeting the needs of various schools. There are eight such three-day meetings annually, with eastern and western Japan having separate meetings to discuss kindergarten, elementary, middle school, and high school programs. These eight meetings draw together actual users of the programs, teachers who have a sense of how effective they are with students and how they could be more useful.

As in the national educational system in general, the budget for educational television is concentrated overwhelmingly on the years of compulsory education. Quality is maintained not only by the outside evaluation but by the high quality of the people planning and developing programs. There are approximately 125 academic specialists working in

the schools division of NHK who were trained in various departments of universities. Winning a job in NHK is a highly competitive exercise. There is a special three-month training program within NHK for all beginning employees. Although the staff draws heavily on academic experts and others especially skilled in writing, they have found that to communicate well in television they must rely on their own staff to write the final program and to handle production.

The result is a high-quality national service readily and easily available without charge to local schools. Programs draw on the best information available to scholars, presented in such a way as to fit in with the course of study for compulsory education. In educational television, as in many fields, national planning has made possible a quality program far ahead of anything the United States with its greater resources is even seriously considering.

8

Welfare: Security without Entitlement

IN 1955 the average Japanese life expectancy was sixty-five years for males, sixty-seven years for females. One might have expected that in the 1960s and early 1970s, with frantic economic development and environmental pollution, health would suffer. Since 1962 companies with fifty employees or more give annual physical examinations to all employees. With the exception of small rises in 1966, 1973, and 1974, the rate of illnesses observed through these examinations has gone down annually. By 1977, when Japanese longevity surpassed Sweden's to become first in the world, life expectancy was 72.7 for males, 77.9 for females.

In the 1950s as urban areas grew rapidly and expenditures on social benefits lagged behind economic development, one might have expected alienated city dwellers. Sewage facilities and park areas still rank behind those of other advanced countries. Although from 1970 to 1975 Japan had more than eighty percent as many new housing starts as the United States (about 8.6 million, compared to 10.5 million) with only fifty percent as much population, the average Japanese still has only about two-thirds as much housing space as his American counterpart. Yet large urban districts with defaced personal

and public property and accompanying degradation and alienation, found so frequently in large American cities, are virtually absent in Japan.

Since pension and old-age security payments are just catching up with modern Western countries, one might have thought that Japanese old people would have been discouraged and forlorn. There are discouraged old people in Japan, and suicide rates rise with old age as in other countries, but as Erdman Palmore finds in his comparative study of aging in the United States and Japan, Japanese old people are more active than their American counterparts, and, based on large sample surveys of different age groups, their sense of satisfaction does not decline with age as in America.

In the 1960s as Japanese production was catching up with world levels, politicians began to talk of the need for more expenditures on social benefits to balance economic growth. Fashionable speakers replaced the term "gross national product" with "net national welfare" in order to show they were not narrow economic animals but were concerned with the quality of life. More funds began to flow into the welfare sector.

However, by the mid-1970s government and business leaders, at first quietly and then increasingly in indirect public comments, began expressing a new consensus. The essence of the consensus is that the welfare state, with "high welfare and high state burden" as found in England, Sweden, and the United States, is undesirable. By emphasizing the tax burden, Japanese leaders have achieved a measure of public support, but because opposing welfare lacks popular appeal, the new consensus has not been sloganized and enshrined with a fully-developed rationale. Nor has it necessarily carried the day with the Diet, which has voted and established more welfare than bureaucrats and business leaders consider desirable. Yet the basic rationale for the new consensus is understood by all

in leadership positions and in muted form ("in a period of low growth, with a heavily strained budget, funds are not available") occasionally appears in the public media. These leaders prefer to keep funds flowing into the productive sectors of the economy, to encourage the working place and the family to share welfare burdens, and to supplement private welfare with state funds only when it is essential to do so.

Minimal State Welfare

The Japanese lag in welfare expenditures is not necessarily permanent, but the new consensus has already slowed down the rate of increase and it is tailoring the welfare program in a certain direction. In part the long-range strategy of Japanese leaders after World War II was to concentrate first on industrial growth, next on wages and consumption, then on welfare expenses. By 1973 only twenty percent of public expenditure in Japan went to social benefits, compared to twenty-six percent in Great Britain, twenty-eight percent in the United States, and substantially more in all other Western European nations. As welfare expenditures increased, they were concentrated in health (in the early 1960s) and pensions (in the early 1970s) while other areas were virtually neglected.

In the health field the percentage of the GNP spent for medical expenditure grew rapidly for several years after national health care was established and then remained fairly steady except for 1973 to 1975, when it grew to keep pace with inflation, while the GNP remained steady. Overall, the percentage of GNP devoted to health care increased from 2.6 percent in 1961 to 4.3 percent in 1975; while the GNP multiplied by seven times in the period, health expenditures multiplied by twelve times. Japanese expenses on health care, including the ratio of doctors, nurses, hospitals, and hospital beds to the population, now compares favorably with the Western European average. In the Japanese system the patient

chooses his private doctor, pays a set fee for service determined by the national plan, with the patient assuming thirty percent of the costs, the rest provided by the national plan. People over seventy have all their medical care provided by the national plan. Because fees for visits are low, doctors encourage patients to come frequently, and a Japanese citizen visits the doctor more often than citizens in other countries. Although brief visits are not necessarily desirable and may be motivated largely by monetary concerns, in balance it gives more opportunity for doctors to diagnose problems, to catch illnesses early. Japanese doctors also make a substantial income from drugs, and Japanese patients consume more drugs than patients in other countries; the merits of this system are now being debated and alternatives are being considered. Government payments for a hospital bed are low, forcing hospitals to cut costs, and the period of hospitalization is much longer in Japan than in other modern countries of North America and Western Europe. In general, Japan has also raised medical costs very rapidly, and their internship and residency training has at times exploited the trainee without providing the well-developed supervision and didactic education about clinical work provided in American teaching hospitals. Yet the system of private physicians, low standard fees for doctors' visits and hospital service, and patient responsibility for as much as thirty percent of health care provides more frequent doctor visits for all elements of the population than the American delivery system.

Following heightened attention to the problems of the elderly in the late 1960s, annuity and pension payments began to increase very rapidly. There are two major pension plans covering about ninety percent of Japanese pensions: those for former company employees (*kōsei nenkin*) and those for unattached independent citizens (*kokumin nenkin*), further divided between contributory payments (for those young

enough to be part of recent payment plans) and noncontributory (those for the very old and infirm unable to pay their own way). In 1971, 1,200,000 former company employees received 176 billion yen (almost 1 billion dollars) in pension payments, but by 1976, 2,400,000 received 950 billion yen (over 5 billion dollars). For noncontributory national pensions, the 165 billion yen (less than 1 billion dollars) paid to 4,400,000 people in 1973 increased up to 706 billion yen (almost 4 billion dollars) paid to 5,100,000 by 1976. For contributory national payments it increased from 50 billion yen (less that 300 million dollars) paid to 750,000 people in 1973 to 563 billion yen (almost 3 billion dollars) paid to 3,000,000 people in 1976. As a whole, the Ministry of Finance has been careful to assure that funds are available in pension funds before rapidy increasing payments, although political pressures have forced them to increase payments more rapidly than they would prefer. Except for the national payment scheme, the government ordinarily contributes up to twenty-five percent, but most of the funds come from reserves. Reserves totaled 14 trillion yen (about 80 billion dollars) in 1975 and are deposited in the Ministry of Finance for public investment.

Aside from health and old age, welfare payments are still minute by American standards. Unemployment insurance is low because of the low unemployment rate; companies find it cheaper to set aside their own funds and pay for disguised unemployment when necessary than to support a very large bureaucratic system of unemployment insurance that is then paid out to workers laid off or fired. Even when workers are unemployed, the length of time for which they receive unemployment compensation is generally shorter than in Western countries. By law, all workers under thirty and all workers with less than one year of employment cannot receive more than ninety days of unemployment insurance payments, and ordinarily they receive considerably less.

Japan has fewer categories of aid programs than the United States. It has a general program of "livelihood protection subsidies" (*seikatsu hogo*) that covers a range of expenses from enough food to avoid starvation, to medical aid (to cover the thirty percent of private expenses that individual citizens cannot afford), to miscellaneous costs such as the modest compulsory education fees. These payments can be much smaller, partly because Japan has so few broken homes and aid for dependent children is therefore a minor expense. In 1975, for example, there were 1,400,000 mother and children households in Japan, compared to 7,200,000 in the United States. Amounts paid are adjusted to need, but in any case they are not sufficient to live on comfortably. Before the period of rapid growth, as many as 1,600,000 people were receiving a livelihood protection subsidy, but with the very rapid economic growth, the number of people receiving such a subsidy declined by the mid-1970s to 1,300,000. In 1975, even after rapid increases, the livelihood protection subsidies for the average recipient household was 67,000 yen (about 350 dollars); the total disbursements for the entire country were 685 billion yen (about 3.5 billion dollars), over two-thirds of which went for medical care. Aside from health care and old-age pensions, people do not have a sense of entitlement about welfare, there is a sense of stigma about accepting it, and it is given out very sparingly. The family (including relatives beyond the nuclear family) and the workplace are expected to bear a much bigger responsibility and to put aside funds to provide for their own security.

GROUP WELFARE

Historically, the Japanese government did not establish a single comprehensive welfare scheme for everyone, but progressively developed special schemes for various occupational categories. It basically followed the Bismarckian model of the

government's encouraging private organizations to set up welfare programs and keeping to a minimum the direct involvement of the state. Early in the twentieth century, plans were devised to provide for government employees, seamen, and minors; other plans gradually included employees in all large companies. After World War II these were expanded to include laborers, farmers, and eventually all self-employed. Just as the government holds to the principle that polluters should bear the costs of polluting, so it has generally accepted the principle that companies should be responsible for all the welfare costs of their employees. These programs did not necessarily stem from the most benevolent motives; many of the original programs concentrated on productive workers with the purpose of keeping a healthy working population, but the programs have since been extended to the nonworking population.

Since the employer in all lines of work is responsible for welfare, the employee knows he will be better looked after if he remains loyal to his company or his government branch. When the economy is very vigorous the individual can find other opportunities, but nonetheless the system tends to reinforce the tie between the individual and his place of work.

In the health system, for example, there is a program of health care for employees of large companies (*kenkō hoken*), employees of small- and middle-sized companies (*kanshō hoken*), public and quasi-public employees (*kyōsai kumiai*), day laborers, ship crew members, and all citizens who are not affiliated with one of the above (*kokumin kenkō hoken*). These programs cover, respectively, about twenty-five, twenty-five, ten, and forty percent of the population. Corresponding to these are pension systems for those working at large companies (*kōsei nenkin*), for public and quasi-public employees (*kyōsai kumiai*), and for nonaffiliated citizens (*kokumin nenkin*).

The scheme of providing welfare through separate oc-

cupational groupings rather than through a single system is quietly but enthusiastically supported by big-businessmen. According to a recent survey, large companies provided twice as many benefits as they were required to provide by law. Businessmen oppose the government's assuming heavy welfare burdens, for they want to pay less in taxes and to avoid the large governmental administrative overhead required for a large public welfare system. Perhaps even more important, they want to maintain the advantage that large companies enjoy over small companies, for if a potential employee is offered an equivalent salary at a large and a small company, other things being equal, he will take the large company because it can provide more security over the long run. This broader sense of security strengthens the identification of the worker with his company. Big-businessmen prefer to offer the benefits because the system reinforces the loyalty of the worker.

Although it is difficult to compare welfare benefits in a Japanese and an American company because the categories are so different, Japanese companies concentrate their benefits in areas that will keep the employee attached to the company over a long period of time. Benefits in the United States include substantial paid sick leave, vacation time, and coffee breaks—benefits rarely provided by Japanese companies in comparable amounts. In contrast, some seven percent of the Japanese population live in housing supplied by employers. An additional fifty percent—almost as much of the population as in the United States—own the dwellings where they live, and over half of the money that company employees borrow to buy housing is lent by employers. In 1975 the average interest rate for money borrowed from employers was three to four percent, compared to nine to ten percent for private loans in general. Even small companies unable to buy housing often lease housing and rent it to their employees below cost.

Large companies often have their own medical facilities, including hospitals and recuperation homes; these provide a much higher level of service than facilities supported by the national health plan. Since company retirement age is usually between fifty-five and sixty, most employees need a second job after retirement, and a company ordinarily assists a faithful employee in finding this post-retirement work. Many benefits provided by the company for longtime employees, such as the use of company mountain and seaside cottages and entertainment halls, are not easily calculated in value. Entertainment allowances are generous, but it is not easy to distinguish what portion should be considered company needs and what portion employee welfare. However difficult to calculate, as Robert Immerman, longtime American labor attaché in Tokyo, has noted, it is clear that the total Japanese company welfare package is larger than the American.

The Japanese company avoids tight contractual arrangements with employees and unions, leaving considerable discretion to company executives. The company tries to keep abreast of worker desires and offer more services than seem minimally necessary to meet union demands. By avoiding contractual agreements, company officials retain the leverage to give more rewards to those who have been faithful and hardworking. Especially in allocating company loans, assisting with postretirement employment, and allowing the use of special company recreation sites, company officials enjoy considerable leeway, conveying the message that perquisites are not automatic and that loyalty will be rewarded.

The Japanese government's intention to maintain strong ties between the individual and his company is perhaps most clearly revealed in the new program developed for depressed industries. As part of the Japanese employment maintenance program initiated in January 1975, if an employer in a depressed industry does not lay off employees, the government

will compensate for half the pay of idle employees, or two-thirds of the pay in small- and medium-sized firms. From January 1975 to April 1977, 69,414 business establishments received such subsidies for some 3,500,000 idle workers for a total of 29,000,000 man-days. Executives of companies in depressed industries are the first to point out that in fact these payments by the government are still totally inadequate, but their very existence is a creative way to maintain social stability and the attachment of the company to the individual employee, something missing in America, where an unneeded employee in a depressed industry is furloughed or fired and paid unemployment compensation.

Although it is difficult to match the security of the large companies, independent professionals and small businesses respectively form groups not only to make payments for mandatory welfare benefits but to provide additional collective security to their members. Their associations commonly offer collective insurance through private companies, and large organizations often create their own independent welfare funds.

With the decline of the growth rate, one might have expected that people in small businesses would suffer greatly. The smaller firms in affected industries indeed suffered many bankruptcies, but the overall number of workers in them remained remarkably steady through the early 1970s and actually increased in 1976 and 1977. Since many large companies anticipated the decline in growth rate, they greatly reduced the number of incoming employees. One result was that, with fewer employees, companies were less able to respond to certain short-range opportunities, and many opportunities fell to smaller companies. As Hiroshi Wagatsuma and George De Vos found in their study of the small business sector, small businesses have been surprisingly adaptable and their pychological profiles are remarkably similar to more successful upper-middle-class people. Individual companies occasionally

fail, but the same people keep forming new companies, drawing on others from small companies that are also going out of business. The same pattern is true not only for artisans and small manufacturers but also for service establishments like restaurants and bars, where the number of workers has continued to increase faster than the very modest population increases.

The Agricultural Cooperative, a very powerful organization to which every farm household belongs, has in effect an extensive program of security benefits for its members. Farmers make mandatory government welfare payments through the Cooperative, and the Cooperative buys and invests on a broad scale, providing greater security for investment than the farmers could hope to attain individually. By 1970 the association had five trillion yen in savings (almost thirty billion dollars) for the five million rural households and a few nonfarm depositors. By 1976 total savings reached fourteen trillion yen (almost eighty billion dollars), or almost three million yen (almost sixteen thousand dollars) per household. In a 1976 survey of farm households, it was found that the average farm household deposited about eight hundred thousand yen (about forty-five hundred dollars) more than it withdrew from savings each year. The retired farmer is thus able to enjoy a higher income as a result of this saving and investment than he would merely by mandatory social security alone.

The family farm also provides a form of social security. The typical farm is small (two or three acres) as a result of the land reform policy of the Allied Occupation and the accompanying legislation discouraging reconcentration. By the mid-1960s, with increased mechanization, much less labor power was required on the farm. Young farmers therefore go out to work in towns and cities, in a variety of industries. With good transport facilities and automobiles, most of them are now able to commute to work from their homes. Even if

they are retired from urban employment at age fifty or fifty-five, they can return to farm work, earning enough to cover food and other expenses for the household until well into old age. This is the dominant pattern for the five million rural households in Japan, one that provides old-age security and a sense of pride and activity for the elders in almost twenty percent of the nation's family households.

In the urban areas the small retail store, often owned by the elderly, also provides an equivalent to a welfare security system, for while it is not economically efficient, it is protected by government rules about the penetration of large stores and is supported by neighborhood shoppers, who appreciate convenience. It provides an opportunity for widows, divorcees, and workers retired from small- and medium-sized enterprises, for it requires almost no capital investment. As of 1978 Japan had 1.61 million retail outlets and the number was continuing to rise, while the United States had 1.55 million and the number was continuing to fall.

Families, rural and urban, have expected to provide funds for themselves in their old age, although it is likely that the very rapid increase in pension payments in the early 1970s will have an impact, lessening family financial responsibility. In 1973 Japanese saved twenty percent of disposable personal income, compared to Americans, who saved eight percent. Survey research data collected during the last several years show increased savings since the mid-1970s. In households where heads are approaching retirement, savings rates have increased beyond the national household average. These surveys show that a higher proportion of savings are now being set aside for retirement than in previous years when a higher percentage of families reported they were saving for household purchases, housing, and the education of their children. In Japan the family has been clearly responsible for the education of its children, and families put aside money for that pur-

pose. In the United States, where there is less clarity about whether the family, the government, or private institutions are responsible for the education of the student, there is virtually no family saving for educational purposes.

Japanese family members also assume a much larger share of the responsibility for caring for the sick than American family members. Hospitals not only encourage family members to help out but often supply mats or cots and cooking facilities at the hospital, providing quality personal care without great financial burden.

The Japanese family still accepts a large responsibility in caring for the aged. In 1953 eighty-one percent of the Japanese over sixty-five were living with their children, and in 1974 this had declined only to seventy-five percent. As John C. and Ruth Campbell have noted, less than two percent of Japanese over sixty-five were in nursing homes and other institutions, compared to almost six percent in the United States. Palmore notes that in 1973, seventy-nine percent of Japanese couples over sixty-five live with one of their children, compared to between fourteen and eighteen percent in Denmark, the United States, and Great Britain. Among Japanese widowers, eighty-two percent over sixty-five live with children, and of widows, eighty-four percent. Only about ten percent of Japanese over sixty-five are not living with a spouse or child. The pattern of elders living with their children does impose a burden on the young couple, especially upon the young housewife, and this is a cost that needs to be considered in this system. The advantage for the elderly is quite clear. Even in old age the Japanese continue to be active, to maintain strong social ties to their families, and to engage in work and hobbies. Although the percentage of working men over sixty-five has declined slightly since the 1960s, in 1973, while forty-eight percent of Japanese were employed compared to forty percent of Americans, forty-seven percent of the Japanese men over sixty-five

Japanese Successes: Welfare

were still in the labor force, compared to about fifteen percent in North America and the west European countries. In 1976 forty-three percent of Japanese men and fifteen percent of Japanese women over sixty-five were still working. Palmore concludes that the relatively high satisfaction of the elderly is related to a high activity level and to their involvement in family affairs. The low pension payments until recently have made this a necessity, but in general Japanese individuals in the household are taught to be more aware of the needs of others and have therefore adapted more easily to three-generation households and to young couples living near elders than in comparable American families.

The Japanese employment system operates to give more encouragement to youth. Middle-age people save for old age because when unemployment comes the burden will fall more heavily on them. In 1977, although the growth rate in Japan had slowed considerably, there were still roughly two openings for each young applicant entering the market because of the permanent employment system, whereby companies are motivated to hire inexpensive young workers. Compared to the United States, where unemployment is especially high among the young, the Japanese system reduces alienation and pessimism at this crucial stage of life when attitudes toward work are in their most formative stage.

There are many in Japan, including the leaders of the Japanese Medical Association, who would argue that the system of having different welfare schemes for different companies and other groups of the population is a feudalistic holdover that should be rationalized by having a more unified standardized national welfare program for everyone. Clearly, the greatest disadvantage of the system is that the unattached individual does not receive as complete a coverage of various benefits as those attached to the largest companies. The large company's health and pension funds thrive and grow while

government sponsored funds for self-employed individuals are in chronic deficit. Certain groups in Japan suffer from these disparities to an extent that many civic-minded Japanese consider undesirable and that the vast majority of Americans would consider undesirable. Minority groups like Koreans (perhaps numbering six hundred thousand) and the descendants of outcasts (perhaps numbering two million) often have much more difficulty finding employment in middle age and have much less adequate welfare provisions. Widows and divorcées not only receive inadequate coverage from protection plans, but even those who wish to enter the labor force are handicapped because they have not accumulated seniority and thus receive far less pay than other workers of their age. Those from small industries who seek new jobs at middle age have very little chance for sharing attractive living conditions.

No benevolent-minded person in Japan or the United States would find the extent of these differentials attractive. Despite ups and downs, the long-term trend for the Japanese welfare programs of the Social Insurance Agency has been to gradually fill the gaps in groups which were inadequately covered. For example, one gap filled in 1973 was the provision for free medical care for all people seventy and older. One could argue, however, that the injustices should be dealt with by reducing the differentials between groups without sacrificing the system of company and group responsibility. Large company funds could be taxed and some of the proceeds given to support those who are unattached. Large companies could be required to bear a larger portion of their former employees' old age expenses. Special programs could be made available for training and employing women heads of households. Since 1976 monthly bonuses have been given to companies for employing widows or women with disabled husbands, and these bonuses could be increased. One could argue that the strength of the company, the professional associations, the village, and

the family is a precious commodity in the postindustrial age with its centrifugal tendencies and that a welfare system which reinforces these ties should not be casually cast aside as a feudal remnant.

MINIMAL BUREAUCRACY, MAXIMUM IMPACT

In the health and welfare fields, as in other fields, the Japanese bureaucracy is highly centralized. It has broad scope but tries to play a minimal role in direct administration. Compared to the United States, which has confusing and overlapping national and state jurisdictions with many inconsistencies, Japan has simpler, more consistent national plans. Although the varying programs for different groups is not without administrative problems, services are nonetheless standardized throughout the country. With less duplication, Japan is able to streamline its welfare bureaucracy.

Just as the economic bureaucracy accepts a broad responsibility for promoting the economic health of the nation, so the national health bureaucracy accepts a broad responsibility for looking after the health of the populace. As in other fields, bureaucrats take more initiative than their counterparts in the United States. For example, they make far more frequent inspections of restaurants, hospitals, and other institutions to see that they observe standards of nutrition and cleanliness. They take a more active role in health examinations for youth, providing dental and medical checkups for all school children. They make more use of schools and neighborhoods for giving vaccinations and injections of all types, and therefore the Japanese population is better protected against such diseases than people in the United States.

In improving nutrition and in trying to prevent damage from charcoal, gas fumes, and the like, the Japanese government takes an aggressive role in using the mass media. NHK and National Education Television give detailed advice to

mothers about nutrition and the health of their children. Mothers are also called in to the public schools and lectured on child care.

In the United States politicians are at the mercy of welfare pressure groups, and the result has been that fees and payments for certain welfare programs have risen astronomically, sometimes at the expense of a coherent, equitable plan. In Japan the bureaucracy, which has a greater measure of power relative to politicians, is somewhat better able to resist special pressures and to provide a sound fiscal base, although it is by no means immune from pressure groups, as John C. Campbell has shown in his analysis of Diet decisions to raise welfare payments prior to crucial elections.

In the case of livelihood maintenance subsidies, the Japanese government relies less on professional welfare workers and more on some 160,000 officially designated volunteers to make home visits. These volunteers, respected senior people in the local neighborhood or village, make recommendations about need for the 1,300,000 people who receive maintenance subsidies. These volunteers consider it an honor to be called on to talk with and visit needy people in their local community. Since advice and suggestions are not standardized, the program suffers from the lack of professional judgment, and it was therefore attacked by the Allied Occupation and is still criticized by some Japanese professional socialworkers. The advantage of the system is that senior people in the community respected for maturity and personal judgment take an interest in family situations, giving advice about how to achieve greater frugality, how to resolve personal difficulties, and how to cope with employment problems. Because they live nearby and visit people in their homes, the volunteers understand the local situation and tend to bring to bear the more enlightened side of community opinion. Over the years the Japanese have built up a roster of such people, one in each neighborhood or local

community, who take an interest in the neighborhood and help look after people with problems. This informal system not only mobilizes local community support but reduces the demands on a welfare budget that has a very small paid staff by American standards. In 1976 the United States Department of Health, Education and Welfare had 155,100 employees; Japanese Ministries of Education and of Health and Welfare had 11,200.

REDISTRIBUTION AND WELL-BEING WITHOUT DEPENDENCE

One of the tenets of the Japanese approach to welfare in the broad sense is that there should be economic employment opportunities for everyone and that those who work and exert themselves for their organizations should be appropriately looked after. The government's policy of distributing wealth throughout the society is not based on public welfare but on fine calibrations of wages, taxes, budget redistribution to poorer prefectures, and subsidized rice price paid to farmers. People are not entitled to anything but the barest essentials unless they contribute to their groups. As a result, there is no sizeable group that feels indignant out of a sense of entitlement or self-deprecatory out of a sense of inadequate achievement. Nor is there the deep social cleavage between taxpayers who object to supporting those who work less and the recipients who object to the inadequacy of their payments, their uncertainty, and the spirit in which they are given.

In the view of Japanese businessmen, the ordinary worker in England, Sweden, or the United States has lost the drive for work. The differential between the low-paid worker and the welfare recipient is too small to retain a strong commitment to the organization. Despite the growth of welfare payments, bureaucrats in various ministries strive to maintain this differential. Bureaucrats in the Finance Ministry, for example, take

care to ensure that the effect of tax policy is to encourage people to save, to accept responsibility for others in the company and the family. Even when Japan's growth far surpassed other countries and unemployment was virtually nonexistent, the Japanese employee sought workplaces that provided security and he exerted himself for his company, for public welfare was not a real alternative for a comfortable life.

In the West in preindustrial times when communities were small, charity, elicited by generosity and appreciated by the recipient, was a humane way of ensuring minimal living standards. In the complex modern world, however, where groups have grown in size and formality, charity, however benevolent in its origins, has been transformed into a government-sponsored system impersonally operated, leading to a sense of entitlement. The recipient has less appreciation for what is received than annoyance at what is not received. The resulting cycle of frustration, lack of motivation for work, unattractiveness to employer, and self-depreciation has disastrous consequences to the social fabric of many Western nations. The Japanese are reluctant to sing the praises of their modest public welfare system, but Japanese who travel to American cities are invariably struck by the run-down nature of American slums, the lack of respect for public property, and the general degradation of American cities. As paradoxical as it may be to Americans, the Japanese, with a poorly financed welfare system aside from health and pensions, have managed much better than we to avoid the despair that underlies this degradation.

Ample employment opportunities help maintain high morale, a sense of purpose, self-respect, and group effort; the opportunity to work more than compensates for the inadequate welfare payments. How well the system would work if the Japanese economy were to decline precipitously is speculative, but with the vigor of the national efforts, this may not

be tested in the foreseeable future. In short, the Japanese have been able to provide for the well-being of their population without requiring many except the very old and infirm to become economically dependent on the state, and they have done it in such a way as to reinforce their communitarian ideals.

9

Crime Control: Enforcement and Public Support

IT HAS BECOME almost conventional wisdom that crime rises in modern industrial countries. This is true for all countries of North America and Western Europe. William Clifford, one-time head of the United Nation's Crime Prevention and Criminal Justice Programs, recalls that in 1969 when international specialists began to notice Japan's falling crime rate, the trend was hardly believed. They confidently predicted that with continued urbanization Japanese rates would begin to soar. In fact, crime rates continued to decline for the next several years and then stabilized. From 1946 to 1973 crime in Japan declined by roughly one-half. Not only are crime rates now lower than during the immediate postwar period, but they are lower than during the early Meiji period, to say nothing of the sixteenth century prior to the establishment of Tokugawa rule, when feudal states engaged in violent warfare.

David Bayley, a political scientist who conducted an excellent study of Japanese police, concludes that Japanese crime reporting is more complete than American, so that when comparisons are made with the American crime rate, the Japanese rate is understated. Using 1973 reports for both countries, he relates that in the United States four times as many serious

crimes were recorded per person (8,638,400 in all) as Japanese crimes of all sorts (1,191,549). There were approximately four-and-a-half times as many murders per person in the United States, five times as many rapes, and 105 times as many robberies. Despite the fact that drug offenders are pursued with more vigor in Japan, in 1973 only five hundred were arrested, six percent of whom were on hard drugs; in America, with twice the population, 629,000 were arrested, twenty percent of whom were on hard drugs. The Japanese are also much more successful in apprehending offenders. In the United States the average rate of clearance of reported crimes through arrest in 1974 was twenty-two percent. In Japan in 1974 the overall clearance rate through arrest was sixty-nine percent and it averaged even higher for serious crimes: seventy-seven percent for robbery, eighty-three percent for rape, ninety-three percent for graft, ninety-seven percent for embezzlement, ninety-six percent for murder, ninety-three percent for bodily injury, and eighty-six percent for arson.

Japanese policemen are in much less danger than their American counterparts. The rate of on-duty policemen killed is approximately sixteen times higher in the United States. In the four years from 1969 to 1973, 16 on-duty policemen in Japan were killed, while in one year, 1973, 127 on-duty American policemen were killed.

Why have the Japanese police recently been so successful in controlling crime? Part of the answer lies in the readiness of citizens to call police (throughout the nation there is a single number to call police which everyone knows), the speed of response to calls, and the thoroughness of pursuit. In 1976 the average time it took police to respond to a call throughout the country was three minutes and twenty-three seconds. America has no national statistics on response time, and notification of police is often slow. Japanese police are distributed in some 5,800 mini police stations (*kōban*) in the cities, each commonly

serving a population of about ten thousand, and some ten thousand residential mini police stations (*chūzaisho*) in the countryside, each serving an average of about five thousand people. Given Japan's crowding, an area covered by a mini police station is of small geographical size.

Second, Japanese police have great advantages in pursuing complaints. Police in mini stations are in close touch with the local community and know about household composition and household valuables. Residents acknowledge the need for police to ask questions in order to gather information and are prepared to be cooperative. When polled as to how they would advise a relative who commits a crime, the Japanese respond overwhelmingly that they would tell the relative to turn himself in to the police. In the United States the suspect is advised that he has the right to seek counsel and not to cooperate in giving information to the police. Japanese find it puzzling that American suspects are not urged to help the police find out about the crime. In Japan the suspect knows that it is prudent to assist the policemen in gathering information. Nor are Japanese offenders likely to receive leniency because they are considered to have psychological difficulties or to be victims of society or because an able lawyer pursues legal technicalities. Japanese punishments are generally mild (in 1974 less than 38,000 Japanese were in jail), but Japanese officials are relentless and systematic in pursuing all cases. If they show leniency, it is because the suspect is especially cooperative. Japanese officials are also not troubled by jurisdictional disputes between regions and local communities as in the United States. Japanese police are attached to the forty-seven prefectural-level governments and enjoy cooperative relations and overall coordination provided by the National Police Agency. Suspects cannot escape to other jurisdictions, nor do local officials hesitate to transfer suspects from one prefecture to another, even in minor cases.

Third, because there are far fewer crimes with almost as many policemen per population, the Japanese police are able to assign larger numbers of policemen to a single case and to pursue the data in all directions until the problem is solved.

Two other factors, police professionalism and public cooperation, are even more important in explaining Japanese success in controlling crime.

Professionalism

Policemen in Japan come more from rural areas than American police, but they tend to have comparable social standing. Despite general full employment and the modest lifestyle of policemen, there have always been, as with other permanent government jobs, at least several applicants for each opening on the Japanese police force. The examinations are not as intellectually demanding as tests administered for entrance to the best universities, but they are taken very seriously by candidates and the educational background of the police compares favorably with the population as a whole. Applicants know that police work is a demanding task and that if they are successful they will be expected to maintain strict discipline. Because there are so many candidates per position, prefectural police officials processing applications know they can require high standards of personal commitment as well as general ability. The officials undertake detailed investigation of the applicant's background and personal connections, rejecting those with antisocial tendencies and those who are judged not to be stable, cooperative, and disciplined.

Rules about police behavior are overly strict by American standards. When a policeman is in uniform he cannot smoke or eat outside the police station. A policeman is expected to be unfailingly courteous to the public, remaining cool even if verbally abused, yet unbending in carrying out his responsibilities.

Bayley found that Japanese police are also better disciplined than American police. In 1973, of the 182,000 policemen in Japan, only 524 were dismissed for misbehavior, about half the number dismissed in New York City alone. There is a Human Rights Bureau of the Japanese Ministry of Justice where the public may complain about policemen without fear of retaliation, but in all of Japan there were 123 complaints made during an entire year. The good relationship between the public and the police did not exist in all periods of Japanese history. In the 1930s and early 1940s Japanese police were known for their haughtiness, sometimes even brutality, and the public kept their distance without complaining. Since World War II, police sensitivity to the public has improved, and the public has become more positive in its attitudes toward police. When Japanese senior police officials are asked to identify the most troublesome problems of police behavior, they now mention off-duty traffic accidents, drunkenness, and indiscretions with women; there were virtually no disciplinary problems on duty.

The National Police Agency, with roughly two thousand police officers and six thousand civilians, sets standards for prefectural police concerning appropriate behavior, salary range, force size, and organizational structure. As in other parts of the national bureaucracy, about fifteen officials are admitted each year into an elite career track in the agency. This corps of elite officials plans overall policy and guides the administrative handling of all major issues, including the standards to be maintained by the prefectural police. Elite officials are rotated between the central office and the prefectural offices, and at any one time several elite officials are assigned to each prefectural police headquarters. They thereby ensure high local standards and coordination between the prefectures and the central government. Also, high officials are aware that in many

countries police desiring information feel it necessary to compromise themselves with local gangs and shady businesses. The constant rotation of senior officials from the national headquarters to the prefectures and comparable rotation of prefectural officers to localities within the prefecture make it more difficult for gangs and illegitimate enterprises to maintain the special relationships with particular people that lead to local police corruption.

The National Police Agency also supervises the training of prefectural police. As Bayley notes, whereas policemen in the United States typically receive about eight weeks' training, in Japan the training program is for one year. In addition to supervising the training program for the prefectures, the National Police Agency itself trains all higher officials in the prefectures and provides various programs for specialized personnel. Patrolmen constitute roughly sixty-eight percent of the Japanese police force; in the United States they commonly make up over seventy-five percent, with considerable local variation. The larger proportion of higher positions in Japan permits more opportunity for advancement and more supervision of patrolmen by higher officials. As in other walks of life, there is an expectation that the younger policemen will be nurtured and trained by their seniors. Bayley concludes that there is much more in-service training and stricter supervision of policemen in Japan than in the United States. Supervisors in the Japanese police are considered responsible for the behavior of their subordinates, even to the extent that they may receive criticism and punishment for mistakes committed by their subordinates whether or not the supervisors were specifically responsible for the errors. As in other spheres of Japanese life, the small group has a high esprit and generates internal discipline over its own members, helping prevent police corruption. Social activities, team sports, and informal recreation greatly

strengthen the bonds between fellow policemen. This helps discipline flow naturally from bonds of loyalty rather than from outside authority arbitrarily imposed.

One group, the riot police (*kidōtai*), receives further specialized training. Tokyo, being the center of government and possessing a high portion of the university students, employs over half of the ten thousand riot police. To handle large demonstrations and other mass activities, they have developed elaborate tactical plans with shields, helmets, masks, and staves, as well as electronic equipment. Compared to the United States, which relies on various state-run National Guards or units of several different local police forces, both of which are unprepared and uncoordinated for handling riots, the Japanese riot police are much better trained, better coordinated, better protected from personal danger, and less prone to use force. Japanese student leaders visiting the United States in the late 1960s were surprised at how unprepared American students were in helmets, poles, and electronic communication equipment, because they assumed American police were as well prepared as the Japanese.

In the United States it is assumed that policemen might act without adequate regard for the rights of the suspect, and judges therefore constrain police action. In Japan the police are expected to have inner discipline so that courts rarely challenge police decisions and the police do not feel on the defensive. American police have at times abused their authority, but it is a vicious cycle. Constantly hemmed in by regulations and overrulings by the court, they have less opportunity to develop group pride and self-discipline. Japanese police, like high-level bureaucrats or section people in the company, have a great deal of professional pride and confidence in their own work, and they enjoy the respect of their superiors.

As in other administrative spheres, the police are permitted flexibility in handling problems as long as the result

conforms to overall goals. Determinations of justice are made less on the basis of technical legal grounds or skillful legal argument than on an overall assessment of whether a person has done something fundamentally wrong and whether he is likely to engage in such misbehavior in the future. In the Japanese view, truth is not best arrived at by adversary relations wherein lawyers try to be as clever as possible in bending the law to favor one side. They are convinced that flexibility avoids contentiousness, reduces the chances of loopholes interfering with justice, and increases the likelihood of finding a sanction that is effective. The notion that a defendant could legally consult lawyers and refuse to talk to the authorities is unthinkable. Authorities may be relentless in their questioning, but in their view truth is arrived at through an open process of information gathering. Japan has about ten thousand lawyers, compared to about three hundred forty thousand in the United States.

The Japanese also do not draw such a sharp line between nonlegal and legal sanctions. They may use quiet warnings or mobilize friends, neighbors, and others to express public disapproval as well as impose fines and imprisonment. They systematically make an effort to assess the attitude of the defendant and his sincerity and determination to avoid future trouble.

In short, policemen are given considerable discretion. The ordinary patrolman handles only the immediate contact and questioning; for further investigation, even in minor misdemeanors, specialists are sent out from the twelve hundred or so police stations that are above the mini police station to gather information and determine the disposition of the case. The scope for discretion is large, but the basic logic for determining how to handle particular cases is clear. In general, what Americans define as crimes without victims are dealt with in a very permissive way unless the acts disturb or endanger others.

In the evening in downtown bar areas it is common to see groups of two or more drunks holding each other up, staggering along and singing happily. The Japanese police, like the public, are more amused by than morally critical of such behavior. They readily assist the large number of drunks who inhabit entertainment quarters each evening in gathering up belongings, avoiding injury, and finding transportation home. If a drunk should hit another person, the police rush to restrain him. And if he should attempt to drive his own vehicle, the Japanese police will be extraordinarily severe. Similarly, gambling is ordinarily considered acceptable. The *pachinko* parlors (which use a kind of pinball machine) with their nonmonetary prizes are so widespread that at one point there was a *pachinko* machine for approximately every twenty-eight people in Japan. Moreover, there is legalized betting, particularly in government-run horse racing, bicycle racing, and boat racing. Police even tolerate the involvement of gangs in this betting and in *pachinko* parlors. Homosexuality has never had the moral disapproval that it has in the United States and has never been treated as a vice. Prostitution began to be regulated only during the Allied Occupation and these regulations have been retained, but the post-Occupation prohibition is not against payment for sexual services but against public solicitation, ownership of a house of prostitution, or management of a group of prostitutes. As long as there is no huge public scene, prostitutes and their customers are allowed to go their way. Local policemen do not chastise a prostitute on their beat as long as she is quiet and discreet.

Many Japanese gangs (*yakuza*) at times engage in illegal activity, but they are often composed of highly disciplined members who identify with conservative nationalistic goals, engage in public activity including publishing magazines, and maintain, by American standards, shockingly open, cordial relations with the police. The police, by constant open inter-

action with these gangs, implicitly allow certain activities not considered dangerous to public order, but they move quickly to curb activities that go beyond.

The one exception to permissive handling of victimless crimes concerns traffic in dangerous drugs. For a while in the 1960s police condoned glue sniffing as it spread among certain avant-garde groups of young people, but they have always been very severe in controlling the growth, manufacture, importation, and use of narcotic drugs. Because of their tight control over the availability of narcotics, they have never arrested more than three thousand persons for use of hard drugs in any single year.

In dealing with automobile traffic Japanese police are decisive and unyielding. First of all, cars are required to be in much better condition than in most states of America. If one were to drive a car in a bad state of repair, he would be stopped quickly by the police. Procedures for obtaining a driver's license are so severe that license seekers commonly pay as much as fifteen hundred dollars for drivers' training programs. Japanese drivers stop more quickly when the traffic light changes to avoid fines. Although the Japanese are given a five- or ten-mile leeway over the speed limit, police are much more systematic in tracking down people going more than ten miles above the speed limit than in America, and one therefore rarely sees cars going too fast. Using loudspeakers, they behave with confidence and authority at major intersections. When accidents occur, in addition to handling the emergency situation by diverting traffic, caring for the injured, and arranging for the removal of damaged vehicles, the police also take a larger role in investigating causes of accidents than in the United States. Very quickly, measurements are taken, facts are ascertained, and the basic determinations of responsibility are made. Decisions as to who should pay for damages are handed down fairly soon, often at the scene of the accident, and generally

both parties are expected to share in the expense, although the party most at fault pays more. The result is that traffic accidents and their consequences are much less likely to result in court cases, cars are repaired more quickly and at a reasonable rate, few large fees are paid to lawyers, and high insurance payments are avoided.

Although the Japanese policeman is given considerable discretion, with detailed supervisory training of some years he, like the teacher, tends to behave as a firm and confident professional who knows the proper way to deal with a particular problem. This in turn reflects a high degree of group consensus about desirable behavior. He is not prone to argue and can be virtually impervious to argument. He aims to be polite but he is rigid, for he has the confidence that his entire organization is prepared to support him as long as he is acting correctly within his jurisdiction.

MAINTENANCE OF PUBLIC COOPERATION

Why does the public cooperate with the police? In the first place, they respect the quality of the police, their professionalism, and their devotion to duty. It is not because the Japanese consider the policeman to be of high social standing but because they recognize his authority and competence within his sphere. Police do not take these attitudes for granted. They exert themselves to maintain the cooperative attitude of the public. In dealing with a suspect or an ordinary citizen individually, a policeman is polite and businesslike. He is self-confident and so he does not need to flaunt his authority. He tries to avoid making comments that might provoke anger. As Bayley notes, a policeman is taught to ask questions indirectly, and, unless pursuing an especially important case, he is unlikely to coerce a person to supply information. The policeman has implicit authority, but he makes every effort to behave as the eagle in the Japanese proverb who hides its claws.

Japanese Successes: Crime Control

The local neighborhood mini police station has several policemen assigned to neighborhood duty. The local policeman is commonly called the *omawarisan*, the one who makes his rounds. Aside from manning the station to be of assistance to neighborhood people, each policeman makes frequent rounds in his respective neighborhood. Because he often meets local residents on his rounds, he tends to develop friendly personal relationships. He usually travels by foot or by bicycle, scarcely distinguishable in attitude and type of dress from the local postman. The mini police station is also responsible for local household registration, and this aids a policeman in knowing his neighborhood. Each household in Japan is expected to register all residents with the local police station, and policemen visit each home semiannually to note any changes in a household. In addition, he gathers information about ownership and the ordinary location of cars and other valuable property. He notes the daily patterns of coming and going. Because the local policeman is generally the best informed person about the neighborhood, he is sought by outsiders who wish to ask directions about how to find a particular house or shop. He aims to be helpful in giving first aid, assisting children across streets, finding lost items, and providing informal neighborhood news. He posts neighborhood announcements on the bulletin board outside the mini police station.

This kind of friendly service to the local community builds a basis for relationships that makes people in the neighborhood feel confident about approaching a policeman when they have seen suspicious people or suspicious activities. A crime prevention association is organized as part of every village (*burakukai*) or neighborhood (*chōnai kai*) to ensure that certain local people specifically have the responsibility of assisting the police. With this background of knowledge and these neighborhood connections, a policeman is in a good position to notice unusual behavior when asked to do so by local people.

When a policeman is pursuing a suspect, he can count on networks of local relationships. The police can thus get information with greater rapidity from broader circles than if they had to rely on new contacts in each case. Since neighborhoods tend to be better organized than in America, the whole effort is much easier. Higher-level police officials may be rotated every two or three years, but low-ranking policemen are commonly assigned to the same location for a longer period of time to cultivate contacts with the community. Even if individual policemen are rotated, local people nonetheless trust the policeman at the mini station, for his behavior is highly predictable.

Police are lenient to those who are cooperative in giving information and who show respect to the police, for this is considered necessary to get the job done. Bayley found that whereas an American suspect is more likely to protest his innocence and argue with the police, the Japanese suspect is more likely to be compliant and cooperate in supplying information and submitting to search. This is not simply a holdover of prewar attitudes when police could bully the frightened public; it reflects a greater tolerance of surveillance and general social control than in America, where individuals are likely to be more assertive about their rights. The attitude is nourished by Japanese police, who are likely to apply longer and less pleasant questioning to those who proclaim their rights, defend their behavior, and criticize the police than those who are more cooperative.

Part of the public's cooperativeness stems from its general deference toward government agencies. The Japanese are more prepared to cooperate with authorities than Americans, whose widespread alienation and tradition of righteous indignation toward authorities cause them to sympathize more with persons committing crimes against the government and big business. In the late 1960s tens of thousands of Japanese protested against the government, and many remain sympathetic with

criticism of the establishment, but probably no more than a few hundred radicals remain committed to physically attacking the basic institutions of society, and the public overwhelmingly unites against anyone who challenges those in authority. Toward anyone who departs significantly from his expected role, the Japanese automatically respond with visible disapproval, whether by gesture, subtle comments, or very strong, even if indirect, criticism. Just as the public is less willing to understand and excuse lateness, sloppiness, and laziness than the American public, so is it less patient with the transgressor and more willing to cooperate with the police in maintaining the public order they so firmly believe in.

The low level of alienation in Japanese society is related to the widespread pride of individuals in their work and workplace. In Japan, as elsewhere, it has been noted that transient populations have much higher crime levels than stable local communities. For example, Japanese government researchers who conducted an intensive study of crime in Kashima found that while many unattached construction workers were present, crime rates were very high. Once these transients were replaced by a more stable population, the crime rate went down precipitously. Because Japan is a relatively stable society with strong group membership, people have a commitment to their own group and to the maintenance of order that unites them firmly against threats to order. Similar attitudes may be found in many small American communities but are unfortunately weaker in large urban areas where cohesiveness has declined.

In virtually all of Japan, as in much of America, there is a feeling that people do have a chance to succeed if they apply themselves. Society values merit and work, not manipulation of the system. The Japanese feel that their efforts will be rewarded, that their compliance to norms will result in gains to themselves and their families. Given sufficient stability and

group cohesiveness, the one who attempts to manipulate the group is unlikely to gain, whereas in disorganized societies there is more room for manipulation and the group has more difficulty maintaining control over deviants. Although some American ethnic enclaves may have internal social cohesion, many American urban areas have so little cohesion and such a high level of alienation toward the wider society that deviants are less subject to the informal bonds of social control.

Because an individual in Japan is identified as a member of a group, the group is affected by the reputation of a deviant and therefore exerts considerable pressure on a potential deviant to live up to standards. The Japanese family, for example, is judged to be much more responsible for an individual's behavior than in America, and no sharp line is drawn between parental responsibility for minors and adults. When members of the Red Army, a small militant radical group of the 1970s, committed crimes, they caused families enormous embarrassment, and at least one parent of such a youth committed suicide. When university demonstrations were so much in vogue in the late 1960s, it was not uncommon for humiliated parents to plead with their children not to participate. Television graphically relayed scenes where mothers were searching out their demonstrating children, even those of college age and beyond, pulling them away from the crowd. Any crime that involves a company member, especially if publicized, is an extraordinary embarrassment to the company. When the story of Marubeni's involvement in the Lockheed scandal broke, popular weeklies featured articles on the humiliated young people who had just become Marubeni employees. A school principal and a school teacher are considered so responsible for the behavior of children under them that they may be asked to resign or at least to apologize publicly when a child under their charge gets in trouble with the police. The effect is not only to create greater group pressure on the deviant, but

to inhibit him by emphasizing the potential shame he will bring to his group by misbehaving. A potential deviant may even be isolated and expelled from the group if he has blatantly violated group norms against the advice and urging of his fellow members.

Police make use of their areas of discretion in such a way as to maintain public support. They tend to be slow in arresting people when there is not a high level of support for their behavior. If anything, they err on the side of not being as severe as most of the public wishes. The calculations of the police can be seen most clearly in their handling of student riots. The police consciously hold off in responding to provocations until the public mood turns into anger at police inaction and into demands for immediate steps. At that point the police move in. They thus keep the public firmly behind them in their activity and avoid stepping beyond bounds set by public opinion. When students occupy buildings, or the Red Army takes over villas, or Japanese terrorists hold international hostages, the Japanese police tend to be patient, maintaining psychological pressure around the clock for days to encourage mass resisters to give in voluntarily and in order to avoid direct violent confrontations that might create or increase sympathy for potential martyrs. They could have cleared the Narita Airport field early in the 1970s but hesitated because of widespread popular support for the demonstrators.

The essence of the strategy of riot police is to minimize the danger of injury, gain the support of the public, and reduce the threat posed by the resisters. The Japanese police are ordinarily quite permissive to demonstrators, and indeed there are far more public political demonstrations in Tokyo than in Washington, D.C. However, it is only when there is a danger of violence or when the group is occupying a place to which the public needs access, such as train stations, airports, or public buildings, that the police feel called upon to take control.

When they do so, they amass overwhelming force. In 1978, for example, when gasoline was first taken to the Narita Airport over the protest of resisters, over six thousand riot police took charge of protecting the oil from the danger of intruders. They failed to prevent damage to the control tower, but thousands of well-trained, courteous riot police prevented any incidents in the first months of the airport's operation despite a group of highly skilled opponents determined to cause trouble. In dealing with massive student demonstrations and clearing an area, the riot police generally used huge shields, slowly pushing back the demonstrators blocking an area. Thus, the police have little worry of being hit by flying objects and do not need to respond precipitously out of fear. They systematically move those blocking public access. Rather than individually shout and yell at rioters or demonstrators to make themselves heard, the police use large public amplifiers, explaining what they are doing in a calm but firm voice.

Because gun control is very tight, because police are well-trained in hand-to-hand combat, because they amass overwhelming numbers when demonstrators assemble, and because they can count on public support, the police are less likely to attack a suspect out of fear. Because they feel quite confident, they can be firm and definite without needing to fight with or overwhelm a suspect. The policeman is so certain that a suspect who has done wrong will be punished by the arm of the law that he can even behave sympathetically to the unfortunate violator.

The Japanese police themselves may detain a person up to twenty-three days for investigation without a court order, but they are cautious about doing so without substantial reason. Having ample time to interrogate subjects, Japanese police do not have to act in haste, although they do make every effort to conclude investigations quickly.

Japanese police also make every effort to be mild in their

punishment. In the United States in 1973 about forty-five percent of those who were convicted were sent to prison, about forty-one percent were allowed out on probation, and about six percent more were fined. In Japan, by contrast, about ninety-five percent of those who were found guilty were fined and less than five percent were sent to prison. In 1972 approximately forty thousand Japanese were in correctional institutions, compared to approximately three hundred and forty thousand Americans. Former Japanese prisoners are, of course, under the surveillance of the local police in the neighborhood to which they return, even without being on probation. Since the local community cooperates in observing any strange behavior and the police know the location of the former prisoner, they can promptly handle any problems that may arise.

If one commits a serious crime in Japan, one is almost certain to be caught, but the punishment is likely to be relatively mild. In the United States the proportion of wrongdoers apprehended is low, but the person who is tried and found guilty is treated much more harshly. As a result the American public harbors doubts about the justice of the criminal system, and the potential wrongdoer has a much greater chance of escaping detection or, through technicalities or use of skilled lawyers, avoiding punishment. In Japan, less public dissatisfaction is generated against the system because most offenders are punished, and punishment is not so severe as to be judged unfair.

As Donald Klein, comparative political scientist, has said, the Japanese handling of crime "demolishes some firmly held theories that enshroud America with veils of pessimism. It's simply untrue that massively populated cities are sure-fire breeding grounds for crime and public disobedience. Japan's history is equally if not more violent . . . Violence is also part and parcel of Japanese television." Yet now, violence in Japan is extremely rare.

As paradoxical as it may seem, Japan is more successful in controlling crime in the highly populated areas than in other areas. William Clifford attributes the differences to underlying philosophy: "Crowding people into cities under a banner of absolute privacy and maximum individual liberty as a right regardless of the interests of others . . . makes crime difficult to control . . . Japan has kept the citizens within social boundaries, group allegiance and community constraints . . . As crime grows across the world and the city dwellers skulk in fear at night in their homes that have truly become protected castles of guards, guard dogs, security services, special alarms and double locks, they may wonder whether Japan has not, for the time being at least, found a happy medium of tolerance with control."

PART THREE
American Response

IO

Lessons: Can a Western Nation Learn from the East?

INTRODUCING BASIC CHANGE is never easy. But to expect Americans, who are accustomed to thinking of their nation as number one, to acknowledge that in many areas its supremacy has been lost to an Asian nation and to learn from that nation is to ask a good deal. Americans are peculiarly receptive to any explanation of Japan's economic performance which avoids acknowledging Japan's superior competitiveness. It is easier to accept such explanations as Japan's industrial plants were devastated by a world war, and it could therefore build modern facilities; Japan copied Western technology; Japanese companies undersell American ones because they dump goods (sell below costs in foreign markets and at lower prices than in domestic markets); Japanese companies succeed because they are subsidized and protected by their government; Japanese workers receive low salaries; Japanese companies exporting to the United States violate antitrust and customs regulations.

It is more comfortable to overlook Japan's continued modernization decades after rebuilding from World War II, its effective organization, its genius in adapting technology, its patience in marketing, its disciplined work force. It is more comfortable not to ask how its businessmen could remain so

zealous in selling goods to America if they were basically selling below cost. It is disquieting to admit that the Japanese have beaten us in economic competition because of their superior planning, organization, and effort. To the extent that our government and business enterprises have begun to study their Japanese counterparts, it is often only to gather information that might prove charges of dumping or antitrust violation. One wonders at our lack of interest in profiting from Japanese successes.

THE COSTS OF INADEQUATE RESPONSE

The American response to the Japanese challenge is perhaps best illustrated by our abortive efforts to develop a foreign trade policy and an industrial restructuring policy. In 1971 when America was acutely worried about its trade imbalance with Japan, the White House trade representative, Peter Peterson, began to develop the outlines of such a policy. With the first dollar devaluation, the sense of urgency disappeared, and key American officials stopped worrying about an overall trade policy. In 1977 Americans faced the same crisis and again began thinking about the desirability of a comprehensive trade policy. Lacking continuous study and consultations, new officials had to start almost from scratch and without the broad public and business understanding necessary to achieve success. Unprepared, the situation became an emergency, as we had little choice but to allow the value of the dollar to decline in 1978 to about fifty percent of its 1971 value while government officials tried to find short-range palliatives to stem the tide of growing protectionism. They hoped that traditional market forces would operate: that as the terms of trade changed and American goods became cheaper, Japanese goods would become more expensive, the market would find its level, and trade would become better balanced. This policy, based on conventional but extremely narrow economic

considerations, brought some temporary relief, but it failed for three important reasons. In the first place, because Japan is so dependent on imports of raw materials, the cost of these imports constitutes about three-fourths of the eventual price of steel and Japanese manufactured goods like cars; when the value of the dollar goes down, Japanese buy raw materials much more cheaply, and therefore the change in Japanese export prices is minor. Japan is now able to buy oil, lumber, and other American resources so cheaply that it could easily disturb the American domestic market in a number of products and create new inflationary pressures. Labor-intensive Japanese companies heavily dependent on exports suffer with dollar revaluation, but companies buying materials from abroad prosper. The Japanese government helps ease the readjustment for those industries that suffer; for example, electric power rates were lowered in 1978 since the cost of energy resources had gone down. The second reason this policy does not work is that the Japanese find new ways to respond to the challenge by cutting costs, while the American companies, temporarily protected because of improved export prices, do not feel the pressure to improve and fall further behind their Japanese counterparts. Third, Japanese goods with a superior reputation for quality continue to sell even if prices are raised. If the Japanese, formally or informally, face quotas in the number of items of a particular product they are allowed to sell, they move into the higher quality market, thus increasing the dollar value of exports to America while continuing to observe the quotas—and without contributing to the correction in the trade balance that Americans had hoped for.

Each round of temporary relief from the fall in the value of the dollar distracts attention from basic problems in governmental organization, economic policy, and company modernization. Appraising American policy toward Japan, William L. Givens, business consultant and former Japanese specialist

in the State Department, concluded, "Like protectionism, the floating exchange rate is the opiate of the inefficient producer and the crutch of ineffective government."

The deterioration of America's competitiveness will have a far greater impact on our national life than we have thus far contemplated. As American industries fall behind, television factories must retrench, watch plants move elsewhere, and steel plants close down, with fewer jobs for American workers. Although Japanese takeover and modernization of some American plants like television factories will ease some of the burden, Japanese and other foreign investment replaces only a small percentage of the American industries that do not remain competitive. With increased Japanese profitability and continued trade imbalances, Japanese companies in America will draw heavily on Japanese banks and capital rather than American, thus reducing América's profits and increasing Japanese ownership of property and companies in the United States. The continued growth of Japanese industries and investment in this country may ease the unemployment problem, but it is questionable how far this process will continue before it arouses nativist resistance against foreign control.

As Japanese companies gain larger shares of international markets from American companies, American companies become less profitable. As the Boston Consulting Group has shown, a company with a large market share is able to sell enough to make considerable profit, to keep up research expenses, and to modernize facilities. But American companies with declining market shares will not make enough profit to finance continued research and modernization, and they will lose even more of the market, caught in a vicious circle.

As American companies become less profitable, America's government income is affected. Because profitability is down, governments must raise taxes to support the level of services to which people are accustomed, making it even more difficult for

companies to reinvest for modernization and creating understandable resistance if not a revolt of individual taxpayers. Local governments are caught in a political bind and must cut services, raise taxes, or both.

The decreasing tax base is already having an effect on American aid abroad. Even where we have made economic and military commitments, the recipient countries, watching the weakness of the American economy, naturally wonder about America's capacity to meet its commitments. Pessimistic foreign leaders may yet prove more accurate in their assessments than American officials who are endeavoring to provide reassurance about the reliability of American friendship.

Not only foreign aid but our basic stance toward developing countries is affected by the weakness of our economy. In 1978, for example, the United States asked some European countries not to pass on steel industry know-how to developing countries since the world's market in steel was satiated. Japan is not entirely open to imports from competitive third world countries, but its stronger and more flexible economy allows it to concentrate on higher quality steel, an area where it could still remain competitive, and to pass on to developing countries the technology for basic steel plants they so greatly desire. The American stance deprives the developing countries of the means to raise their industrial skills and can only lead to greater conflicts between the developed and the developing countries regardles of our humanitarian intentions.

With serious trade imbalances, the United States is becoming increasingly protectionist not only toward Japan but toward Korea, Taiwan, Hong Kong, Singapore, and other rapidly developing countries. Whether the Japanese and Koreans use voluntary restraints or America uses formal measures, the effects of protectionism are the same: even more directly than the falling value of the American dollar, it preserves the inefficient producer unable to meet international competitive

standards, and it requires the addition of sizeable bureaucratic machinery. At best, it can never be entirely effective, for there are many ways of going around barriers in such a porous society as America.

Superior foreign competitiveness creates an increasingly defensive mood in the United States. American company officials, straining to meet foreign competition, cut corners in quality and treat employees less generously, while labor unions, afraid of increasing financial stringencies, become more determined to maintain their benefits and to block modernization that might reduce jobs. Government workers, worried about the declining tax base, try first to guarantee their own security and income levels. Lack of competitiveness and increasing protectionism affect American self-confidence, contributing to internal divisiveness and discouragement about many of our difficult domestic problems.

The impact of all these trends would be serious enough if they were anticipated and dealt with in an orderly fashion. However, Congress, suddenly confronted with a shortage of funds, slashes aid or military assistance to countries that have grown to depend on it. National and state administrators impulsively cut budgets when confronted with tax shortages or taxpayer revolts. In declining industries decisions based on legal criteria like bankruptcy, dumping, and anti-trust lead to abrupt closing of plants, allowing insufficient time for planning the relocation of workers. By the time legal procedures in a dumping case are completed, for example, it may be too late for the injured party to regain a competitive position. When such stringencies create a sense of emergency, political pressures force trade negotiators to visit Japan to demand immediate action in dealing with trade imbalances that in fact require long-term solutions. Foreign nations, like American workers suddenly confronted with decisions affecting their lives, are becoming understandably annoyed and less willing to cooper-

ate with America at a time when our declining hegemony requires greater international cooperation.

It is tempting for Americans, having achieved affluence, to feel they no longer need to worry about economic competitiveness and should turn their attention to problems connected with the quality of life. Yet in an era of international economic interdependency, it is not possible to ignore a nation's international competitive position, as England discovered a while ago. America's problems at a national level are rather like those of a family that purchases a new home to relax and enjoy life, only to find that it is unable to make the mortgage payments and to afford the repairs needed to keep the house in order as prices rise faster than income.

If all countries had governments that devoted little attention to international competition, many of America's problems would be less severe. But other countries have developed a system to achieve superior performance, and America cannot effectively respond to the challenge with the old system, no matter how much we devalue the dollar and no matter how many protectionist barriers we erect.

A New Basic Model

Any country's practices are deeply rooted in its traditions and cannot easily be transplanted, as all developing nations, including Japan, have found in bringing Western patterns to their countries. Even if America borrows fewer ideas and institutions from Japan than Japan borrowed from us, it is unlikely that the process can be controlled easily by planning, and it may well require many years to define problems, discuss approaches, prepare people to undertake appropriate studies, carry out research, and evaluate conclusions. There is every reason to believe that despite our best efforts at sorting, sifting, and choosing, new practices will turn out to require more adjustments than originally anticipated. Given these caveats,

if America wanted not only to profit from individual lessons in various spheres but to develop an integrated program for profiting from Japan's experience, what would be its most critical features? The following features should certainly be included:

An industrial and trade policy. In the past America's economic philosophy has been to preserve the free operation of the market place, and it may be that market forces could eventually correct imbalances and adjust for the rapid decline of American industries that are being lost to other countries. However, the world can no longer tolerate the human, social, and political consequences of waiting for these market forces to reach a new equilibrium.

Rather than escape from the market place into state socialism, Japan accepts the ultimate value of market forces, but aims to hasten institutional adjustment to long-term trends while easing the human readjustments necessitated by changing economic forces. Japan provides key research and financial resources to assist key developments in the national interest when private sources are inadequate. Japan has been a pioneer in the development of such an industrial and trade policy, and many European countries have rapidly been following suit. The United States government—despite all its resources and reserves—can no longer afford not to give more positive guidance through a trade and industrial policy if our country is to continue to provide world leadership and an optimal quality of life for its own citizens.

We should make an effort to distinguish those industries in America that can be competitive on the world market and to support them through tax policy, monetary policy, antitrust policy, and administrative cooperation. We should make an effort to provide temporary cushions for those industries such as textiles that cannot remain competitive. We should not wait for legal action to show that damage has been done to declin-

ing industries but should guide them in reducing their capacity gradually while personnel are being retrained and relocated. In our trade negotiations, instead of spending our political capital on the defense of small, dying industries, we should defend the large, strong industries that can be effective in the future. We should create enough awareness of these overall problems in business and labor circles and provide them with a steadier, more predictable government policy. We need an on-going program, supported by careful research on the role of various American industries in the future. We should be bolder in assisting third world countries to develop their own industry, working toward an international division of labor in light of each nation's comparative advantages. We should reduce the number of regulations and regulatory agencies that operate independently of these overall goals.

A small core of permanent high-level bureaucrats. The capacity to provide long-range direction to society requires a continuity of leadership at high levels, a leadership that has the power and responsibility to oversee specific areas of activity whether they are in foreign policy, finance, energy, environment, transportation, or regional planning. Great issues require long time horizons and great continuity before solutions are found; it is not possible to pursue long-term policies when all key personnel change every two to four years. The issues are so complex that bright, noncareer outsiders who are brought in by changing political leaders cannot match a small core of highly able, dedicated professionals in respective spheres who have been given the best possible training, have been exposed to the most progressive thinking of private and governmental groups in America and abroad, and have been seasoned as junior officials working on problems they will face as they acquire greater responsibilities.

The American bureaucracy as now constituted is simply too large and unwieldly, and its talent too uneven, to provide

a high degree of coordination and direction in such basic fields. The White House staff is too prone to influence on the basis of short-range political considerations. Many people with great potential are not given the kinds of training, broad experience, and responsibility they need to play a central role in shaping these policies. Bureaucrats responsible for the health of organizations under them have no power over government regulatory agencies that may be operating at cross purposes. In short, there is no substitute for a select group of highly trained professionals, small enough in number to have effective communication with each other, who are not burdened down with the details of management and administration and can work effectively as a unit to give overall guidance in specific areas.

In the beginning, to start the core group of leading specialists, some of the ablest midcareer bureaucrats and non-bureaucrat specialists prepared to make a long-term commitment would have to be recruited. But a system should be established for recruiting and training a small number of the ablest young people of their generation. Along with extensive training and experience, they should be given broad responsibilities and monetary incentives to remain in these positions until they retire from this service at a moderately young age. They should be given enough leeway to develop and guide the implementation of long-range programs in their respective spheres. White House aides in these respective fields should be restricted to members of this group, and the group should be encouraged to maintain liaison with Congress and private leaders to gain the level of understanding required to make policies effective.

A communitarian vision. In bygone days of more genuinely free enterprise, the model of the independent trader or businessman, like that of the cowboy, was not only appealing but appropriate. As George Lodge has noted from his study, business leaders now recognize that this model is no longer ap-

propriate in an era when large organizations confront complex problems, but they nevertheless lament the passing of our individualistic past. Americans at large seem to share the same predilections, for charismatic critics of organizations are cheered while hard-working executives who exert themselves to hold organizations together are criticized. Organizational leaders are constrained by an enormous number of regulations and excessive red tape, and yet we wonder why they cannot make their organizations function more effectively. We clamor to protect the academic freedom of intellectuals, the free enterprise of business, the rights to confidentiality of lawyers, physicians, journalists, and clergymen, the rights of the accused, the privacy of the individual citizen. These are all values worth preserving, but they need to be balanced with equal concern for public responsibility, the interests of the group or society at large. In the guise of pursuing freedoms, we have supported egoism and self-interest and have damaged group or common interests. We are often more concerned with the rights of the deviant than the rights of the responsible citizen. Thus crime control, high educational standards, and effective organizations have been difficult to achieve, for they require that groups have the leverage to give moral approval to the member who restrains his self-assertion and is sensitive to the needs of others.

The Japanese have been on the forefront of making large organizations something people enjoy. Americans tend to think of the organization as an imposition, as an outside force restraining the free individual. Japanese from an early age are taught the values of group life. They learn to make school life and the life of work organizations more pleasurable. Japanese are uncompromising in requiring individual performance, but they can then take this performance for granted and concentrate on camaraderie, games, ceremonies, parties, and celebrations. Employees come in to their workplace on vacation and weekends in large part because they enjoy the camaraderie.

In contrast, while Americans acknowledge the need for large organizations, we have yet to tame them; the communitarian values so essential for successful group living which we once treasured in our villages and towns have not been revitalized in modern cities and complex organizations.

At the organizational level, we need to give more flexibility to universities, companies, and government offices: responsible people in these organizations are now more often concerned with satisfying scores of special regulations or avoiding lawsuits than with accomplishing the overall purpose of their organization. To achieve the purpose for which regulations were created, Americans would do well to follow the Japanese model and rely on moral suasion, on creating a consensus of concerned people who can exert their positive influence. The use of specialized regulatory agencies not responsible for the overall health of the organizations they supervise leads to legalistic rigidities and adversary relationships, thus weakening the force of the moral community. Without this moral force, regulations cannot fully accomplish their original purpose. At all levels, from the individual to the highest government offices, we must restrain the use of adversary relations if we are to avoid the divisiveness that makes cooperation for mutual benefit untenable.

Aggregation of interests. Complex problems of international trade negotiations, energy policy, pollution control, and readjustment of declining industries now require high levels of cooperation between companies within a given industrial sector and between the companies and the American government. Antitrust legislation should be adjusted to encourage this cooperation, and flexible administrative rather than rigid legal procedures should be found for dealing with the dangers of monopoly and oligopoly not in the public interest. The legal risks of working together now encourage companies to make individual arrangements with the bureaucracy and politicians,

thus weighting down the government with special concessions, and it makes it impossible for any group to represent common purposes against a single well-organized group not acting in the interests of the majority. Branches of government in various sectors should welcome the cooperation of independent companies under them and should work with these associations on issues of overall public interest.

Aggregation of interests works well when representatives of different groups meet frequently without immediate business in order to build up friendship and trust which become invaluable at the time of difficult negotiations. The representatives must not only have the trust of their own members but must also know thoroughly the interests and inclinations of their constituents. This in turn requires frequent meetings of persons in the same group, sufficient discussion and "root binding" so that there is a consensus which can be represented in higher level discussions. American labor leaders and management seldom see each other except in confrontational situations, but in Japan the frequent informal social gatherings between them creates a better basis for understanding and reduces the mutual antagonism. When various groups send representatives to negotiate, they do not use attorneys but "go-betweens," intermediaries who are known for their capacity to gain the trust and confidence of all groups because of their personal reputation and social position. They are often chosen by one group for their special connections with the group to be negotiated with or at least for their capacity to relate to people in that group. American mediators are often more skilled at articulating a position, but the Japanese have developed the ability to be sensitive to the wishes of the other parties and to win their trust. Americans may more easily win an argument, but the Japanese more easily win an agreement. Japanese make full use of informal consultations and social occasions at the golf course and the geisha house to create the

kind of mood where people can achieve agreements. Without importing geisha houses, Americans have ample social mechanisms that should be used to create and maintain trust between key groups so that, when necessary, important matters can be negotiated under optimal conditions.

Costs and Dangers

Some of the most serious problems likely to be encountered in importing Japanese patterns are the following:

Smothering individual rights, individuality, and creativity. At the national level the United States has many safeguards, legal and customary, to protect the rights of the individual and the private group. Japanese people, private organizations, and local governments are more at the mercy of central government bureaucrats and politicians because the traditional attitude of *kanson minpi* (respecting the bureaucrats and looking down on the citizenry) has not entirely disappeared. Firms that do not cooperate with central government officials encounter greater difficulties in dealing with bureaucrats than those that cooperate, and firms that are punished for noncooperation have no real appeal. The leaders of the Japanese Teacher's Union have been frightened of granting power to educational officials to establish merit ratings because they fear this could be used as an excuse to fire teachers with deviant political views; and indeed it was used in this way in 1949–1950.

In Japan the deviant in a group can be isolated, ridiculed, ignored, and banished (*mura hachibu*) from the group as in the traditional village. It is difficult for a deviant to stand against a group or for a creative misfit to gain the support he would gain in America. Those who do not conform to narrow guidelines are criticized and pressured until they fall within those guidelines.

In Japanese schools there is almost no flexibility in the

curriculum during the years of compulsory education that could encourage the development of creative imagination. One should not underestimate Japanese capacity to engage in original research, especially in projects requiring group co-operation; indeed, this capacity has begun to increase. Yet in basic research that relies on individual creativity, the Japanese achievements lag behind those in other fields.

Ignoring the variant, the opposition, and the little man. Although Japanese do make an effort to give all recognized groups a fair share, in fact Koreans and small numbers of Chinese and Westerners, even second and third generation, are not treated as full citizens. *Burakumin*, descendants of the outcasts from the Tokugawa period, are citizens, but most desirable employers and potential marital partners take great pains to avoid taking them in legally and socially. While one cannot exclude the possibility that the growing awareness of these injustices will lead to progress as it has toward blacks in the United States, Japanese are less willing to absorb foreigners than European countries and America.

Although opposition groups are given some shares, their shares are distinctly smaller. Opposition parties, labor unions, consumers' groups, and radicals are often ignored or given conspicuously less prestigious positions. They may be excluded from private meetings and treated as outsiders by those in the dominant power positions. There are even gradations within the accepted group, and members of the newly rising group, like the newcomer to a village or club, are treated as conspicuously less than equal by old revered members.

The elite bureaucrats who are so busy solving the larger problems of economic development and local regional construction often ride roughshod over opposition, as they did over the protesting farmers at Narita Airport before the public became aroused. Because of the intimate contacts within the inner circle, those aspiring groups that are left out, such as

student protest groups, some consumer groups, and local anti-pollution groups, feel a kind of social exclusion absent in a less cohesive society like America. Over a long time frame, new groups are admitted to inner circles and able individuals from protest groups are absorbed into the networks of friendly relations, but there is a real danger that bureaucrats with a firm power base might become insensitive to popular pressures. The problem may be more severe in France, but it is not absent in Japan and it is a problem that could prove divisive within America if a powerful professional elite were created, especially given widespread antielitist sentiment.

Condemning the misfit. Because there are few opportunities for individuals to change their place of work, one who does not get into a place of work that he or his family considered desirable suffers from an enormous sense of failure. By extension, the student who does not enter a desired high school or university may be equally miserable. Suicide rates are high among Japanese youth, and those who are discouraged by not making the proper organization may be more depressed than their American counterparts, who will have a variety of later options open to them.

Japanese who enter a place of work are not totally devoid of opportunities if they were to leave, but given the difficulty of obtaining a secure position with comparable benefits, most have little real option but to endure. Those who might be able to start a new life under different surroundings find that it is too late to make that kind of change. Those not valued highly by their peers or superiors have no place to turn. They therefore remain in the same organization, without particular satisfaction until they retire and go elsewhere.

The unhappy wife is often subject to the same fate. Officially, there is no problem in getting a divorce, and the procedures are not difficult. However, the weight of social pressure is on the wife to make adjustments to avoid divorce.

Courts may require the husband to divide property with his wife upon divorce, but there is no alimony. After years without employment, the divorcée or widow has difficulty making a satisfactory entry into the labor market. This forces the wife who is unhappy with her marriage into making the best of it. The system causes great economic and social hardship on the unfortunate widow or on the unhappy wife of modest means who proceeds to get a divorce.

Stimulating excessive nationalism. In an effort to stimulate internal cooperation and consensus, Japanese leaders have a way of publicizing international developments so that Japan is seen to be the victim of foreign pressure. One often seeks in vain for articles in the Japanese press that fully give the foreign side of the disputes.

Whether officially violating the General Agreement on Tariffs and Trade (GATT) or not, Japanese bureaucrats use a variety of ways to support Japanese products that are not competitive on the international market. When foreign cars were more competitive, the Japanese required that foreign cars off the assembly line had to be inspected in Japan before they could be sold there. It was not enough to send a model of the car, although it is safe to assume that Japanese automobile manufacturers had close working relationships with the necessary officials. By the time foreign cars arrived in Japan, the new model was so far along in production that it was extraordinarily expensive to make adjustments, and Japanese inspectors could find problems as small as location of mirrors or door handles. It thus was difficult for the foreign car maker, subject to such tactics and sometimes delays as well, to enter economically into the Japanese market. Japanese public corporations, although not officially part of the government, generally do not buy any foreign-made materials, even if they are cheaper and superior. The Japanese Telephone and Telegraph, for example, refuses to buy foreign computers whether or not

they are superior, as a spur to the domestic computer industry. When a foreign kidney dialysis machine began to take over the market because it was able to do in several hours what it took Japanese-made machines fourteen hours to do, the Japanese health service changed its rules to pay for use of dialysis machines on the basis of length of time machines were used, so that Japanese health facilities again began to buy Japanese products, subjecting patients to fourteen hours of time for what could have been done in several hours. When foreign pleasure boats began to penetrate the Japanese market, the inspector was granted the power to drop them from several meters high and then subject them to lengthy examinations, the expenses to be borne by the foreign company. Japanese pleasure boat makers simply submitted a model for approval and did not need to endure such testing. When an American soft drink maker began to expand its share of the Japanese market beyond what Japanese officials considered proper, it was required to use no artificial sweeteners while Japanese competitors could still use artificial sweeteners. When an American company wished to erect a caustic soda plant in Japan that was far superior to Japanese competitors, it was given one delay after another for well over a year. Because foreign drug manufacturers are often such superior competitors in Japan, when a Japanese company develops a new product, competitors are not allowed to enter the market for three years, thus effectively keeping out many foreign firms. If a foreign firm develops a new product, it may have such a right for only one year.

Some such practices are finally terminated after several years of foreign protest, but Japanese officials use bureaucratic haze to create delays, without full explanation of reasons or standards, thus further discouraging the foreign competitor and giving Japanese competitors a chance to catch up. Not all

foreign complaints prove to be justified, but many such practices continue, though virtually unreported in any Japanese medium despite foreign objections. The problems of the foreign firm are generally known only in a narrow circle of officials and business leaders responsible for such policies.

Japanese children who study abroad and learn foreign languages are given virtually no recognition for their achievements. Even Japanese children who have studied abroad and become fluent in English may be required by their teachers in Japan to go through various archaic exercises to prepare for English entrance examinations rather than encouraged to continue to develop their natural fluency. Japanese employees who serve abroad for a very long period of time have virtually no chance to rise to the very top positions in their firms, for they are considered a bit too *gaijin kusai* (contaminated by foreignness). Employees with foreign experience who do rise may first have to prove their superior loyalty to Japan even if it means rejecting part of the foreign experience.

The major universities in Japan are national universities, and since foreigners cannot be regular government employees, no foreigners are allowed to become full professors in Japanese universities. This is beginning to change, but the number of foreign faculty is unlikely to grow substantially. In most Japanese companies virtually no foreigners are allowed to enter the regular managerial career route even if they can handle the language.

Foreigners are generally excluded from Japanese press clubs and from briefings of the press by Japanese officials, except at special press centers for foreigners, even if they are competent to speak Japanese.

In international economic aid and in international organizations Japan has generally exerted itself in matters of immediate national interest. Although generally taking a respon-

sible and cooperative role in developing an international order, the Japanese have taken little initiative in matters beyond their own narrow self-interest.

Although foreigners are generally treated with courtesy and kindness, Japanese groups rarely accept them in their inner councils. Many large organizations have "managers of foreigners," people skilled in English and foreign ways, who mediate between foreigners and regular line officers. Foreigners may be taken as true friends by many Japanese individuals, but with some notable exceptions most Japanese organizations treat foreigners as honored guests outside the inner circle.

Becoming immobilized. One of the most troubling problems within and between Japanese groups is the deadlock brought about when one important partner refuses to go along. It is generally not considered proper to force a decision on an unwilling party. Narita Airport was long delayed partly because of the deadlock between the bureaucracy and the protesters. Universities are unable to progress because the Ministry of Education and faculties at the various universities are deadlocked over how much government control to permit if there are to be greater government expenditures. Because it is sometimes so difficult to resolve internal problems by means of consensus, a sense of outside pressure must sometimes be used. At other times when groups remain divided it may be that no one has the authority to resolve the dispute since everyone's views must be considered and no one wants to push through something when one group does not agree.

The Japanese have achieved success at a considerable price, the price of strong pressure toward conformity and consensus, sometimes at the expense of the deviant, the opposition, the little man, the outsider. These are excesses that Americans who may wish to copy Japanese patterns will have to consider seriously and devise ways to avoid. At the same time, it may be suggested that America is in little danger of

going to Japanese extremes in any of these spheres. America's problem is rather that American groups do not have enough power to maintain their own standards, that they do not have the confidence to carry out the will of the majority against the egoistic deviant. It may be suggested that America needs all the help it can get in moving toward group cooperation.

CAN THE JAPANESE MODEL SURVIVE SUCCESS?

Before Americans begin studying the Japanese model, they need to consider the question raised by many Japanese and some foreigners as well, whether the Japanese model of the last twenty years will remain effective, even in Japan. The Japanese model, so the argument goes, was appropriate to a period of very rapid growth when Japan had many comparative advantages and a receptive international economic and political climate. It worked when there was a high internal consensus about growth, but this consensus is now drawing to a close. Ordinary citizens are now more interested in social benefits than economic growth, and the new generation of youth reared in affluence have very little interest in economic growth at all.

The pessimists note that growth has already slowed down. During rapid expansion the banks had high leverage over firms, and banks were in turn dependent on the government to help provide financing for new investment. Now companies have accumulated more capital and will undertake less new investment. They therefore have less need for the banks and the government and are more prepared to go on their own. The domestic market was lively when one product after another was introduced into Japan, but now Japan is satiated with all the basic electrical and other equipment, so the market is limited only to replacement of old goods. Many Japanese goods have already begun to saturate other world markets, which will no longer be able to absorb products from rapid

expansion of Japanese industry. Manufacturers are fully aware of these trends and no amount of government encouragement can make them continue their rate of investment in modern facilities.

Korea, Taiwan, and other countries with lower labor costs and new plants sometimes more modern than Japan's will be able to undersell Japan on world markets in a broad range of products, enjoying the comparative advantage that Japan once did. Japan will therefore give up many of its labor-intensive industries to those countries, and the high technology sector where America still has strength and the service sector toward which Japan is moving do not provide the same growth opportunities that Japan enjoyed during its heyday as a heavy manufacturer.

The Japanese system, as seen by such critics, is in jeopardy as the growth rate declines. Companies are heavily indebted to banks, but when growth was high they could easily repay loans. When they were expanding rapidly, they could hire many young employees at low wages. Now that growth rates have declined, companies have trouble repaying loans and, with permanent employment, they are stuck with a highly paid older work force. With less expansion, they often do not have enough work for everyone, and disguised unemployment is rising rapidly. Firms are so strained maintaining the permanent employment system that the whole system is beginning to crack. The population over sixty-five has doubled in the last twenty-five years and is expected to double again in the next twenty-five years when the proportion of old people will reach European levels. The nation will be confronted with a smaller work force and a larger welfare bill, increasing companies' tax burden, reducing the growth rate, and creating a vicious cycle.

In the past, younger workers, workers in small and me-

dium enterprises, temporary workers in large enterprises, women and other underprivileged groups could be kept under control by the government and big business establishment because they stood to gain some benefits from rapid growth. In difficult times these groups will be the first to be sacrificed. During rapid growth the large number of rural youth who entered the urban industrial work force were willing to endure low wages and difficult woking conditions because it was an improvement over earlier rural conditions, but now that the rural-to-urban transition has been essentially completed, expectations are higher, there are fewer opportunities for rising, and consequently people in lower positions are less easily satisfied. Those who once took pride in their work in middle-level specialties are no longer as content to remain subservient to those in the elite track.

With a slower growth rate, political leaders must make more difficult decisions that require some groups to pull in their belt. Social cleavages will become more severe and the broad-based support for the conservative leadership will decline. The Liberal Democratic Party in the Diet is already eroding so that a coalition government is likely. As opposition parties and the disadvantaged groups they represent gain power, the great triad of leading politicians, elite bureaucrats, and big-business leaders will be unable to rule unilaterally. With a broader and more diverse base of rule, leaders will lose their capacity to achieve the consensus needed to act quickly. Government will be less effective.

Until now, Japan could selectively control imports of foreign ideas and customs, maintaining a tight national solidarity. With stronger foreign pressures on Japan to further open its import market, with increasing foreign contact and internationalization of Japanese companies, Japan will have more difficulty controlling foreign impact. It will become in-

creasingly difficult to preserve the strong distinctive features of Japanese society and to prevent the spread of some of the less attractive features of Western society.

Japan, always fragile because of its dependence on the international system, faces even greater dangers than previously. Raw materials like oil could be cut off, European and American markets could be curtailed by protectionism, and the productivity of rising countries like Korea, Taiwan, and Brazil could destroy Japan's comparative advantage. Japan profited from a period of great stability in resources and great receptivity to its products, but this era is ending and future crises could have a devastating impact.

During growth the grand vision of catching up with and overtaking modern, affluent countries gave the entire society a sense of purpose. The victory won and the vision achieved, Japan no longer has any clear direction. The optimism, discipline, and hard work that resulted from the pursuit of these visions, according to the pessimists, will now go the ways of affluent Europe and America.

The above arguments embody very real fears and they are not without some foundation. Americans who are hopeful for an end to Japanese competitive power as well as Japanese spokesmen who are trying to counter foreign pressure on Japan to further relax import controls and to restrain exports are likely to repeat them often in a variety of forms. In making estimates about Japan's future, informed reasonable men do not entirely agree, and a scholar can do no more than offer his best professional judgment.

The Japanese for the last two decades have been caught up in a series of crises, shocks, disasters, and so-called "depressions" when growth rate goes down as low as five percent. Each time there was a wave of panic, and each time Japan rallied to astound the pessimists. According to the best estimates of Japanese and foreign economists, Japan in the decade

ahead will still be able to maintain a growth rate of perhaps five to seven percent a year, substantially higher than the United States'. It is true that companies must repay loans to banks, but many are already finding ways to pay back some of their debts; and because of the policies of the Finance Ministry and the Bank of Japan, interest rates have already gone down far lower than during the rapid growth years. There are bankruptcies, but enough companies do well for the total employment to continue to rise; official unemployment is unlikely in the foreseeable future to reach three percent, and companies have expanded new product lines and further rationalized to control disguised unemployment. Companies have decreased seniority pay differentials and increased incentive pay systems without sacrificing the seniority system. Small and medium-sized enterprises are sometimes exploited by large manufacturers, but productivity and salary differentials between small and large firms continues to decline, and the small and medium-sized sector still continues to grow. Many large manufacturers want reliable subcontractors and therefore help modernize smaller companies; the result is that subcontractor workers are increasingly brought into a regularized employment situation similar to that of workers in large companies.

It is true that the service sector has grown relative to other sectors, but Japan is likely to turn this stage to its advantage as it has the stages of light industry, heavy industry, and high technology. As information processing becomes more important, Tokyo has the potential for becoming the information capitol of the world. Its six largest trading companies are probably each superior to any foreign company in range of economic and political information. Telephone facsimiles are already much more widespread in Japan than anywhere else. Because of its rapid advances in putting all published material on tapes and arranging patent and other laws to make this feasible, Japan is further along in having all library informa-

tion integrated into a single system than any other country. Although part of its computer capacities still lag behind IBM, the national government's commitment to making Japanese companies superior in computer and telecommunication systems gives it distinct advantages over other countries where there is no such policy and where antitrust suits threaten to break up the strongest multinational companies of American origins. Meanwhile, Japanese investment overseas will bring Japan new opportunities. The Tokyo-based economist Tait Ratcliffe estimates that in 1980 Japanese investment overseas will have tripled in five years and will continue to expand. Purchase of foreign firms with high technology is growing.

It is true that the proportion of voters supporting LDP had been declining, but the decline now appears arrested and in local elections the LDP has been regaining power. Every opposition party that has grown in recent years soon peaked far short of a serious challenge to LDP supremacy. Since coalition government came to be considered a possibility, bureaucrats have become increasingly cooperative with key opposition Diet members, in preparation for working together if a coalition government is necessary. So many moderate opposition leaders are prepared to cooperate with the LDP that even with a coalition, the government is unlikely to be fundamentally changed.

It is true that young workers had been less enthusiastic about subordinating themselves to the group, but the fears of petroleum shortages after the oil shock and of foreign protectionism after Europe and America complained in 1977 has greatly strengthened discipline and has kept groups from different circles united.

It is true that Japan would be in great trouble if natural resources were cut off, but wise Japanese bureaucrats have managed to keep open many petroleum options (between the Middle East, Indonesia, Russia, China, Australia) and many

coal and atomic energy options, all of which are supplemented by an excess supply of tankers and approximately ninety days on-shore petroleum storage capacity. With these efforts and their vigorous conservation program, the danger of a serious energy problem in Japan seems remote. With dollar devaluation, Japanese can now import oil so cheaply that some of the previous plans to reduce energy-intensive industrial production now seem unnecessary. As for international resistance to Japanese products, this will undoubtedly cause problems in certain selected industries, but the flexibility of the Japanese government's guidance, the capacity of the Japanese system to rapidly absorb information concerning trends, and the responsiveness of Japanese firms gives Japan many options. The fact is that the Japanese are likely to remain extraordinarily competitive in the world markets for a long time. What they reluctantly give up in labor-intensive industries like textiles and low-level electronics can more than be replaced by their rapidly growing capacity in new high-technology fields such as copiers, computers, and telecommunication equipment—a capacity that already threatens to weaken some of America's few remaining areas of competitive strength. Not only do exports of consumer goods continue to increase, but huge integrated Japanese construction projects in many parts of the world are growing rapidly, providing an outlet for Japanese production without attracting political reactions as do consumer products. Japanese investments throughout the world are already catching and surpassing American investments in many areas. Although investments in America have begun slowly, they can be expected to increase rapidly in the years ahead.

Within Japan, female temporary workers are generally the first laid off in times of economic difficulty, but in the "recession" year of 1977, for example, the number of women in the labor force increased almost two percent, far more than the growth of women in the population. The much heralded

cleavages in Japanese society are sufficiently quiet that leftist political leaders still bemoan the low level of consciousness of Japanese workers. The Japanese fear of inundation by foreigners has receded as the value of the dollar has fallen because so few foreigners can afford to live in or visit Japan. In short, within the next decade at least Japan appears to have the leadership, cohesion, and group support necessary to maintain a highly effective postindustrial society without any great changes in its institutions.

CREATING AND BORROWING

Can the United States, with its strong tradition of individualism, acquire a system, however admirable and effective, that is based on very different premises? When Japan began borrowing from the West in the late nineteenth century, it had hoped it could get technology without giving up the Eastern spirit. In the end Japan had to change its own spirit and institutions far more than originally intended. Japan's ultimate success should not mask the turmoil of the process, but Japan found that it could effectively transplant institutions that, with its tradition, it had not been able to create. It is no accident that the early, basic discoveries of modern science, technology, and industry originated in Western Europe and the United States, where individuality and creativity flourished.

The first generation of industrialists in Europe acquired their skills through their own experiences, but the first generation of industrialists in Japan spent many years in training programs acquiring the experience of others. In the turmoil of the early Meiji period some great individual entreprenurs and charismatic leaders played a crucial role, but the dominant pattern for catching up was of central government planning and guidance, close government–business cooperation, and rapid creation of large, private institutions through centralized capi-

tal accumulation and formal training programs. As Ronald Dore put it, Japan, even more than Germany, is a "late modernizer," with a particular set of institutions designed for rapid catching-up. In the later part of the twentieth century these institutions, originally developed for providing central direction for rapid change, turned out to be better adapted to the complex problems of postindustrial society than the institutions of Western countries that were developed for creating industrialization. In the current era of rapid change, a highly politicized population, environmental pollution, and shortage of resources, the Japanese have found that institutions which provide more central direction, more flexibility, and more consensus outperform those which lack these capacities.

Until a few decades ago America's institutions, which grew out of the Western European experience, worked extraordinarily well. Doctrines of private enterprise, civil liberties, and states' rights allowed creative individuals and institutions to adapt to local situations. With its scientific and technological inventions, America was on the forefront of world creativity. Laws developed in response to European tyranny gave individuals their highly prized personal freedom. Benevolent charities and academic institutions provided a level of humanity and decency lacking in many nations. When these institutions were at the height of their success, Americans were proud of and devoted to their country.

By the 1970s, however, institutions that once served our country effectively have often been found wanting and have been strained almost to the breaking point. Organizations lost the power and flexibility to function effectively. In a loosely organized urban society, ordinary citizens are defenseless against crime and license. Government regulations have multiplied, creating endless litigation that burdens society financially and organizationally. Commitments made when resources were seemingly inexhaustible have created expectations that

cannot be realized. Benevolent impulses and government programs have proliferated in a mass of confusion without adequate consideration of the financial burden on the taxpayer, of the divisiveness between taxpayer and recipient, of the motivation of the low-paid worker, and of the self-depreciation of the recipient in an achievement-oriented society.

The pace of economic change has accelerated and foreign trade increased, but America's institutions are not strong enough to guide these developments or to respond effectively to the problems of its declining economic competitiveness. When sudden dislocation can cause enormous human misery, as in the excessive migration from the rural south to northern cities in recent decades, the United States has had no migration policy. Our institutional practices promote adversary relations and litigation at a time when the complexity of our organizations requires greater consideration of overall goals and when divisiveness threatens to disrupt the society. As a result, judges are called upon to make complex rulings concerning social and economic situations, a task for which they are most often professionally unprepared.

Japan, with its greater sense of group orientation, more recent emergence from feudalism, and government-led modernization, has developed solutions for many of these problems that America, with its more individualistic and legalistic history, might never have invented. America's transition to industrialization did not require the central direction nor the high level of government and business cooperation required of a borrower. Now that postindustrial America, too, requires higher levels of cooperation and more central leadership oriented to a modern economic order, there is no reason why America could not borrow and adapt Japanese models which, with a different tradition, it could not have originally created.

No one should underestimate the difficulty of pulling out specific practices from their context. Nonetheless, while Japa-

nese practices are in many ways significantly different from American ways, they are surprisingly consistent with America's basic values. America values free enterprise, and even more of Japan's gross national product is located in the private sector than America's. America is committed to freedom of speech and freedom of the press, and so is Japan. America strives for a more equal society, and although the Japanese have higher requirements for performance before granting underprivileged groups equality, they have exerted themselves in reducing differentials of opportunity and have achieved income differentials smaller than America's. Japan is group-oriented, but as George Lodge points out, communitarianism is an integral part of the American tradition, going back to the early New England village. America's many voluntary associations, its history of community organization, and the positive value it attaches to teamwork suggest that group-oriented activities, if not dominant, are at least not alien to the American tradition.

America's problem of recreating a sense of community now that group ties have been attenuated is infinitely more difficult than Japan's problem of maintaining group ties that were never dissolved. But there is no reason why, with greater central direction and sensitivity to the needs of various groups, to the mechanisms of maintaining solidarity, and to the practice of broad consultation, America could not adopt policies more suited to the postindustrial age and recreate a sense of community in a form adapted to postindustrial society.

It is not clear that Americans are ready to respond to the challenges now posed by Japan's success and that will soon be posed by the success of Korea and other Asian nations. Unlike other nations inundated by Western dominance, the Japanese beginning in the late nineteenth century moved with eagerness and speed to bring in foreign patterns rather than have them brought in; thus they became the masters of change

rather than the victims. Other countries were devastated by foreign influence, but Japan was invigorated. This work is written with the hope that America, like Japan, can master the new challenges, that we will respond with foresight rather than hindsight, with planning rather than crisis management, sooner rather than later.

Bibliography

Index

Bibliography

CHAPTER 2

Abegglen, James C., Thomas Hout, and C. Tait Ratcliffe. *Japan in 1980*. London: The Financial Times, 1974.

Boston Consulting Group. *Trade between Japan and the United States*. Prepared for the U.S. Department of the Treasury, April 1978.

Financial Times, London, July 26, 1977. [Special issue on Japan.]

Gibney, Frank. *Japan: The Fragile Superpower*. New York: Norton, 1975.

Jorgenson, Dale. "U.S. and Japanese Economic Growth, 1952–1973: An International Comparison." Presented at the Fifth World Congress of the International Economic Association, Tokyo, August 29–September 3, 1977.

Patrick, Hugh, and Henry Rosovsky, eds. *Asia's New Giant*. Washington, D.C.: Brookings Institution, 1976.

Reischauer, Edwin O. *The Japanese*. Cambridge: Harvard University Press, 1977.

Scott-Stokes, Henry. *The Japanese Competitor*. London: The Financial Times, 1976.

[Statistical data is contained in annual government white papers published by various Japanese ministries (*White Papers of Japan*, Japan Institute of International Relations.) Various statistics are also summarized in such

annuals as: *Japan Almanac*, Mainichi Newspapers; *Japan Statistical Yearbook*, Prime Minister's Office; *Nippon: A Chartered Survey of Japan*, Kokusei-sha; *Statistical Handbook of Japan*, Prime Minister's Office. Statistics are also frequently reported in international English weeklies such as *Japan Times* and *The Japan Economic Journal*.]

CHAPTER 4

Abegglen, James C. *Business Strategies for Japan*. Tokyo: Sophia University Press, 1970.

Amaya, Naohiro. "On Japan's Trade and Industrial Policies." MITI Report JR-1 (73-2). Tokyo, February 1974.

Campbell, John Creighton. *Contemporary Japanese Budget Politics*. Berkeley: University of California Press, 1976.

Frank, Isaiah, and Ryokichi Hirono. *How the U.S. and Japan See Each Other's Economy*. New York: Committee for Economic Development, 1974.

Fukui, Haruhiro. "Economic Planning in Postwar Japan." *Asian Survey* (April 1972) 12:327–348.

Johnson, Chalmers. *Japan's Public Policy Companies*. Stanford: AEI Hoover Institute, 1978.

Kaplan, Eugene. *Japan: The Government-Business Relationship*. Washington, D.C.: U.S. Department of Commerce, 1972.

Komiya, Ryutaro. "Planning in Japan." In Morris Bornstein, *Economic Planning East and West*. Cambridge, Mass.: Ballinger, 1975.

MITI. *Japan's Industrial Structure—A Long Range Vision*. Report BI-23. Tokyo, 1976.

———. *Japan's Industrial Structure—A Long Range Vision*. Report NR-140 (77-26). Tokyo, 1977.

OECD Secretariat. *Environmental Policies in Japan*. Tokyo, April 1977.

Ojimi, Yoshihisa. *The Industrial Policy of Japan.* Paris: OECD, 1972.

Sato, Hideo. "The Crisis of an Alliance: The Politics of U.S.–Japanese Textile Trade." Ph.D. thesis, University of Chicago, 1976.

Scalapino, Robert A., ed. *The Foreign Policy of Modern Japan.* Berkeley: University of California Press, 1976.

Tanaka, Kakuei. *Building a New Japan.* Tokyo: Simul, 1973.

Vogel, Ezra F., ed. *Modern Japanese Organization and Decision Making.* Berkeley: University of California Press, 1975.

Watanabe, Tsunehiko. "National Planning and Economic Development." *Economics of Planning* (1970) 10:21–51.

CHAPTER 5

Austin, Lewis, ed. *Japan: The Paradox of Progress.* New Haven: Yale University Press, 1976.

Baerwald, Hans H. *Japan's Parliament.* Cambridge: Cambridge University Press, 1974.

Curtis, Gerald. *Election Campaigning Japanese Style.* New York: Columbia University Press, 1971.

Destler, I. M., Hideo Sato, Priscilla Clapp, and Haruhiro Fukui. *Managing an Alliance.* Washington, D.C.: Brookings Institution, 1976.

Fukui, Haruhiro. *Party in Power—The Japanese Liberal Democrats and Policy-making.* Berkeley: University of California Press, 1970.

Langdon, Frank. *Politics in Japan.* Boston: Little, Brown, 1967.

Maruyama, Masao. *Thought and Behavior in Modern Japanese Politics.* London: Oxford University Press, 1963.

Morley, James W., ed. *Prologue to the Future: The U.S. and Japan in the Postindustrial Age.* Boston: D.C. Heath, 1974.

Patrick, Hugh, ed. *Japanese Industrialization and Its Social Consequences*. Berkeley: University of California Press, 1976.

Pempel, T. J., ed. *Policy Making in Contemporary Japan*. Ithaca: Cornell University Press, 1977.

Thayer, Nathaniel B. *How the Conservatives Rule Japan*. Princeton: Princeton University Press, 1969.

Watanuki, Joji. *Politics in Postwar Japanese Society*. Tokyo: Tokyo University Press, 1977.

CHAPTER 6

Abegglen, James C. *Management and Worker*. Tokyo: Kō-dansha, 1973.

Cole, Robert E. *Japanese Blue Collar*. Berkeley: University of California Press, 1971.

Dore, Ronald P. *British Factory–Japanese Factory*. Berkeley: University of California Press, 1974.

Marsh, Robert M., and Hiroshi Mannari. *Modernization and the Japanese Factory*. Princeton: Princeton University Press, 1976.

Okochi, Kazuo, Bernard Karsh, and Solomon B. Levine. *Workers and Employers in Japan*. Princeton: Princeton University Press, 1974.

OECD. *Manpower Policy in Japan*. Paris, 1973.

Pascale, Richard Tanner. "Personnel Practices and Employee Attitudes: A Study of Japanese- and American-Managed Firms in the United States." *Human Relations* (1978) 31:597–615.

Ratcliffe, C. Tait. *Japanese Corporate Finance, 1977–1980*. London: Financial Times, 1977.

Rohlen, Thomas. *For Harmony and Strength*. Berkeley: University of California Press, 1974.

Tsurumi, Yoshi. *The Japanese Are Coming*. Cambridge, Mass.: Ballinger, 1976.

Yoshino, M. Y. *Japan's Multinational Enterprises*. Cambridge: Harvard University Press, 1976.

———. *The Japanese Marketing System*. Cambridge, M.I.T. Press, 1971.

———. *Japan's Managerial System*. Cambridge: M.I.T. Press, 1968.

CHAPTER 7

Bereday, George Z. F., and Shigeo Masui. *American Education through Japanese Eyes*. Honolulu: University of Hawaii, 1973.

Comer, L. C., and John P. Keeves. *Science Education in Nineteen Countries*. New York: Halsted, 1973.

Cummings, William K. *Education and Equality in Japan*. Princeton: Princeton University Press, 1979.

———. "The Effects of Japanese Schools." In Antonina Ktoskowska and Guido Martinotti, eds., *Education in a Changing Society*. London: Sage, 1977.

Glazer, Nathan. "Social and Cultural Factors in Economic Growth." In Hugh Patrick and Henry Rosovsky, eds., *Asia's New Giant*. Washington, D.C.: Brookings Institution, 1976.

Halloran, Richard. *Japan: Images and Realities*. New York: Random House, 1969.

Kobayashi, Tetsuya. *Society, Schools, and Progress in Japan*. New York: Pergamon Press, 1976.

Ministry of Education. *Course of Study for Elementary Schools in Japan*. Tokyo, 1976.

———. *Course of Study for Lower Secondary Schools in Japan*. Tokyo, 1976.

———. *Educational Standards in Japan*. Tokyo, 1970.

Monbushō. *Chihō kyōikuhi no chōsa hōkokusho* (Survey of local educational expenses). Tokyo, 1976.

————. *Waga kuni no kyōiku suijun* (Educational standards in Japan). Tokyo, 1976.

OECD. *Reviews of National Policies for Education: Japan.* Paris, 1971.

Passin, Herbert. *Society and Education in Japan.* New York: Columbia University Teachers College, 1965.

Singleton, John. *Nichū.* New York: Holt, Rinehart & Winston, 1967.

Vogel, Ezra F. "Infernal Entrance Examination." In *Japan's New Middle Class.* Berkeley: University of California Press, 1963.

CHAPTER 8

Bennett, John W., and Solomon B. Levine. "Industrialization and Social Deprivation." In Hugh Patrick, ed., *Japanese Industrialization and Its Social Consequences.* Berkeley: University of California Press, 1976.

Campbell, John C. "Entrepreneurial Bureaucrats and Programs for Old People in Japan." Presented at the American Political Science Association, New York, August 31–September 3, 1978.

————. "Programs for the Aged in Japan." Presented at the Midwest Regional Seminar on Japan, December 3, 1977.

Japan Institute of Labor. *Japan Labor Bulletin.* Tokyo, monthly.

Kōseishō. *Kōsei hakusho* (Welfare white paper). Tokyo, 1975.

Kōsei Tōkei Kyōkai. *Kokumin eisei no dōkō,* "Kōsei no Shihyō" (Social welfare indicators). Tokyo, 1976.

Husby, Ralph D. "Public Assistance (*Seikatsu Hogo*) in Japan." Unpublished manuscript, 1975.

Nihon Keieisha Dantai Renmei Jimukyoku. "Fukuri Kōseihi chōsa kekka hōkoku" (A survey of [employee] welfare benefit payments). Tokyo, 1976.

Nishimoto, Kōichi. "Nōkyō" (Agricultural cooperatives), *The Japan Interpreter*, 1972, 321–331.

Palmore, Erdman. *The Honorable Elders*. Durham, N.C.: Duke University Press, 1975.

Plath, David. "Japan: The After Years." In *Aging and Modernization*, ed. Donald Cowgill and Lowell Holmes. New York: Appleton-Century-Crofts, 1972.

Social Insurance Agency, Japanese Government. *Outline of Social Insurance in Japan*. Tokyo, 1977.

Yamaguchi Shin'ichirō, ed. *Nihon no fukushi* (Japanese welfare). Tokyo, Zaikeishōhōsha, 1976.

Chapter 9

Ames, Walter L. "Police and Community in Japan." Unpublished manuscript, 1978.

Bayley, David. *Forces of Order: Police Behavior in Japan and the United States*. Berkeley: University of California Press, 1976.

Clifford, William. *Crime Control in Japan*. Boston: D.C. Heath, 1976.

Hōmushō. *Hanzai hakusho* (Crime white paper). Tokyo, 1976.

Chapter 10

Lodge, George C. *The New American Ideology*. New York: Knopf, 1976.

Index